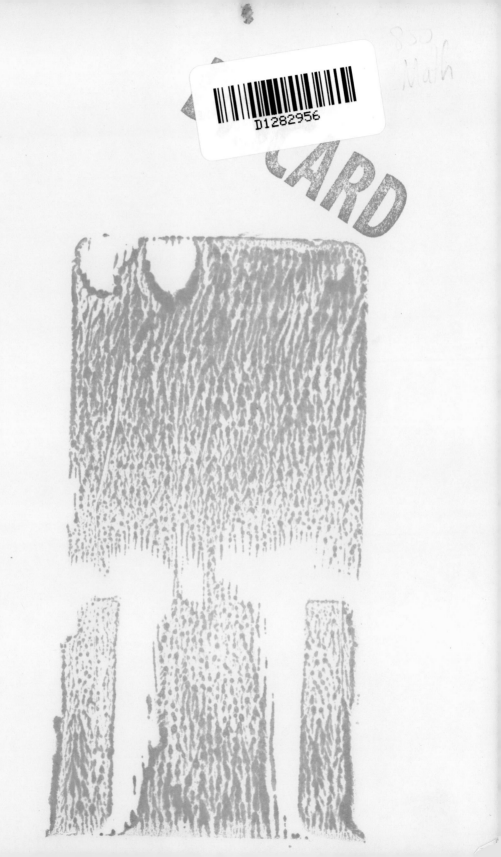

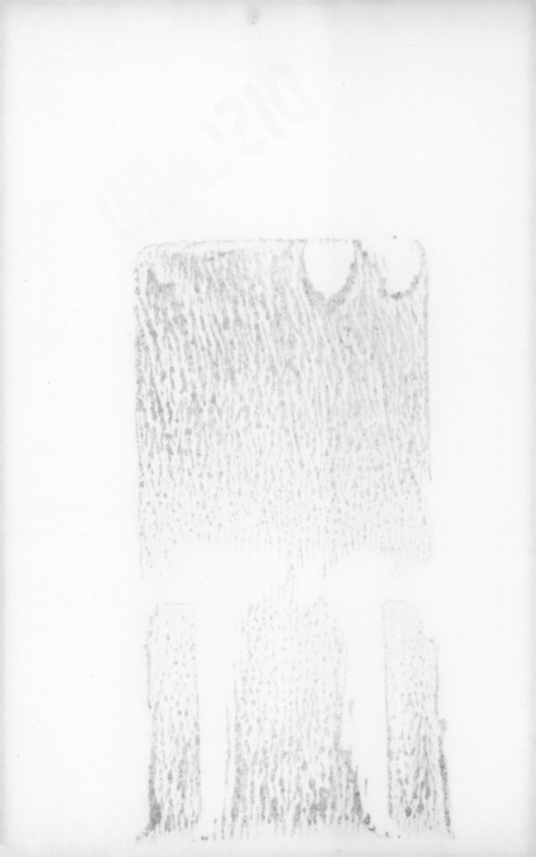

PLANE GEOMETRY
AND ITS GROUPS

HOLDEN–DAY SERIES IN MATHEMATICS

Earl E. Coddington and Andrew M. Gleason, Editors

Introductory Calculus
S. Bell, J. R. Blum, J. V. Lewis, and J. Rosenblatt

Modern University Calculus
S. Bell, J. R. Blum, J. V. Lewis, and J. Rosenblatt

Elementary Partial Differential Equations
P. W. Berg and J. L. McGregor

The Structure of Lie Groups
G. Hochschild

Abstract Algebra
A. Lindstrum, Jr.

Set Theory for the Mathematician
J. Rubin

Elements of General Topology
Sze-Tsen Hu

Elements of Modern Algebra
Sze-Tsen Hu

Elements of Real Analysis
Sze-Tsen Hu

Introduction to Contemporary Mathematics
Sze-Tsen Hu

Introduction to General Topology
Sze-Tsen Hu

Homology Theory
Sze-Tsen Hu

PLANE
GEOMETRY
AND ITS
GROUPS

Heinrich W. Guggenheimer

University of Minnesota

Holden-Day, Inc.
San Francisco, Cambridge, London, Amsterdam

To my wife

PREFACE

In this book the main theorems of plane euclidean geometry are proved on a university level. In the opinion of the writer, a reasonable training of high-school teachers must present them with a good working knowledge *of* geometry before starting to speak about foundations, i.e., *about* geometry.

The approach to geometry chosen in this book goes back to some papers by Ch. Wiener in the early 1890's. In particular also, I am indebted to the great book on plane geometry by Jacques Hadamard, and to modern works by G. Thomsen, H. Freudenthal, and F. Bachmann. Freudenthal has remarked that geometry today suffers from a low level of formalization as compared to other parts of mathematics. I am trying to remedy the situation by the use of a consistent formalism which is in keeping with the notations both of set theory and of traditional geometry. The deviations from the usual notations are kept to a minimum. Sometimes, however, they are unavoidable; for example, to untangle the different notions of angle that appear in elementary geometry, or, to distinguish between the point set of a segment and the vector which is its length.

Drawings are a major tool in the book. In the opinion of the writer, American instruction in geometry has been occupied too much with formal proof in geometry and, on the way, has forgotten the main points of geometry. Geometry was the model of abstract proof in Euclid's time, but algebra and general topology are the paradigms in our time. Geometry is partially based on intuition, and instruction in geometry is needed for a good training of one's intuition. The fallacies in proofs usually quoted as a warning against intuition only show that uninstructed intuition is bad intuition. The book also hopes to stimulate some interest for the role of clean drawings in the teaching of geometry. Some proofs in the text are referred to illustrations. This should not mean that the drawing *is* the proof, but that the reader should read from the drawing a formal proof along the lines presented in the text.

The treatment of geometry in this book is based on mappings. Geometry is constructed as the study of a transitive group of transformations on a set. The algebraic structures of geometry (addition of angles and vectors, multiplication of segments) are derived from a study of the transformation group. This approach has many advantages over the fashionable one using a reduction of geometry to analytic geometry over the field of real numbers. First, geometry is much simpler than real numbers. It is possible to understand geometry at a level at which a thorough grasp of the real-number system is out of the question. Second, the completeness of the real-number system is rather irrelevant in classical geometry. Since a complete non-archimedean field need not contain the square roots of its positive elements, completeness is of no importance for non-archimedean geometries. From the viewpoint of methodology, the introduction of completeness is harmful since it directs attention to a categorical axiom system. The treatment given here tries to be modern and, hence, avoids categorical system in order to enlarge the meaning of the theorems proved. The axiom system is chosen so that problems unsolvable in the classical sense really become "unsolvable in general." In a further defense of the use of incomplete axiom systems, it may be said that the penetrating analysis of elementary geometry given by Bachmann shows that many more geometries classify as "non-euclidean" than the usual three. Also, modern work in topology and Lie groups has shown that hidden separation properties of orbits are essential if categoricity is required in the group theoretical space problem. Therefore, the use of continuity arguments is avoided in this book. Ideal points are introduced as pencils of lines, and tangents to a circle are treated as lines of support of a convex set.

Even though the text is written mainly for future high-school teachers, its group theoretical approach may serve to re-introduce the study of geometry into the regular curriculum of all mathematics and physics majors on an upper-division level.

The axioms are introduced in the first chapter. Congruence is defined by the existence of an isometric mapping and the usual congruence theorems are proved. The second chapter contains a detailed study of the group of motions generated by reflections in lines. Oriented angles and vectors are defined and shown to form abelian groups. The addition of lengths appears as a special case of vector addition.

In the third chapter, the general notions of a group and that of a homogeneous space are taken up. The main result is the identification of the plane with the quotient of the group of motions by the isotropy group. The whole discussion is algebraic; the topological structure is not considered. As an application, the seventeen groups of ornaments in the euclidean archimedean plane are determined. The proof of the completeness of the list and the elimination of multiple appearances of the same group are rather tedious. Therefore, the arguments in the text are presented with some hand-waving. The details are worked out in the exercises. The section also gives a first discussion of the role of the archimedean axiom in classification problems.

Chapter four deals with circles. Oriented angles allow a formulation of the theorem about angles subtended by a chord which is easier to manage than that in elementary angles. The power of the formulation is illustrated in the proofs of the affine Pappus, affine Desargues, and Pascal theorems.

In chapter five, a field structure is defined on the set of lengths of segments.

The construction is based on Euclid's book II; the field is obtained simultaneously with an area function. As an application, the main metric theorems are proved. The field obtained from the axioms of free mobility is pythagorean, i.e., for all x in the field it contains an element $\sqrt{1 + x^2}$. This leads into a discussion of the geometric meaning of the existence of $\sqrt{1 - x^2}$ and $\sqrt{|x|}$.

Chapter six deals with homothety and similitude, in particular the classification and composition of similitudes. In keeping with the spirit of the text, all applications of similitude use mappings. The metric relations implied by the equality of angles in triangles have been treated in chapter five.

Chapter seven deals with geometric inequalities. The triangle inequality leads to extremal problems (with and without solutions) and to a problem in topological dynamics. This is treated following an eighty-year-old paper by R. Sturm, whose results have been partially rediscovered many times. The Erdös-Mordell inequality is derived with a set of related inequalities due to Sir A. Oppenheim. The isoperimetric inequality is derived without increasing the number of edges to avoid the use of limits.

In chapter eight, it is first proved that the circle and line preserving maps of an archimedean plane onto itself are the similitudes. Then the plane is extended to make inversion a one-to-one map. The remainder of the chapter is devoted to a study of the group of circular transformations and to some applications. In the last chapter, the hyperbolic group is defined on the Poincaré model as a subgroup of the group of circular transformations. The structure theorems of the preceding chapter allow a very rapid treatment of hyperbolic geometry. The classical formulae for angle and length are derived over the field of real numbers. After a discussion of the inadequacy of these formulae over general fields, the analytic geometry of the hyperbolic plane is based on Hilbert's calculus of ends. The field of ends is used to prove the isomorphy of the hyperbolic group with the group of 2 by 2 matrices of determinant ± 1 and to show that, in hyperbolic geometry, the existence of the perpendicular bisector implies the existence of the angle bisector and of square roots in the field of ends. The chapter closes with a simple proof of the isomorphy of the Poincaré and Klein models of hyperbolic geometry and with a rapid treatment of elliptic geometry in its conformal and spherical models.

An appendix deals with the Hilbert non-archimedean plane and its analytic geometry. The underlying field is also an example of a pythagorean field in which $\sqrt{|x|}$ need not exist but which is complete.

I have tried to keep the text close to the essentials and to relegate the niceties to the exercises. Also, some topics related to the main exposition, such as the theory of signed areas and hyperbolic trigonometry, appear in the exercises. However, all theorems needed in later proofs are established in the text itself. This accounts for a number of detailed results that otherwise might appear to be too special for inclusion in the text. The approximately

600 exercises contain very few construction problems. Most problems ask for proofs and give complements to the theory of the text. Indications for the solution of the problems are given for all but the obvious ones.

The book is written for a two-quarter course in plane geometry. With some selectivity in the topics, it can also serve for a one-semester course. It is hoped that it may be useful not only for education students, but for the liberal arts major in mathematics and physics as well.

A one-quarter course in the basic facts of geometry could consist of chapters I, II, chap. III. sec. 1 stopping short of (3.5), chap. IV. secs. 1 and 2, chap. V, chap. VI. secs. 1,2,3, chap. VIII. secs. 2 and 3, chap. IX. secs. 1,2,3,6, and as much of chap. VII as there is time available.

A short introduction to the foundations of geometry could cover chapters I,II,III, chap. IV. through (4.17), chap. V. secs. 1,2,3, chap. VI. secs. 1 and 2, chap. VIII. secs. 1,2, and 3, chap. IX, the Appendix, and, eventually, chap. VII. secs. 1 and 4.

I hope to follow up this book by one on n-dimensional geometry and a high-school course in geometry.

Even though this book does not contain any material that can be considered new, its preparation was helped by the support of my researches into various aspects of geometry given by the Air Force Office of Scientific Research and the National Science Foundation. In the revision of the manuscript, I leaned greatly on critical remarks by Brother Abel, F.S.C., Andrew Gleason, William Pohl, and Shlomo Sternberg, to all of whom I express my thanks.

H. GUGGENHEIMER

January 1967

CONTENTS

PLANE GEOMETRY
AND ITS GROUPS

Chapter I

AXIOMS

1. Sets in the plane

Any systematic theory must start with an enumeration of its assumptions. Therefore, we shall first describe some basic features of plane geometry as known from high school, intuition, or experience, in order to formulate a system of assumptions, or *axioms*, upon which our deductions will be based.

The axiomatic method has two goals. The first one is obvious and goes back to Euclid, *viz.*, to give a firm foundation to mathematical reasoning by a complete enumeration of the basic notions and hypotheses. The second direction of axiomatics is more subtle, but it is characteristic of modern mathematics. A detailed enumeration of the hypotheses of a theory gives us unlimited possibilities of experimentation. We may try to prove the same theorems with other hypotheses, or study the new theories which are obtained by replacing some familiar axioms with some contradicting statements. This is a completely legitimate procedure since axioms are not theorems and do not have to follow from anything. As a matter of principle, an axiom is legitimate in a system if it does not contradict any consequence of the preceding axioms. With a moral simile we may say that, in axiomatics, every exercise of the human freedom of invention is legitimate unless it is specifically outlawed. As a matter of practice, a system of axioms has to pass the further test that it should yield beautiful theorems.

Historically, both aspects of the axiomatic method were developed first on the example of geometry. The deductive method found its expression in Euclid's text, and the experimental aspects of axiomatics were developed on the example of the non-euclidean geometries. However, geometry is a rather complicated structure which leans on algebra, topology, and analysis. These simpler structures are today the main fields of application of the axiomatic method. In this book we are concerned with plane euclidean geometry, and we shall not do any experimenting with axioms for its own sake. However, we shall see that a certain amount of flexibility in the choice of the axioms will lead us to a much better understanding of the basic facts of geometry than we

1

could possibly obtain by a rigid axiomatic frame. In this sense, the book wants to be a practical guide to modern axiomatics. No abstract considerations of axiomatics are given.

Plane geometry is the study of certain sets called *planes*. The elements of a plane are called *points*. Certain sets of points are singled out and called *straight lines*, or *lines* in short. We do not define lines and points since we are not interested in their essence but in their properties. The properties of systems of points and lines will be described in the axioms. In keeping with the spirit of modern mathematics, we shall use only the minimum number of axioms necessary to derive the theorems of euclidean geometry. These axioms are not sufficient to characterize the plane of analytic geometry. The plane of analytic geometry is only one very special case for which our theorems will be true. The same theorems will be true in an infinity of other planes. This means that the axiomatic method helps us to obtain theorems in many different cases for the labor needed to prove one single theorem. We shall discuss later the special algebraic and analytical properties that single out the plane of analytic geometry among all planes of euclidean geometry.

Points will be denoted by capital letters, lines by lower-case letters. We shall also use the symbolism of set theory. If A is an element of the set a, we write

$$A \in a.$$

The fact that A is not an element of a is expressed by

$$A \notin a.$$

b is a *subset* of a, or a contains b, if all elements of b are also elements of a. In a formula,

$$b \subset a \text{ means: } A \in b \text{ implies } A \in a.$$

The *intersection* of two sets is the set of elements common to both sets:

$$a \cap b \text{ is the set of elements } A \text{ such that } A \in a \text{ and } A \in b.$$

The *null set* $\emptyset$ is the set without elements. Two sets are *disjoint* if they have no elements in common, i.e., if their intersection is the null set:

$$a \cap b = \emptyset.$$

Disjoint lines are usually called *parallel*. In this case we write $a \parallel b$ as a shorthand for $a \cap b = \emptyset$. Lines are *concurrent* if they are not parallel.

The *union* $a \cup b$ is the set of all elements which are either in a or in b:

$$A \in a \cup b \text{ if and only if at least one relation } A \in a, A \in b \text{ is true.}$$

The axioms will be introduced in three stages. They will be numbered by roman numerals.

axiom I.   *For any two distinct points A, B, there exists a unique line l(A,B) containing these points.*

axiom II.   *All points in the plane but not on a line l form two non-null disjoint sets.*

In geometry, we use the expressions "*A* is on *l*, *l* passes through *A*, *l* contains *A*" as synonyms of $A \in l$. The two sets mentioned in axiom II are called the *halfplanes* defined by the line *l*. A point *C* is *between* two points *A* and *B* if $C \in l(A,B)$ and if there exists some line *g* through *C* for which *A* and *B* are in different halfplanes. The set of points between *A* and *B* is the *segment* (A,B).

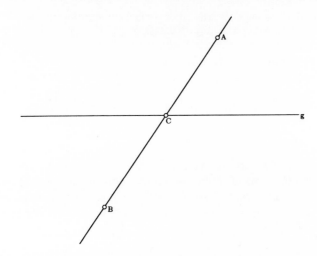

FIG. 1-1

By our definition, the points *A* and *B*, the *endpoints*, are not elements of the segment defined by themselves. It is often of advantage to use the *closed segment*

$$[A,B] = (A,B) \cup A \cup B,$$

which is the union of the segment with its endpoints. The next two axioms give a definite sense to these definitions.

Without further axioms, II implies only that there are two distinct points in the complement of a line. It becomes meaningful by the next two axioms.

axiom III.   *Two distinct points A and B are in different halfplanes of a line l if and only if $l \cap (A,B) \neq \emptyset$.*

axiom IV.   *If $B \in (A,C)$, then $C \notin (A,B)$.*

The null set satisfies axioms I through IV since it contains neither points nor lines. We are interested only in a geometry which actually contains points and lines. In fact, we shall need the existence of a number of special points and lines. These additional requirements will be introduced when they will be needed. Here we exclude the null set by the next axiom.

axiom V.   *There exists a line.*

Now we may start proving our first theorems.

(1.1)   *Two distinct lines have at most one point in common.*

Otherwise, two distinct points would be contained in two distinct lines. This is excluded by axiom I.

The next statement is just a convenient re-wording of the "if" part of axiom III.

(1.2)   *If C is between A and B, then A and B are in different halfplanes*
           for all lines g through C and distinct from l(A,B).

A set is *convex* if with two points it contains their segment:

$$S \text{ convex: } A \in S \text{ and } B \in S \text{ imply } (A,B) \in S.$$

By axiom III, two points are in different halfplanes of a line if and only if that line intersects the segment of the two points. This implies that the segment of two points in the same halfplane does not contain points either on the line or in the other halfplane; it is completely in the halfplane which contains the two points:

(1.3)   *A halfplane is a convex set.*

If A and B belong to every one of several convex sets, then their segment (and also $[A,B]$) belongs to the intersection of all the sets:

(1.4)   *The intersection of convex sets is convex.*

The elements of a subset of a straight line are called *collinear* points. Three non-collinear points, the *vertices*, define a *triangle*. The triangle is the union of the closed segments (the *edges*) between the vertices:

$$\triangle(A,B,C) = [A,B] \cup [B,C] \cup [C,A].$$

The edges are subsets of the lines $a = l(B,C)$, $b = l(C,A)$, and $c = l(A,B)$. The union of these three lines is sometimes referred to as the *complete* triangle defined by A, B, and C. The lines a, b, and c are the *sides* of the complete

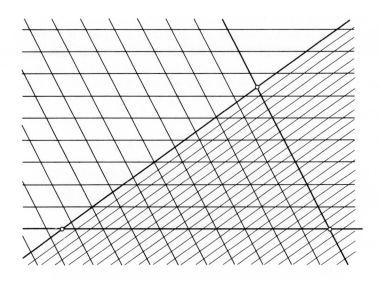

Fig. 1–2

triangle. Let us call π_A the halfplane of a which contains the vertex A. Similarly, we define π_B and π_C. The *interior* of $\triangle(A,B,C)$ is the intersection $\pi_A \cap \pi_B \cap \pi_C$. As a corollary to (1.3) and (1.4) we obtain:

(1.5)   *The interior of a triangle is a convex set.*

The next statement, known as *Pasch's* theorem, is another re-wording of axiom III.

(1.6)   *If a line intersects one of the edges of a triangle and does not pass through a vertex, it intersects exactly one other edge.*

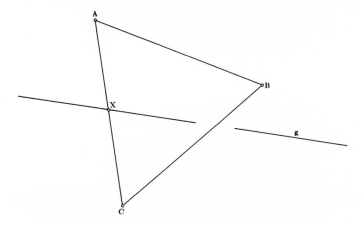

Fig. 1–3

For definiteness, we assume that the line g intersects (C,A) at X. The vertex B is either in the halfplane of A or in that of C relative to g. By axiom III, exactly one of the sets $g \cap (B,C)$ and $g \cap (B,A)$ is not the null set.

Our axioms imply the existence of an infinity of points in the plane. The proof for this assertion is rather complicated. We leave it for the exercises since later we shall be able to obtain the same result without effort. At this point we prove only:

(1.7)   *A line contains at least three points. There exists a triangle.*

Let l be the line whose existence is postulated in axiom V. By axiom II, there exists at least one point in each of the halfplanes of l; we call them A

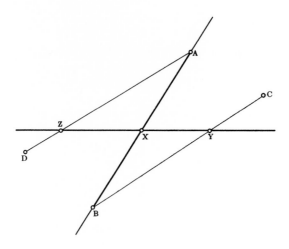

FIG. 1–4

and B. By axiom III, l contains the point $X = l \cap (A,B)$. Again by axiom II, there exist two distinct points C and D in the two halfplanes of $l(A,B)$. This gives us two triangles $\triangle(A,B,C)$ and $\triangle(A,B,D)$. If C or D is on l, we obtain an additional point on the line. If no vertex is on l, there exists an additional point of intersection of l with each one of the two triangles, by Pasch's theorem (1.6). The argument is valid for an arbitrary line l.

Exercise 1–1

    1. Prove that $(A,A) = \emptyset$.
    2. Prove: (a) $l(A,B) = l(B,A)$; (b) $(A,B) = (B,A)$, $[A,B] = [B,A]$.
    3. Prove: if $B \in (A,C)$, then $(A,B) \cap (B,C) = \emptyset$.

4. Prove that the following sets are convex:
(a) $\emptyset$; (b) (A,B); (c) $[A,B]$.

5. In the definition of convexity, show that (A,B) can be replaced by $[A,B]$ without changing the meaning of the notion.

6. Prove that the plane contains an infinity of points. [A set is infinite if, for any number N of its points, it contains an $(N+1)$st point distinct from the former.]

7. Prove: if $D \in (A,C)$ in the $\triangle(A,B,C)$ and $E \in (B,D)$, there exists $F \in (B,C)$ such that $E \in (A,F)$.

8. The *kernel* of a plane set S consists of all points A with the following property: for all $X \in S$, $[A,X] \subset S$. Prove that the kernel of any set is convex.

9. What are the convex subsets of a line?

2.   Reflections

In informal approaches to geometry, two figures are usually said to be congruent if there exists a motion which brings one onto the other. For an axiomatic approach we have to give a clear and definite meaning to the ideas expressed in this sentence. A first interpretation of the idea of motion would be to consider the plane as an unchangeable entity and only to move certain point sets (e.g., triangles) within it. But it is also possible to visualize two identical copies of one plane which both contain the same figure. A congruence may then be realized by moving one plane (thought of as a transparent sheet) rigidly over the other plane until the two figures lie one over the other. Two points in different planes will correspond to one another in this movement if they end up one above the other. If, finally, we identify the two planes, we can say in mathematical language that a movement is a special kind of function $Y = f(X)$ of points in the plane whose values also are points in the plane. Following the axiomatic approach, we shall single out certain functions, or *maps*, of the plane onto itself. Then we shall describe two figures as congruent if they are maps of one another in one of the admissible maps.

Our first example of such a map is the *reflection in a line l*. This is a function which to any point A associates a point $\sigma_l(A)$ such that the line l is the perpendicular bisector of $[A,\sigma_l(A)]$.

In this preliminary discussion we have used notions of informal geometry which now we have to re-introduce in a systematic way. In order to simplify our formulae we shall drop parentheses and write $\sigma_l A$ for $\sigma_l(A)$ and $\sigma_m \sigma_n A$ for $\sigma_m[\sigma_n(A)]$, in particular also σ^2 for $\sigma[\sigma(\ )]$.

The associative law holds for the composition of functions. This means that $h\{g[f(X)]\}$ can be computed in steps either by finding first $Z = g[f(X)]$ and then $U = h(Z)$, or first $Y = f(X)$ and then $U = h[g(Y)]$. In the special case of reflections,

$$(\sigma_3\sigma_2)\sigma_1 = \sigma_3(\sigma_2\sigma_1).$$

Hence the composite function may be denoted without ambiguity by $\sigma_3\sigma_2\sigma_1$, and we can drop the use of parentheses altogether. As suggested by our notation, we shall prefer to speak about the *product* of maps rather than about the composition of functions. All the formulae involving such a product have to be read from right to left: $\sigma_m\sigma_l\sigma_k A$ is obtained by reflecting, first A in the line k, then the result in the line l, and finally the resulting point in the line m.

The special symbol ι will be used for the *identity* map defined by $\iota A = A$ for all A in the plane.

The properties of reflections are described by eight axioms which we shall present in two groups.

axiom VI.   *For any line l there exists a map σ_l which maps the points of one halfplane of l onto the points of the other halfplane.*

axiom VII.   *σ_l maps all straight lines onto straight lines.*

axiom VIII.   *$\sigma_l^2 = \iota$.*

axiom IX.   *For all points $L \in l$, $\sigma_l L = L$.*

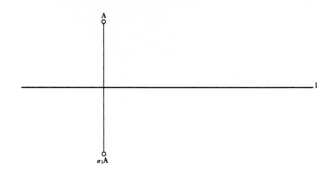

FIG. 1–5

An operation which on repetition yields the identity $(\sigma^2 = \iota)$ is called an *involution*. We shall reserve the symbol σ for maps of the plane which are involutions.

(1.8)   *An involution is a one-to-one function of the plane onto itself.*

If $B = \sigma A$ and $B = \sigma C$, then

$$\sigma B = \sigma^2 A = A = \sigma^2 C = C.$$

This proves that no point in the plane can be the image of two distinct points in an involution. On the other hand, by definition $A = \sigma(\sigma A)$; hence every point is an image under σ, and σA is defined for all points.

A one-to-one map of a set onto itself is also called a *transformation* of the set. Reflections are transformations of the plane.

From axioms III and VI it follows that

(1.9) $[A,\sigma_l A] \cap l \neq \emptyset.$

For the final set of axioms we need some additional definitions. A point P on a line l determines two *rays*. Each ray is the union of P and the intersection

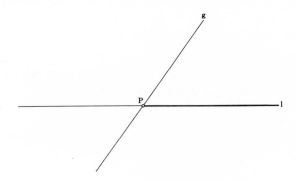

FIG. 1–6

of l with one halfplane of some line g ($\neq l$) through P. The point P is the *vertex* of the ray. If no confusion can result, we denote the two rays by l_1 and l_2. A ray of vertex P which contains a point $Q \neq P$ will be denoted by $P[Q]$.

The union $a_1 \cup b_1$ of two rays with a common vertex P is the *angle* $\angle (a_1,b_1)$ formed by the *legs* a_1, b_1. If $a_1 = P[A]$, $b_1 = P[B]$, we also write

$$\angle (a_1,b_1) = \angle APB = \angle BPA.$$

An *angle bisector* of an angle $\angle (a_1,b_1)$ is a line $t = t(a_1,b_1)$ such that

$$b_1 = \sigma_t a_1.$$

A *perpendicular bisector* of two points A, B is a line $m = m(A,B)$ such that

$$B = \sigma_m A.$$

The *midpoint* $M(A,B)$ of A and B is the point $m \cap [A,B]$ which exists by (1.9).

A line a is *perpendicular* to a line b ($a \perp b$) if $a \neq b$ and $\sigma_b a = a$. By axiom VI, no point of a other than $a \cap b$ can be a fixed point of σ_b (i.e., such that $\sigma_b A = A$). The intersection of a and b exists by (1.9). The perpendicular to a line l through a point A will be denoted by $p(l,A)$. Its existence and uniqueness will be discussed later. If a and b are perpendiculars to $l(A,B)$ at A and B, then we also write $m(a,b)$ for $m(A,B) = p(l(A,B), M(A,B))$ and call it the *midline* of a and b.

A finite product of reflections is called a *motion*. In general, we shall denote unspecified motions by the symbol Σ.

Our last axioms are:

axiom X.   *For any angle there exists an angle bisector.*
axiom XI.   *For any pair of points there exists a perpendicular bisector.*
axiom XII.   *If a motion leaves a ray fixed, then it is either the identity or the reflection in the line carrying the ray.*
axiom XIII. *If a $\parallel$ b and d $\perp$ a, then d $\perp$ b.*

We shall see that XIII implies the euclidean statement that through a point not on a given line there exists a unique parallel to that line.

Axiom XII is due to the Danish geometer *Hjelmslev*. If Σ maps a ray onto itself, it must map the vertex of the ray onto itself. In order to use the axiom to replace a product of reflections by one reflection, we have to find a line which is fixed under Σ, a point which is a fixed point of Σ, and finally, we have to check whether Σ maps the rays defined by the fixed point onto themselves or not. In the next chapter we shall use the axiom to prove that every motion can be reduced to a product of at most three reflections.

If S is a set contained in the domain of definition of a function f, we denote by $f(S)$, or fS, the set of all points $Y = fX$, $X \in S$. We need this convention for our last basic definition:

Two plane sets S and S' are congruent (S $\cong$ S') if there exists a motion Σ such that S' is the image of S in the transformation $\Sigma : S' = \Sigma S$.

Axiom VIII implies that

(1.10) $S \cong S$,

as was to be expected.

A map T is an *inverse* of a map Σ if $T\Sigma = \iota$. In our case, the relation between a point and its image under Σ is one-to-one by (1.8); hence it is possible to speak of *the* inverse Σ^{-1} of Σ. To simplify the computations, we shall write σ_i for σ_{l_i}. The following computation by recursion uses the associative law for the composition of maps and the fact that reflections are involutions:

$$(\sigma_1\sigma_2 \cdots \sigma_{k-1}\sigma_k)(\sigma_k\sigma_{k-1} \cdots \sigma_2\sigma_1)$$
$$= (\sigma_1\sigma_2 \cdots \sigma_{k-1})(\sigma_k\sigma_k)(\sigma_{k-1} \cdots \sigma_2\sigma_1)$$
$$= (\sigma_1\sigma_2 \cdots \sigma_{k-1})(\sigma_{k-1} \cdots \sigma_2\sigma_1)$$
$$\cdots$$
$$= \sigma_1\sigma_1 = \iota.$$

This means that

(1.11) $(\sigma_k\sigma_{k-1} \cdots \sigma_2\sigma_1)^{-1} = \sigma_1\sigma_2 \cdots \sigma_{k-1}\sigma_k.$

The inverse of a product of reflections is the product of the reflections taken in the inverse order. A direct computation shows that this inverse $T = \Sigma^{-1}$ also satisfies

(1.12) $\qquad \Sigma\Sigma^{-1} = \iota.$

The same result could have been obtained by some abstract reasoning. From

$$S = \iota S = \Sigma^{-1}\Sigma S = \Sigma^{-1}S'$$

we obtain:

(1.13) $\qquad$ *if* $S \cong S'$, *then* $S' \cong S$.

If $S' = \Sigma_1 S$ and $S'' = \Sigma_2 S'$, then $S'' = (\Sigma_2\Sigma_1)S$:

(1.14) $\qquad S \cong S'$ *and* $S' \cong S''$ *imply* $S \cong S''$.

$\qquad$ Any relation $\cong$ between sets which satisfies the conditions (1.10), (1.13), and (1.14) is called a *relation of equivalence* of the sets. Congruence is a relation of equivalence of plane sets. Much of modern mathematics can be formulated in terms of relations of equivalence. In this book, many different relations of equivalence will be introduced.

$\qquad$ We are now able to compute the result of a reflection in the image Σa of a line a as a function of Σ and σ_a. For any $X \in \Sigma a$, axiom IX implies that

$$\sigma_a\Sigma^{-1}X = \Sigma^{-1}X$$

or, by multiplication by Σ from the left,

$$\Sigma\sigma_a\Sigma^{-1}X = X.$$

Therefore, $\Sigma\sigma_a\Sigma^{-1}$ leaves every ray of Σa pointwise fixed and, by axiom XII, it is either ι or $\sigma_{\Sigma a}$. The first alternative would imply

$$\Sigma\sigma_a\Sigma^{-1} = \Sigma\Sigma^{-1},$$

hence $\sigma_a = \Sigma^{-1}\Sigma\sigma_a\Sigma^{-1}\Sigma = (\Sigma^{-1}\Sigma)(\Sigma^{-1}\Sigma) = \iota$, which is impossible by axiom VI. It follows that the second alternative is true:

(1.15) $\qquad \sigma_{\Sigma a} = \Sigma\sigma_a\Sigma^{-1}.$

This is a most important formula. As a first application, we derive a formula for the angle bisector. By definition,

$$b = \sigma_{t(a_1,b_1)}a,$$

hence by (1.15)

$$\sigma_b = \sigma_{t(a_1,b_1)}\sigma_a\sigma_{t(a_1,b_1)}.$$

Multiplication by σ_b gives the result:

(1.16)   *Any angle bisector t of an angle defined by rays of two concurrent lines a and b satisfies the identity*

$$\sigma_b\sigma_t\sigma_a\sigma_t = \iota.$$

The identity (1.16) does not quite characterize angle bisectors; it holds also for the midline of two parallel lines.

   The remainder of this section is devoted to a study of the properties of perpendicular lines.

   $a \perp b$ means $\sigma_b a = a$, hence, by (1.15),

$$\sigma_a = \sigma_b\sigma_a\sigma_b$$

and

$$\sigma_b\sigma_a = \sigma_b^2\sigma_a\sigma_b = \sigma_a\sigma_b.$$

Conversely, the equation $\sigma_b\sigma_a = \sigma_a\sigma_b$ implies

$$\sigma_a = \sigma_b\sigma_a\sigma_b = \sigma_{\sigma_b a}.$$

By axiom IX, $\sigma_{\sigma_b a}$ maps every ray of a onto itself. By axiom VI, no reflection is the identity. Hence, by axiom XII, $\sigma_b a = a$. To sum up:

(1.17) $a \perp b$ *if and only if* $a \neq b$ *and* $\sigma_a\sigma_b = \sigma_b\sigma_a$.

In this case we say that σ_a and σ_b *commute*. The condition (1.17) is symmetric in a and b:

(1.18) $a \perp b$ *implies* $b \perp a$.

   The last argument in the proof of (1.17) can be formulated as

(1.19) $\sigma_a = \sigma_b$ *implies* $a = b$.

This argument is the basis of many uniqueness proofs. For example,

(1.20)   *The bisector of an angle is unique.*

Let us assume that both t and t^* are bisectors of $\angle(a_1,b_1)$. The map $\Sigma = \sigma_t\sigma_{t^*}$ maps a_1 onto itself and the halfplane of a which contains b_1 onto itself. By XII and VI, $\Sigma = \iota$, i.e., $\sigma_t = \sigma_{t^*}$.

The uniqueness of the perpendicular bisector of two distinct points is proved in the same way.

Perpendicularity is not destroyed in any product of reflections. If $a \perp b$, we put $c = \Sigma a$, $d = \Sigma b$. Then

$$\sigma_c \sigma_d = \Sigma \sigma_a \Sigma^{-1} \Sigma \sigma_b \Sigma^{-1} = \Sigma \sigma_a \sigma_b \Sigma^{-1}$$
$$= \Sigma \sigma_b \sigma_a \Sigma^{-1} = \Sigma \sigma_b \Sigma^{-1} \Sigma \sigma_a \Sigma^{-1}$$
$$= \sigma_d \sigma_c.$$

$a \neq b$ implies $c \neq d$ since Σ is one-to-one. Hence

(1.21) $a \perp b$ *implies* $\Sigma a \perp \Sigma b$.

The existence of perpendiculars is assured by the next theorem.

(1.22)   *Through any point P there exists a unique perpendicular $p(g,P)$ to a given line g.*

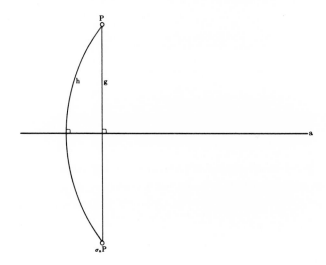

Fig. 1–7

For the proof we need consider two cases. The easy one is $P \notin g$. By axioms VIII and I,

$$\sigma_g l(P,\sigma_g P) = l(P,\sigma_g P).$$

Hence $l(P,\sigma_g P)$ is a line through P and perpendicular to g. If there were two lines through P and perpendicular to g, both must contain the points P and $\sigma_g P$ ($\neq P$). This is impossible by axiom I. We may note that in this proof we also have justified the name "perpendicular bisector" since $B = \sigma_{m(A,B)} A$:

(1.23) $m(A,B) \perp l(A,B)$ *for* $A \neq B$.

    In the case $P \in g$, choose a point $A \in g$ distinct from P. This is possible by (1.7). On $m(P,A)$ (axiom XI) there is a point C distinct from $M(A,P)$. By (1.23),

$$m[M(A,P),C] \perp m(A,P).$$

By construction, g and $m[M(A,P),C]$ do not intersect on $m(A,P)$. Therefore, $g \parallel m[M(A,P),C]$ since otherwise there would be two distinct perpendiculars

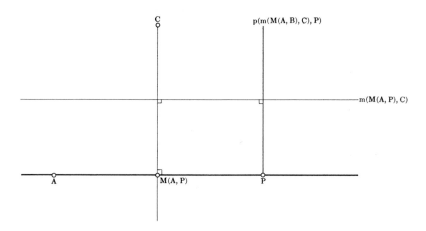

FIG. 1–8

to $m(A,P)$ from their point of intersection. By the proof in the case $P \notin g$, there exists $p\{m[M(A,P),C],P\}$. By axiom XIII,

$$p(g,P) = p\{m[M(A,P),C],P\}.$$

Since a perpendicular to g is also a perpendicular to all lines parallel to g, the uniqueness of $p(g,P)$ in the case $P \in g$ follows from the uniqueness in the case $P \notin g$.

    We note some elementary consequences of (1.22). The first is the euclidean axiom, which in our system becomes a theorem.

(1.24)   *If a line l through a point $P \notin g$ is not perpendicular to $p(g,P)$, then it is not parallel to g.*

    By XIII, a perpendicular to g must be perpendicular to all its parallels.

    Next we prove that a line contains an infinity of points and that the order on a line, defined by the notion of between-ness, is, in the language of set theory, total and dense.

(1.25)   *For any two distinct points A and B there exists an $X \in (A,B)$ and a Y such that $B \in (A,Y)$.*

Take $X = M(A,B)$ and $Y = \sigma_{p[l(A,B),B]}A$.

(1.26)   *Of three distinct collinear points, one is between the two others.*

If the points are A, B, and C on the line g, define $a = p(g,A)$ and $b = p(g,B)$. We denote by π_a^1 the halfplane of a which contains B, by π_a^2 the other one. Similarly, π_b^1 is the halfplane of b which contains A and π_b^2 the second halfplane of b. It follows from the definition that the convex sets $\pi_a^1 \cap \pi_b^1$, $\pi_a^2 \cap \pi_b^1$, and $\pi_a^1 \cap \pi_b^2$ are not empty. We prove first that $\pi_a^2 \cap \pi_b^2 = \emptyset$. If there were an $X \in \pi_a^2 \cap \pi_b^2$, then, by definition, there

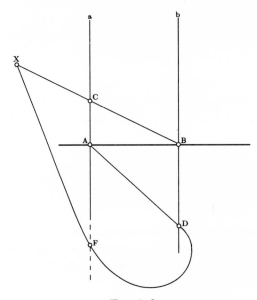

Fig. 1–9

would exist the points: $C = a \cap (X,B)$ and $D = b \cap (X,A)$. Assume first that $X \notin g$. The line a meets $\triangle(X,B,D)$ at C. Since $a \parallel b = l(B,D)$, Pasch's theorem implies that $F = a \cap (X,D)$ exists. But then the two distinct lines a and $l(X,A)$ meet in the two distinct points A and F. This is impossible by axiom I. If $X \in g$, then we replace it by any point of $p(g,X)$ distinct from X.

Finally, if $C \in \pi_a^1 \cap \pi_b^1$, then $C \in (A,B)$. If $C \in \pi_a^2 \cap \pi_b^1$, then $B \in (A,C)$. If $C \in \pi_a^1 \cap \pi_b^2$, then $A \in (C,B)$. This argument shows in particular that

(1.27) $(A,B) = l(A,B) \cap \pi_a^1 \cap \pi_b^1.$

Exercise 1–2

1. If the T_i $(i = 1, 2, \ldots, n)$ are transformations of a set, prove that

$$(T_n T_{n-1} \cdots T_2 T_1)^{-1} = T_1^{-1} T_2^{-1} \cdots T_{n-1}^{-1} T_n^{-1}.$$

2. Let f be a map of a set A into a set B, g a map of B into C, and h a map of C into D.

    (a) Which sets are mapped into which by gf and hg?

    (b) Prove that the three maps f, g, and h are one-to-one if the two maps gf and hg are one-to-one *onto* their image sets.

3. Use (1.25) to prove that a line contains an infinity of points.

4. Prove that the sides of a complete triangle divide the plane into seven convex sets (and the lines).

5. Let P be the vertex of an angle $\angle\,(a_1, b_1)$, and a_2 the other ray of a defined by P. Prove that

$$t(a_1, b_1) \perp t(a_2, b_1).$$

$[t(a_2, b_1)$ is the *external* bisector of the given angle.$]$

6. Prove that (1.16) holds also for the midline of two parallels.

7. For $C \in m(A, B)$, $C \neq M(A, B)$, compute $\sigma_{l(B, C)}$ as a function of $\sigma_{l(A, C)}$ and $\sigma_{m(A, B)}$.

8. Prove that the perpendicular bisector of two distinct points is unique.

9. Prove that the definitions of angle bisector and perpendicular bisector imply also $a_1 = \sigma_t b_1$ and $A = \sigma_m B$.

10. What is $m(A, A)$? $M(A, A)$?

11. What is $\sigma_{m(A, B)} p(l(A, B), A)$?

12. If Σ is a transformation and T the inverse of Σ, prove that Σ is the inverse of T.

13. If $\simeq$ is a relation of equivalence in a set, consider the maximal subsets which contain only equivalent elements. Show that these subsets are disjoint.

14. The *projection* of a point A on a line g is

$$A^g = g \cap p(g, A).$$

This is a map ^{g} of the whole plane onto a line.

    (a) Prove that the projection of a closed interval is a closed interval.

    (b) What are the sets whose projection on a line g is a point?

    (c) Prove that every projection of a triangle is a closed interval.

15. Prove that through a point $P \notin g$ there exists a unique parallel to g.

16. a_1, b_1, c_1, d_1 are four rays with common vertex. If $t(a_1, b_1) = t(c_1, d_1)$ and $t(b_1, c_1) = t(d_1, a_1)$, show that the four rays lie in pairs on two lines.

17. Show that $a \parallel b$ implies $\Sigma a \parallel \Sigma b$.

18. Prove that two concurrent lines define four angles.

19. In (1.25), prove that $B \in (X, Y)$.

3. Congruence Theorems

Any motion is one-to-one and maps lines into lines, halfplanes into half-planes. By (1.27) this implies

$$(1.28) \qquad (\Sigma A, \Sigma B) = \Sigma(A,B) \simeq (A,B).$$

The theory of congruent figures is based on a uniqueness theorem for segments.

(1.29)   *If B and C are on the same ray a_1 of vertex A and $(A,B) \simeq (A,C)$, then $B = C$.*

By hypothesis, there exists Σ such that $(A,B) = \Sigma(A,C)$. If $\Sigma A = A$, we retain it. If $\Sigma A = B$, we replace Σ by $\sigma_{m(A,B)}\Sigma$. Then we have a map of (A,C) onto (A,B) for which $\Sigma a_1 = a_1$. By axiom XII, either $\Sigma = \sigma_a$ or $\Sigma = \iota$. In both cases, $\Sigma C = C = B$.

The preceding theorems are the basis for a comparison of segments. We define

$(A,B) < (C,D)$ *if there exist points* X, Y, Z *such that* $(A,B) \simeq (X,Y)$, $(C,D) \simeq (X,Z)$, *and* $Y \in (X,Z)$.

If two segments s_1 and s_2 are congruent to segments (X,Y) and (X,Z) such that Y and Z are on the same ray of vertex X, the previous results show that one and only one of the relations

$$s_1 < s_2 \qquad s_1 \simeq s_2 \qquad s_2 < s_1$$

must hold. The next result shows that this situation holds for any pair of segments. Hence two segments can always be compared in size.

(1.30)   *For any segment (A,B) and any ray p_1 of vertex P there exists $Q \in p_1$ such that $(A,B) \simeq (P,Q)$.*

The proof is contained in Fig. 1–10:

$$Q = \sigma_{t(p_1, \sigma_{m(A,P)}A[B])} \sigma_{m(A,P)} B.$$

The comparison of angles can be established in the same way. We start with a theorem analogous to (1.29).

(1.31)   *If b_1 and c_1 are rays of vertex $A \in a$ in the same halfplane of a and $\angle(a_1,b_1) \simeq \angle(a_1,c_1)$, then $b = c$.*

By hypothesis, there exists Σ such that $\angle(a_1,b_1) = \Sigma\angle(a_1,c_1)$. If $\Sigma a_1 = a_1$, we retain it. If $\Sigma a_1 = b_1$, we replace Σ by $\sigma_{t(a_1,b_1)}\Sigma$. (One of the two cases must

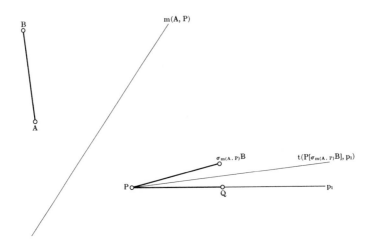

Fɪɢ. 1–10

hold since $\Sigma A = A$.) Then we have a map for which $\Sigma a_1 = a_1$. By axiom XII, either $\Sigma = \sigma_a$ or $\Sigma = \iota$. The first case is impossible since Σ maps halfplanes of a onto themselves, but σ_a does not.

If a_1 and b_1 are not collinear, we define the *interior* of the angle $\angle (a_1, b_1)$ to be the intersection of the halfplane of a containing b_1 (minus its vertex) and the halfplane of b containing a_1. If a_1 and b_1 are collinear, then either $b_1 = a_1$ or $b_1 = a_2$. In the first case the interior is the null set (there is no interior). In the second case we have a *straight* angle, and its interior is either halfplane (suitably chosen) of the line a which carries the angle. We define

$$\angle (a_1, b_1) < \angle (a_1, c_1)$$

if b_1 without its vertex is in the interior of $\angle (a_1, c_1)$. In general, we define $\angle (a_1, b_1) < \angle (c_1, d_1)$ if there exist x_1, y_1, and z_1 such that $\angle (a_1, b_1) \cong \angle (x_1, y_1)$, $\angle (c_1, d_1) \cong \angle (x_1, z_1)$, and $\angle (x_1, y_1) < \angle (x_1, z_1)$. Then (1.31) implies that it is well defined whether two angles are congruent or one is bigger than the other if they are at all comparable. The next proposition guarantees that any two angles can be compared in size.

(1.32)   *For any angle $\angle (a_1, b_1)$, any line p, ray p_1 on p, and halfplane π_1 of p, there exists a unique ray q_1 such that $\angle (a_1, b_1) \cong \angle (p_1, q_1)$ and the interior of $\angle (p_1, q_1)$ is in π_1.*

Depending on the halfplanes, either

$$q_1 = \sigma_{t(p_1, \sigma_{m(A,P)} a_1)} \sigma_{m(A,P)} b_1$$

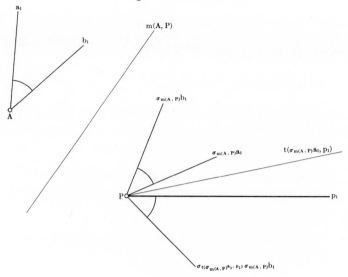

FIG. 1–11

or

$$q_1 = \sigma_{t(p_1, \sigma_{m(A,P)}b_1)}\sigma_{m(A,P)}a_1.$$

The uniqueness follows from (1.31).

The definition of $<$ makes it possible to prove comparison theorems like

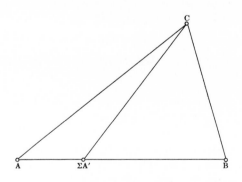

FIG. 1–12

(1.33)   If $(B,C) \cong (B',C')$, $\angle ABC \cong \angle A'B'C'$, and $\angle BCA > \angle B'C'A'$,
then $(A,B) > (A',B')$.

Let Σ be the map, defined by (1.32), which brings (B',C') onto (B,C) and A'
into π_A. Then $\Sigma C'[A']$ is in the interior of $\angle BCA$, hence $\Sigma A' \in (A,B)$ and
$\Sigma(A',B') = (\Sigma A', B) \subset (A,B)$.

A *right* angle is defined by a pair of perpendicular rays. An angle smaller than a right angle is *acute*, an angle bigger than a right angle is *obtuse*. No angle is bigger than a straight angle. By (1.21) we have the following.

(1.34)   *All right angles are congruent.*

If two triangles are congruent, all corresponding subsets of the two triangles are images of one another and, therefore, are congruent. The converse statements are known as the congruence theorems.

(1.35)   (asa) *If in two triangles one pair of edges and the two pairs of adjacent angles are congruent, then the two triangles are congruent.*

In a triangle we shall use the abbreviation $\hat{A}$ for $\angle BAC$ and, similarly, $\hat{B}$ and $\hat{C}$. We have to show that from the hypotheses

$$(A,B) \cong (A',B') \qquad \hat{A} \cong \hat{A}' \qquad \hat{B} \cong \hat{B}'$$

there follows the existence of a Σ such that $\Sigma A = A'$, $\Sigma B = B'$, and $\Sigma C = C'$. By the first hypothesis, Σ_0 exists such that $\Sigma_0 A = A'$, $\Sigma_0 B = B'$. If $\Sigma_0 C$ is in $\pi_{C'}$, we put $\Sigma = \Sigma_0$, otherwise $\Sigma = \sigma_{c'} \Sigma_0$ $[c' = l(A',B')]$. By (1.32),

$$\Sigma A[C] = A'[C'] \qquad \Sigma B[C] = B'[C'],$$

hence

$$\Sigma C = \Sigma A[C] \cap B[C] = C'.$$

(1.36)   (sas) *If in two triangles two pairs of edges and the angles between them are congruent, then the triangles are congruent.*

The hypotheses are

$$(A,B) \cong (A',B') \qquad (A,C) \cong (A',C') \qquad \hat{A} \cong A'.$$

If $\hat{B} \cong \hat{B}'$, the two triangles are congruent by (asa). If, say, $\hat{B} > \hat{B}'$, then the first and the last hypotheses imply $(A,C) > (A',C')$ against the second hypothesis. Therefore, the theorem (sas) holds.

The proof of the (sss) theorem needs some preparation. A triangle with two congruent edges is called *isosceles*. The congruent edges are the *legs*, the third edge is the *base*. If $\triangle(A,B,C)$ is isosceles with $(C,A) \cong (C,B)$, then, by (sas), $\triangle(A,B,C) \cong \triangle(B,A,C)$. It follows that $\sigma_{m(A,B)}$ maps the triangle onto itself, hence C is a fixed point for this map.

(1.37)   *In an isosceles triangle, the angles at the base are congruent, and the perpendicular bisector of the base contains the third vertex.*

Since A and $m(A,B)$ uniquely define B, the last result implies:

(1.38)   *On a given line, not more than two points can be equidistant from a fixed point in the plane.*

A and B are equidistant from C if $(A,C) \cong (B,C)$.

Consider now triangles $\triangle(A_1,A_2,A_3)$ and $\triangle(A_1',A_2',A_3')$ whose edges are congruent:

$$(A_i, A_j) \cong (A_i', A_j').$$

We may assume $A_1 = A_1'$, $A_2 = A_2'$. If $A_3 \neq A_3'$, then

$$\triangle(A_1, A_3, A_3') \quad \text{and} \quad \triangle(A_2, A_3, A_3')$$

are isosceles and, by (1.37), $m(A_3, A_3') = l(A_1, A_2)$. Hence

$$\triangle(A_1, A_2, A_3') = \sigma_{l(A_1, A_2)} \triangle(A_1, A_2, A_3).$$

(1.39)   (sss)   *If in two triangles the three pairs of edges are congruent, then the triangles are congruent.*

Exercise 1–3

1. Prove that $s_1 < s_2$, $s_2 < s_3$ imply $s_1 < s_3$
   (a) for segments   (b) for angles.

2. Prove that $s_1 < s_2$, $s_1 \cong s_1'$, $s_2 \cong s_2'$ imply $s_1' < s_2'$ both for segments and for angles.

3. Show that (1.33) admits a converse.

4. Prove that the interior of an angle is convex.

5. Prove that the interior of a triangle is the intersection of the interiors of the angles of the triangle.

6. Prove that in a triangle the biggest edge is opposite the biggest angle.

7. On the legs of an angle of vertex P one has four points A_1, $A_2 \in a_1$, B_1, $B_2 \in b_1$, such that $(P,A_i) \cong (P,B_i)$ $(i = 1,2)$. Prove that $l(A_1,B_2) \cap l(A_2,B_1) \in t(a_1,b_1)$.

8. Let t_1 be the ray of $t(a_1,b_1)$ which is defined by the vertex P of $\angle(a_1,b_1)$ and is in the interior of that angle. Justify the name "bisector" by proving that

$$\angle(a_1,t_1) \cong \angle(t_1,b_1).$$

9. Prove that $[A, M(A,B)] \cong [M(A,B), B]$.

10. Find conditions for congruence of two quadrilaterals.

11. Prove that $\triangle(A,B,C)$ is isosceles if $t(C[A], C[B]) \perp c$.

12. Show that $(C,A) < (C,B)$ implies $\angle ACM(A,B) > \angle BCM(A,B)$.

4. Isometry

Our definition of isometry may seem artificial and restricted, since we allow only finite products of reflections as maps in a congruence. In this section we show that, nevertheless, our definitions have all the generality that can be desired.

A map of the plane onto itself is an *isometry* if it maps pairs of points into pairs defining congruent segments:

> $Y = fX$ *is an isometry if* $(X_1,X_2) \cong (fX_1,fX_2)$ *for all* X_1, X_2 *in the plane.*

It is not required in the definition of an isometry that it map straight lines into straight lines, or, that

$$f(X_1,X_2) = (fX_1,fX_2).$$

These properties are consequences of the next theorem.

(1.40)   *An isometry is a finite product of reflections.*

Another formulation of the same statement is:

> *If a map of the plane onto itself maps any set consisting of two points onto a congruent set, it maps all sets onto congruent sets.*

We start from an arbitrary triangle $\triangle(A,B,C)$. By (1.39) there exists a finite product of reflections Σ such that

$$\Sigma\triangle(fA,fB,fC) = \triangle(A,B,C).$$

We prove that $\Sigma f = \iota$, or that $f = \Sigma^{-1}$ is a product of reflections. We need to show that $\Sigma fP = P$ for all points P in the plane.

We assume first that P is not on one of the sides of the complete triangle defined by A, B, and C. The hypothesis implies by (sss) that

$$\triangle(A,B,\Sigma fP) \cong \triangle(A,B,P),$$

hence [see the proof of (1.38)] either $\Sigma fP = P$ or $\Sigma fP = \sigma_c P$. From $\triangle(A,C,P)$ we obtain by the same argument: either $\Sigma fP = P$ or $\Sigma fP = \sigma_b P$. Since $b \neq c$, it follows that $\Sigma fP = P$. If P is on one of the sides of the complete triangle, we choose three points R, S, T not on the sides of the complete triangle and so that P is not on the sides of the complete triangle defined by R, S, and T. By the preceding argument, Σf maps R, S, and T onto themselves. By the same argument, Σf maps P onto itself (just change the names of R, S, and T into A, B, and C). Therefore, our assertion is true in all cases.

Exercise 1–4

1. Prove that $f (= \Sigma^{-1})$ can be found as a product of at most three reflections.

5. The Triangle

We introduce standard notations for interesting lines and points connected with a triangle. All notations allow cyclic permutations $A \to B \to C \to A$ and $a \to b \to c \to a$.

Edges and sides have been defined in section 1. The *altitude* from A is $h_a = p(a,A)$. The projection $A^a = a \cap h_a$ is the *foot* F_a of the altitude. The

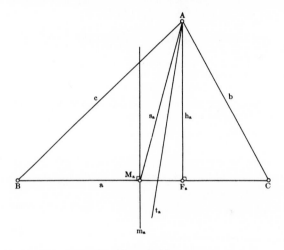

Fig. 1–13

perpendicular bisector $m(B,C)$ is denoted m_a. Its intersection $M(B,C)$ with a is the midpoint M_a. The *median* is $s_a = l(A,M_a)$. The bisector of the angle $\angle BAC$ is t_A.

If $O \in m_a \cap m_b$, then

$$(O,B) \cong (O,C) \cong (O,A);$$

hence, by (1.37), $O \in m_c$. O is called the circumcenter of the triangle.

(1.41) *The perpendicular bisectors of the edges of a triangle are concurrent at the circumcenter.*

The perpendiculars from a point of an angle bisector to both legs of the angle are congruent by reflection in the angle bisector. Conversely, this property is characteristic for angle bisectors.

(1.42)   *If the segments from a point X to its projections onto two con-*
         current lines a and b are congruent, then the line $l(a \cap b, X)$ is the
         angle bisector of $\angle X^a \, a \cap b \, X^b$. If $a \parallel b$ and $XX^a = XX^b$, then
         $X \in m(a,b)$.

In the first case put $u = t(X[X^a], X[X^b])$. Then $\sigma_u X^a = X^b$ and, by (1.21),
$\sigma_u a = b$. Hence $\sigma_u a \cap b = a \cap b$ and

$$t(X[X^a], X[X^b]) = t(a \cap b[X^a], a \cap b[X^b]).$$

In the second case one proves similarly that the parallel to a and b through X
is $m(a,b)$.

We note two consequences. For $I = t_A \cap t_B$ it follows that

$$(I,I^b) \cong (I,I^c) \cong (I,I^a);$$

hence $I \in t_C$. I is called the incenter of the triangle.

(1.43)   *The angle bisectors of a triangle are concurrent.*

A *right* triangle is a triangle one of whose angles is right. The edges
adjacent to the right angle are usually called the *legs*. The third edge is the
hypotenuse, since it subtends the right angle ($\acute{v}\pi o\tau\epsilon\acute{\iota}vo\upsilon\sigma\alpha$ = the subtending).
The $\triangle(a \cap b, X^a, X)$ considered in the proof of (1.42) is a right triangle.
That proof then shows

(1.44)   *Two right triangles are congruent if the hypotenuses and one pair*
         of legs are congruent.

Exercise 1–5

1. Prove that $\triangle(A,B,C)$ is isosceles of vertex C if

    (a) $t_c = h_c$ (c) $t_c = s_c$

    (b) $s_c = h_c$ (d) $h_c = m_c$.

2. Is it true that $\triangle(A,B,C) \cong \triangle(A',B',C')$ if

    (a) $\triangle(A,B,O) \cong \triangle(A',B',O')$?

    (b) $\triangle(A,B,I) \cong \triangle(A',B',I')$?

3. Three non-collinear points are given in the plane. Does a triangle always
exist for which the three points are

    (a) A, B, I?   (b) A, B, O?

4. In every triangle, is the biggest edge opposite the biggest angle?

5. Justify (1.41) and (1.43) by showing that $m_a \cap m_b \neq \emptyset$, $t_A \cap t_B \neq \emptyset$.

6. Prove that a triangle is isosceles if it has two congruent altitudes.

7. Given three distinct lines which are concurrent at a point P, and a point A on
one of the lines, prove that there exists a triangle $\triangle(A,B,C)$ for which the given
lines are angle bisectors. The theorem has to be qualified; there is one case in which
no such triangle exists.

Chapter II

PRODUCTS OF REFLECTIONS

1. Pencils

The proof of (1.40) shows that two products of reflections are identical if their actions on one triangle are identical. Since a triangle can be mapped onto a congruent one by three reflections at most, it follows that any product of reflections is equal to the product of at most three reflections. Our next goal is to obtain more detailed information about the minimal number of reflections required in an isometry. This analysis is rather lengthy, but most of our intermediate results are important in their own right. We first state the result at which we are aiming.

(2.1)   *A product of an even number of reflections is equal to the product of two reflections. A product of an odd number of reflections is equal to either one reflection or the product of three reflections.*

As a consequence, a count of the number of reflections in a product Σ will eliminate the ambiguity in the applications of axiom XII. Theorem (2.1) will be established near the end of this section, after some preliminary arguments.

(2.2)   *No product of two reflections is equal to one reflection.*

The proof is by contradiction. If $\sigma_c = \sigma_b \sigma_a$, three cases are possible. If $a = b$, then $\sigma_c = \iota$; this is impossible by axiom VI. If $a \neq b$, the hypothesis is equivalent to

$$\sigma_a C = \sigma_b C \text{ for all } C \in c.$$

If $a \cap b = O$, the condition says that both a and b are $p[l(C,\sigma_a C),O]$; hence $a = b$, against our hypothesis. If $a \parallel b$, the same contradiction is obtained because both a and b must be $m(C,\sigma_a C)$.

(2.3)   *If three lines are either concurrent or parallel, then the product of the three reflections defined by these lines is equal to one reflection.*

If the lines are a, b, and c, we have to find d such that

$$\sigma_d = \sigma_c\sigma_b\sigma_a.$$

We may assume $a \neq b$, $b \neq c$, otherwise the result is trivial. If the lines are concurrent at O, let a_1 be one of the rays defined on a by O. Then

$$d = t(a_1, \sigma_c\sigma_b a_1).$$

In fact, it follows from

$$\sigma_d\sigma_c\sigma_b\sigma_a a_1 = a_1$$

by axiom XII and theorem (2.2) that

$$\sigma_d\sigma_c\sigma_b\sigma_a = \iota.$$

If the three lines are parallel, we choose an $A \in a$ and call a_1 one of the rays defined on a by A. Then

$$d = m(A, \sigma_c\sigma_b A).$$

The proof can be copied word for word from the first case.

We shall prove later in this chapter that the product of three reflections is equal to one reflection only if the lines are either concurrent or parallel. For the theory of reflections it is therefore convenient to have a common name for both cases. A set of lines is called a *pencil* if either (a) all lines are concurrent or (b) they are all parallel. A *maximal pencil* is either (a) the set of *all* lines through one point or (b) the set of *all* parallels to a given line. Maximal pencils are also called *ideal points* and, in particular, maximal pencils of parallel lines are *points at infinity*. The visual image behind this name refers to analytic geometry: if two lines tend to become parallel, their intersection will be removed farther and farther from any fixed point of reference. In our development of geometry we do not need any limit processes; therefore, we shall discard the imagery and retain the name. If a line belongs to a certain maximal pencil, we shall say that it passes through the ideal point. In many cases, this language lets us dispense with a separate treatment for concurrent and parallel lines. In this new language, (2.3) may be reformulated to read

(2.4)   *If three lines belong to an ideal point, any product of the three reflections defined by the lines is a reflection in a fourth line of the pencil.*

By axiom VIII, the theorem implies

$$(\sigma_c \sigma_b \sigma_a)^2 = \iota,$$

which, by (1.11), is the same as

(2.5) $\sigma_c \sigma_b \sigma_a = \sigma_a \sigma_b \sigma_c$ *if a, b, and c form a pencil.*

The next step in the proof of (2.1) is

(2.6)   *Any product of four reflections is equal to a product of two reflections.*

As before, we may assume that in the product $\sigma_d \sigma_c \sigma_b \sigma_a$ any two consecutive reflections are distinct. If three consecutive reflections are at lines of a pencil, they can be replaced by one reflection. Otherwise, a,b and c,d form two pencils. Here we have to consider two cases. If one of the pencils at least consists of concurrent lines, we may assume for definiteness that $a \cap b = P$. Through P there exists a line g in the maximal pencil defined by c and d. Then

$$\sigma_d \sigma_c \sigma_b \sigma_a = (\sigma_d \sigma_c \sigma_g)(\sigma_g \sigma_b \sigma_a)$$

is a product of two reflections by (2.4). If both pencils are formed by parallel lines, then $P = b \cap c$ does exist. Let x be a line through P distinct from b and c and define y by

$$\sigma_y = \sigma_x \sigma_b \sigma_c.$$

y is distinct from b and c. By (2.5),

$$
\begin{aligned}
\sigma_d \sigma_c \sigma_b \sigma_a &= \sigma_d (\sigma_c \sigma_b \sigma_x) \sigma_x \sigma_a \\
&= \sigma_d (\sigma_x \sigma_b \sigma_c) \sigma_x \sigma_a \\
&= \sigma_d \sigma_y \sigma_x \sigma_a.
\end{aligned}
$$

The last product is defined by two pencils of concurrent lines for which the statement (2.6) holds.

Theorem (2.1) follows from (2.6) by recursion. Any product of $n \geqslant 4$ reflections is the product of 4 and $(n - 4)$ reflections; hence, by (2.6), it is equal to a product of $2 + (n - 4) = n - 2$ reflections. Repeated application of this argument leads to (2.1).

As an application of (2.3), we compute the product of the reflections at the angle bisectors of a triangle. Since

$$\sigma_{t_C} \sigma_{t_B} \sigma_{t_A} b = \sigma_{t_C} \sigma_{t_B} c = \sigma_{t_C} a = b,$$

the fourth line, which belongs to the pencil of I, must be perpendicular to b:

$$\sigma_{t_C} \sigma_{t_B} \sigma_{t_A} = \sigma_{p(b,I)}.$$

For this and all similar formulas, the reader should draw a picture of the operations involved, in their action on an arbitrary point in the plane.

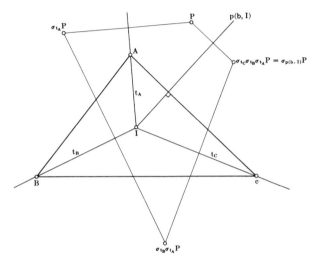

$$\text{FIG. 2–1}$$

Exercise 2–1

1. Compute $\sigma_{m_c}\sigma_{m_b}\sigma_{m_a}$.

2. If a product of n reflections is the identity, show that n is even.

3. If a, b, and c do not form a pencil, prove that

$$\sigma_a\sigma_h\sigma_a\sigma_b\sigma_c\sigma_h\sigma_b\sigma_c = \iota$$

is true only for $h = h_a$.

4. p,q,r are three lines through the vertices A,B,C of a triangle. Define $p' = \sigma_{t_A}p$; similarly for q' and r'.

    (a) Prove that $\sigma_{p'} = \sigma_c\sigma_p\sigma_b$.

    (b) Prove: if p,q,r form a pencil, so do p',q',r'.

Note: p' is called the *isogonal* of p with respect to the triangle. The ideal points defined by the pencils p,q,r and p',q',r' are *isogonal images* of one another. The same name applies to the vertices of the two pencils, if they exist.

5. (Sequel to 4.) The *reflection triangle* of a point S with respect to a $\triangle(A,B,C)$ is the $\triangle(\sigma_a S,\sigma_b S,\sigma_c S)$ if it exists.

    (a) Prove that the isogonal image of $l(S,A)$ is $m(\sigma_b S,\sigma_c S)$.

    (b) Prove that the isogonal image of S is the circumcenter of the reflection triangle, unless the vertices of the reflection triangle are collinear and the isogonal of S is an ideal point defined by a pencil of parallel lines.

6. What is the isogonal image of a point on a side of the complete triangle defined by A,B,C?

7. Compute $\sigma_{t_C}\sigma_{t_A}\sigma_{p(b,I)}$.

2. Rotations

If two lines a and b intersect at a point P, the product of their reflections is called a *rotation* about P, or of *center* P. Its symbol is

$$\rho_{P,2\alpha} = \sigma_b\sigma_a,$$

where α stands for the "oriented angle" from a to b. The reason for this notation can be seen from Fig. 2–2:

$$(P,X) \cong (P,\rho_{P,2\alpha}X),$$

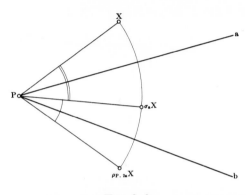

FIG. 2–2

and the angle at P of the isosceles triangle $\triangle(X,P,\rho_{P,2\alpha}X)$ is "twice" the angle from a to b, for an arbitrary X in the plane. In order to give sense to these statements, we must define oriented angles and addition of angles. We shall do so after some preliminary observations.

(2.7)   *If a rotation has more than one fixed point, it is the identity.*

If $\rho_{P,2\alpha}Q = Q$ and $Q \neq P$, then the rotation leaves $P[Q]$ fixed. By axiom XII and (2.2), it is the identity.

(2.8)   *Two ordered pairs of lines in the pencil of a point define the same rotation about that point if there exists a product of an even number of reflections in lines of the pencil which maps the lines of the first pair onto the lines of the second pair.*

Let the pairs be (a,b) and (c,d) in the maximal pencil of P. By (2.1) the hypothesis implies that there exist x and y in the pencil of P such that

$$c = \sigma_x\sigma_y a \qquad d = \sigma_x\sigma_y b.$$

Hence

$$\sigma_c\sigma_d = \sigma_x\sigma_y\sigma_a\sigma_y\sigma_x\sigma_x\sigma_y\sigma_b\sigma_y\sigma_x$$
$$= (\sigma_x\sigma_y\sigma_a)(\sigma_b\sigma_y\sigma_x)$$
$$= \sigma_a\sigma_y\sigma_x\sigma_x\sigma_y\sigma_b = \sigma_a\sigma_b.$$

An immediate consequence of this result is

(2.9)   *Any rotation can be given by an ordered pair of lines of which one can be prescribed arbitrarily in the pencil of lines through the center of the rotation.*

If $\rho = \sigma_b\sigma_a$ and c is given in the pencil of $a \cap b$, then

$$c = \sigma_c\sigma_{t(a_1,c_1)}a,$$

where the rays are defined somehow by the center of the rotation. Therefore, ρ is also equal to $\sigma_d\sigma_c$ if we put

$$d = \sigma_c\sigma_{t(a_1,c_1)}b.$$

We are now ready for the basic definitions. Two ordered pairs of lines belong to the same *oriented angle* if they are images of one another in a motion which is a product of an *even* number of reflections.

Oriented angles can be viewed in two different ways. We may represent any oriented angle in the plane by a rotation about a fixed point P. In fact, if $a \cap b = Q$, we simply have to transform a and b by $\sigma_{l(P,Q)}\sigma_{m(P,Q)}$ to obtain a pair of the same angle which defines a rotation about P. If we choose a fixed line a_0 through P, then, by (2.9), each oriented angle α defines a unique line $b(\alpha)$ through P such that $(a_0,b(\alpha))$ belongs to α.

(2.10)   *The oriented angles are in one-to-one correspondence with the lines through a fixed point.*

Alternately, the relation of belonging to the same oriented angle is a relation of equivalence in the set of ordered pairs of concurrent lines. The three conditions (1.10), (1.13), and (1.14) of a relation of equivalence are easily checked on the definition. The symbol α of an oriented angle stands for the set of all ordered pairs of concurrent lines which are equivalent by this definition. We shall allow ourselves the abuse of language to write $\alpha = (a,b)$, instead of $(a,b) \in \alpha$.

The composition of reflections lets us define an algebraic structure on the set of oriented angles. The additive notation is preferred for angles instead of the multiplicative notation used for the composition of functions. The reason for this preference will be discussed in chapter III. We define

(2.11)(i) $\gamma = \alpha + \beta$ *means* $\rho_{P,\gamma} = \rho_{P,\beta}\rho_{P,\alpha}$,

   (ii) $\gamma = -\alpha$ *means* $\rho_{P,\gamma} = (\rho_{P,\alpha})^{-1}$,

   (iii) $\gamma = 0°$ *means* $\rho_{P,\gamma} = \iota$,

   (iv) $\gamma = 180°$ *if* $\rho_{P,\gamma}$ *is the product of reflections in a pair of perpendiculars.*

By definition, it is clear that

(2.11)(v) $\alpha + 0° = 0° + \alpha = \alpha.$

By (2.9), it is always possible to represent two oriented angles by couples of lines in a pencil such that the first line of the first angle is the second line of the second angle:

$$\rho_{P,\alpha} = \sigma_b\sigma_a \qquad \rho_{P,\beta} = \sigma_c\sigma_b.$$

Then

$$\rho_{P,\alpha+\beta} = \sigma_c\sigma_a.$$

It is also possible to find b' such that $\rho_{P,\beta} = \sigma_{b'}\sigma_a$ and then c' such that $\rho_{P,\alpha} = \sigma_{c'}\sigma_{b'}$. Here

$$\rho_{P,\beta+\alpha} = \sigma_{c'}\sigma_a.$$

By definition,

$$\sigma_{c'}\sigma_{b'} = \sigma_b\sigma_a \qquad \sigma_{b'}\sigma_a = \sigma_c\sigma_b;$$

hence

$$\rho_{P,\beta+\alpha} = \sigma_{c'}\sigma_a = \sigma_{b}\sigma_a\sigma_{b'}\sigma_a = \sigma_{b'}\sigma_a\sigma_c\sigma_b$$
$$= \sigma_b\sigma_b\sigma_c\sigma_a = \sigma_c\sigma_a = \rho_{P,\alpha+\beta}.$$

This shows that the addition of angles is commutative:

(2.11)(vi) $\alpha + \beta = \beta + \alpha.$

The associative law

(2.11)(vii) $\alpha + (\beta + \gamma) = (\alpha + \beta) + \gamma = \alpha + \beta + \gamma$

follows from the associativity of the composition of functions. Since all the usual rules are valid for the addition of oriented angles, it is reasonable to write

(2.11)(viii) $\beta = n\alpha$ *if* $\rho_{P,\beta} = (\rho_{P,\alpha})^n.$

The distinction between the elementary angle $\angle (a_1,b_1)$ and the oriented angle (a,b) is important. To one elementary angle $\angle (a_1,b_2)$ there correspond two oriented angles (a,b) and (b,a) which are inverses of one another. To one oriented angle (a,b) there are four elementary angles $\angle(a_1,b_1)$, $\angle(a_1,b_2)$, $\angle(a_2,b_1)$, and $\angle(a_2,b_2)$. An elementary angle is a point set; an oriented angle is an equivalence class of rotations. The notion formalized by the definition of oriented angles is that which is used in analytic geometry. The main tool of analytic geometry is the slope of a line, i.e., the tangent of the angle between x-axis and line. Since the tangent function is periodic of period π, the slope is a function only of the ordered pair (x-axis, line) and is independent of the orientation given to the line. The formulae of analytic geometry give only the tan-function of the angle of two arbitrary lines; again, this is a function of the oriented angle of the lines in our sense.

Oriented angles are sets of ordered couples of lines, not of rays. They are distinct not only from elementary angles but also from the angles used in trigonometry. The latter are represented by a ray a_1 of vertex P and its image a_1 in a rotation of center P. That rotation is defined only up to multiples of a full turn. Since we consider rotations as mappings, we do identify the full turns to the identity map. Indeed, this is axiom VIII. Therefore, we have no need for trigonometric angles. They will be replaced by the individual rotations. (A further discussion of the nature of trigonometric angles will be found in chap. III, sec. 2.)

We want to stress again that the oriented angles defined by the legs of the angle $\angle APP_{P,\alpha}A$ are 2α and -2α. (a,b) represents a rotation which, according to our definitions, will have

twice

the angle of the rotation which brings a ray a_1 onto the corresponding ray b_1.

Oriented angles do not have interiors, and we are not going to define an order relation to compare them in size. Elementary angles (point sets) only will be compared in size. Trigonometric angles usually are also compared in size. We shall define the notion of a positive turn in chapter III. This notion is used usually to define an order relation for trigonometric angle by identifying positive turns and positive angles. However, we shall not follow this method since *it is not possible to identify the formal system of oriented angles to one derived from the real numbers without an additional axiom.* The use of numbers in geometry will again be discussed in later chapters. Here we note only that, by (1.17),

$$(2.11)(ix) \qquad 180° = -180°,$$

and, in our present framework, $360°$ is identified with $0°$. We shall see in section 5 that sometimes $360°$ or $0°$ need not correspond to any angle at all. The notation $°$ shall remind us of the symbolic character of the system.

In a triangle, it is possible without ambiguity to prefer one orientation of an elementary angle over the other. Therefore, we may use the symbols of the elementary angles also for the particular oriented angles defined by

$$\rho_{A,\hat{A}} c = b,$$

and similarly for the other angles by cyclic permutation. The definition means

$$\hat{A} = (b, t_A) = (t_A, c).$$

We want to emphasize again in this connection that (a,b) is *twice* the angle of the rotation which brings a into b.

Since

$$(b,a) = \sigma_{t(a,b)}(a,b),$$

it follows from the definition of oriented angles that

(2.12)   *Oriented angles that are images of one another by an odd number of reflections are negatives of one another.*

Next we show that the angle bisector deserves its name. Since

$$\big(t(a,b),b\big) = \sigma_{t(t(a,b),b)}\sigma_{t(a,b)}\big(a,t(a,b)\big),$$

we have

$$\big(t(a,b),b\big) = \big(a,t(a,b)\big).$$

By definition (2.11)(i), we have in general

(2.13) $(x,y) + (y,z) = (x,z)$

since the product of the corresponding rotations is

$$\sigma_z\sigma_y\sigma_y\sigma_x = \sigma_z\sigma_x.$$

In particular, this implies that

$$(a,b) = \big(a,t(a,b)\big) + \big(t(a,b),b\big) = 2\big(a,t(a,b)\big).$$

Consequently, axiom X can be reformulated to read:

axiom X.   *For every angle α there exists an angle $\alpha/2$.*

It is not true that our plane has to contain enough points and lines to assure the existence of an $\alpha/3$ for all α. In this sense our axiomatics is incomplete. We could replace axioms X and XI by much stronger axioms stating, e.g., that there is a one-to-one correspondence between oriented angles and real numbers in the interval $0 \leqslant r < 360$, and between segments and positive real numbers. Such axioms would identify the plane with that of analytic geometry. This approach is much too heavy since it uses the notion of limit, or some equivalent notion, without which the real numbers cannot be defined, and which not only is alien to the spirit of elementary geometry but also is very difficult. On the other hand, this approach will make us poorer since it will restrict the validity of our theorems to one particular type of plane only.

We shall see in chapter IV that our axioms can be made strong enough to assure the existence of the points of intersection of circles and lines. In the language of analytic geometry this means the existence of real solutions of quadratic equations. It is interesting to see that the constructions of euclidean geometry make sense if we admit in the plane of analytic geometry only, say, those points whose coordinates are numbers which appear as roots of quadratic equations with coefficients taken from the coordinates. The investigation of these "partial planes" is a major part of research in the foundations of geometry. We shall not treat these questions in this text. We only remark that a problem is called *unsolvable in elementary geometry* if the existence of a solution cannot be proved with our existence axioms II, III, X (or X*, sec. 4–1), and XI, i.e., as it will turn out, by intersections of lines and circles (straight edge and ruler). The famous examples of these problems are: the trisection of the angle, the existence of a segment equal to the circumference of a circle, and, in solid geometry, the duplication of the volume of a cube. As soon as we use analytic geometry and allow the full use of real numbers and of limit processes, all three problems become simple exercises in algebra or in calculus.

Naturally, all our results will be true in the full plane of analytic geometry based on real numbers. This will be shown later.

Exercise 2–2

1. Prove that the equality of oriented angles is an equivalence relation.

2. Prove that $(a,b) = (c,d)$ and $a \parallel c$ imply $b \parallel d$.

3. If a,b,c,d are four concurrent lines, show that $t(a,b) = t(c,d)$ if and only if $(a,c) = (b,d)$.

4. Are two congruent segments images of one another in a rotation if and only if they are not parallel?

5. To two parallels draw a common perpendicular such that the segment between the parallels subtends a given angle at a given point.

6. Given three parallel lines. Find an isosceles triangle whose vertices are on those parallels and which has a given angle as angle at the vertex opposite the base.

7. A and B are two points in the same halfplane of a line g. Find a point $X \in g$ such that

$$(l(A,X),g) = (g,l(X,B))$$

(problem of the reflection of light rays under equal angles).

8. *A* and *B* are two points in the interior of one of the elementary angles defined by two concurrent lines *a* and *b*. Find points $X \in a$ and $Y \in b$ such that a light ray issued from *A* and reflected at *X* and *Y* will pass through *B*.

9. *A* and *B* are two points in the same halfplane of a line *g*. Find a point $X \in g$ such that

$$(l(A,X),g) = 2(g,l(X,B)).$$

10. Prove that the set of rotations about a fixed point has an infinity of elements.

3. Point Reflections

The rotation $\rho_{P,180°}$ is the product of the reflections at *any* pair of perpendiculars through *P*. It is an involution since $a \perp b$ implies

$$\sigma_b\sigma_a\sigma_b\sigma_a = \sigma_b\sigma_b\sigma_a\sigma_a = \iota.$$

In line with our notation we give $\rho_{P,180°}$ the special symbol σ_P and call it the *reflection in the point P*.

If *A* is any point distinct from *P*,

$$\sigma_P = \sigma_{p[l(A,P),P]}\sigma_{l(A,P)}.$$

This implies:

(2.14) σ_P *maps every line through P onto itself. For all points A,*

$$P = M(A,\sigma_P A).$$

These properties characterize the reflection in P among all rotations of center P.

Another expression for the first statement of (2.14) is

(2.15) $\sigma_P\sigma_a = \sigma_a\sigma_P$ *if and only if* $P \in a.$

By (1.15), the relation is equivalent to $a = \sigma_P a$.

For any line *g*, σ_P maps $p(g,P)$ onto itself. By (1.21), this implies

$$\sigma_P g \perp p(g,P).$$

Hence $g \parallel \sigma_P g$ since both lines are perpendicular to $p(g,P)$, unless $P \in g$.

(2.16) σ_P *maps lines not through P onto parallel lines.*

A point reflection is a product of two line reflections and therefore maps oriented angles onto equal angles. By (2.14), $\sigma_{(MP,Q)}$ maps P into Q. Together with our last result, this proves

(2.17)   *An oriented angle can always be realized by ordered pairs of lines attached to arbitrary points.*

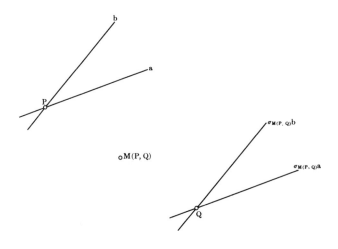

FIG. 2–3

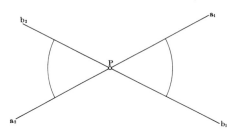

FIG. 2–4

Vertical angles are formed by opposite rays of a given angle at a vertex P. As elementary angles,

$$\angle\,(a_2,b_2) = \sigma_P \angle\,(a_1,b_1).$$

(2.18)   *Vertical angles are congruent.*

The two vertical angles define only one oriented angle. In the same way, one obtains the theorems about *alternate* angles. These are the angles formed by a transversal with two parallels. Alternate *interior* angles are the elementary angles lying in opposite halfplanes of the transversal in the strip between the parallels [see the proof of (1.26)].

(2.19)   *Alternate angles at parallels are equal as oriented angles. Alternate interior angles are congruent as elementary angles.*

The proof can be read from Fig. 2–5. The preceding theorems have the usual consequences for the exterior angles of a triangle and the sum of the angles in a triangle. The reasoning indicated in Fig. 2–6 shows (by (2.14)) that

$$\rho_{C},\hat{c}\rho_{C},\hat{A}\rho_{C},\hat{B} = \sigma_{C} = \rho_{C,180°}$$

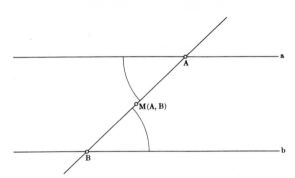

FIG. 2–5

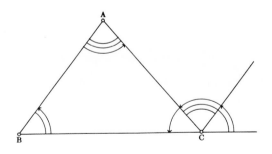

FIG. 2–6

or

(2.20) $\hat{B} + \hat{A} + \hat{C} = \hat{A} + \hat{B} + \hat{C} = 180°.$

For point reflections we have an analogue to (2.3).

(2.21)   *For any three points A, B, C, there exists a point D such that* $\sigma_{C}\sigma_{B}\sigma_{A} = \sigma_{D}.$

If $C \notin l(A,B)$, we denote by q the parallel to $l(A,B)$ through C. Otherwise, we put $q = l(A,B)$. Then

$$\sigma_C \sigma_B \sigma_A = \sigma_q \sigma_{p[l(A,B),C]} \sigma_{p[l(A,B),B]} \sigma_{l(A,B)} \sigma_{l(A,B)} \sigma_{p[l(A,B),A]}$$
$$= \sigma_q \sigma_{p[l(A,B),C]} \sigma_{p[l(A,B),B]} \sigma_{p[l(A,B),A]}.$$

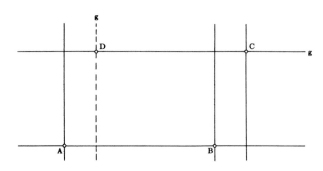

FIG. 2–7

By (2.3) there exists a line g in the pencil of perpendiculars to $l(A,B)$ such that

$$\sigma_g = \sigma_{p[l(A,B),C]} \sigma_{p[l(A,B),B]} \sigma_{p[l(A,B),A]}.$$

Hence $D = q \cap g$ by

$$\sigma_C \sigma_B \sigma_A = \sigma_q \sigma_g = \sigma_{q \cap g}.$$

Four points form a *parallelogram* if $\sigma_D \sigma_C \sigma_B \sigma_A = \iota$. (2.21) can be reformulated to read:

(2.22)   *Any three points in given order uniquely define a parallelogram.*

(2.21) implies that the product of three point reflections is an involution:

(2.23)   *For any three points A, B, and C,*

$$(\sigma_C \sigma_B \sigma_A)^2 = \iota, \ i.e., \ \sigma_C \sigma_B \sigma_A = \sigma_A \sigma_B \sigma_C.$$

Also by (2.21), any product of $n \geqslant 3$ point reflections is equal to the product of $n - 2$ point reflections. If n is odd, we are back to one reflection after a finite number of steps.

(2.24)   *A product of an odd number of point reflections is equal to one point reflection and hence is an involution.*

In particular, for any three points in the plane the operation $\sigma_C \sigma_B \sigma_A \sigma_C \sigma_B \sigma_A$ brings any point P in the plane onto itself. A similar result holds for any odd number of points.

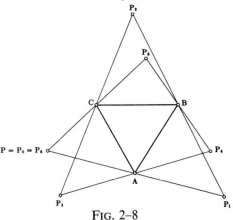

FIG. 2–8

Exercise 2–3

1. Prove the converse of (2.19).

2. If a product of n point reflections is the identity, is n even?

3. What is the sum of the angles of a convex n-gon? What is the angle at a vertex of a convex n-gon of only equal angles?

4. Prove that if P and Q are isogonal images of one another in a triangle $\triangle(A,B,C)$ (exercise 2–1, problem 4), then

$$(l(P,A),l(P,B)) + (l(Q,A),l(Q,B)) = 2\hat{C}.$$

5. If $\hat{A}$ is the greatest angle in a triangle, obtain a proof of (2.20) from Fig. 2–9.

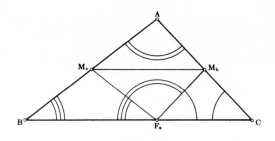

FIG. 2–9

6. For $P \neq Q$, prove that the midpoint is the only point R for which

$$\sigma_P \sigma_R \sigma_Q \sigma_R = \iota.$$

7. Which line x is characterized by

$$\sigma_Q \sigma_x \sigma_P \sigma_x = \iota?$$

8. A set S is *point symmetric* if there is a point P such that $\sigma_P S = S$; it is *line symmetric* if there is a line a such that $\sigma_a S = S$. Then P is called a *center*, and a an *axis* of symmetry of S.

(a) If a point symmetric figure is also line symmetric, then is $p(a,P)$ also an axis of symmetry?

(b) Find a set which has exactly three concurrent axes of symmetry. Is the point of concurrence a center of symmetry?

(c) Find a set that has more than one center of symmetry.

9. Find a point symmetric hexagon inscribed in a parallelogram (i.e., whose vertices are on the closed segments defined by successive vertices of the parallelogram).

10. Let S be a set having two axes of symmetry meeting under an angle which is an integral part of $180°$, say $180°/q$. ($\beta = \alpha/q$ if $q\beta = \alpha$.) Show that the intersection of the axes is a center of symmetry if q is even. If q is odd, the intersection of the axes may be distinct from the midpoint of the segments cut off by the set on the axis of symmetry, but the segments defined by that intersection on alternating axes of symmetry are congruent.

11. Find the triangle for which three given points are the midpoints of the edges.

12. Find the pentagon for which five given points are the midpoints of the edges.

13. a',b',c' are three lines perpendicular to the sides a,b,c of a complete triangle. Define $a'' = \sigma_{M_a} a'$ and similarly b'' and c''. Prove:

(a) $\sigma_{a''} = \sigma_C \sigma_{a'} \sigma_B$.

(b) If a',b',c' are concurrent, so are a'',b'',c''. In this case, $P'' = a'' \cap b'' \cap c''$ is the *isotomic image* of $P' = a' \cap b' \cap c'$. Pencils of parallel lines cannot appear.

(c) $P'' = \sigma_O P'$.

14. Given A, b, and c. A is not on one of the two lines. Find a square having one vertex at A and one vertex each on b and c.

15. Three points M,P,Q are given. Find a square of center M such that P and Q are on two consecutive sides (lines which carry edges) of the square.

16. Prove: if $t(P[A],P[B]) = t(P[C],P[D])$ and $t(P[B],P[C]) = t(P[A],P[D])$, then the four rays $P[A]$, $P[B]$, $P[C]$, and $P[D]$ lie by pairs on two lines.

17. Show that the two angle bisectors of two concurrent lines are perpendicular to one another.

18. To three given points P,Q,R and two lines a and b find a point $X \in a$ such that $\sigma_R \sigma_Q \sigma_P X \in b$.

19. Prove: if two parallelograms have either two consecutive vertices or two nonconsecutive vertices in common, then the remaining four points also define a parallelogram. (Compare the little Desargues and little Pascal theorems, sec. 4–3.)

20. Given three points P,Q,R, nine lines $k,l,m,k',k'',l',l'',m',m''$. Prove: if five of the equations

$$\sigma_{k'}\sigma_{k''} = \sigma_l \sigma_m \qquad \sigma_{l''}\sigma_{m'} = \sigma_R \sigma_Q$$
$$\sigma_{l'}\sigma_{l''} = \sigma_m \sigma_k \qquad \sigma_{m''}\sigma_{k'} = \sigma_P \sigma_R$$
$$\sigma_{m'}\sigma_{m''} = \sigma_k \sigma_l \qquad \sigma_{k''}\sigma_{l'} = \sigma_Q \sigma_P$$

are valid, so is the sixth.

4.   Translations

A *translation* is the product of two reflections in parallel lines

$$\tau = \sigma_b \sigma_a, \ a \parallel b.$$

The proof of (2.9) applies here also to show

(2.25)   *Two ordered pairs (a,b) and (c,d) of lines in a pencil of parallel lines define the same translation if there exists a Σ, product of an even number of reflections in lines of the pencil, which maps a into c and b into d. In particular, a translation can be given by a pair of lines of which one can be prescribed arbitrarily in its pencil.*

If a, b, c are given, $d = \sigma_c \sigma_{m(a,c)} b$.
The last case of the proof of (2.2) also shows:

(2.26)   *A translation has no fixed point unless it is the identity.*

If p is a perpendicular to a and b and $A = p \cap a$, $B = p \cap b$, then

$$\sigma_b \sigma_a = \sigma_b \sigma_p \sigma_p \sigma_a = \sigma_B \sigma_A.$$

Conversely, any product of two point reflections can be represented in this way.

(2.27)   *The translations are identical with the products of two point reflections. Any translation can be given by a pair of points of which one can be prescribed arbitrarily.*

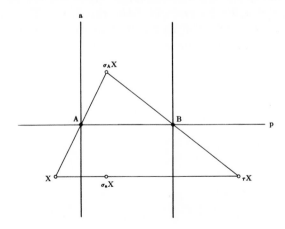

FIG. 2–10

The last statement follows from the fact that through any point there exists a line in any maximal pencil of parallel lines, and a perpendicular to the lines of the pencil.

(2.28)   _The product of two translations is a translation._

If $\tau_1 = \sigma_B \sigma_A$, then any other translation can be written $\tau_2 = \sigma_C \sigma_B$, hence $\tau_2 \tau_1 = \sigma_C \sigma_A$.

Just as rotations lead a double life as operations and as elements of oriented angles, so translations appear as operations and as _vectors_. Vector addition is a language parallel to the multiplication of translations, just as angle addition corresponds to multiplication of rotations. However, one angle as an equivalence class contains an infinity of distinct rotations, whereas vectors are identical to translations. The reason for this discrepancy will be discussed in the next chapter. Note also that our definition of a vector does not differ from the elementary one by a factor 2, as was the case for angles. This also can be justified by group theory.

> _The vector $a = [\![AB]\!]$ is defined to be the translation which maps A into B._

The translation of vector $a = [\![AB]\!]$ will be denoted by τ_a or by $\tau_{[\![AB]\!]}$. The notation makes sense since

(2.29)   _A translation is uniquely defined by a point and its image._

A possible candidate for $\tau_{[\![AB]\!]}$ is $\tau_1 = \sigma_{M(A,B)}\sigma_A$. If there is a τ_2 such that $\tau_2 A = B$, then $\tau_2^{-1}\tau_1 A = A$. By (2.27), the inverse of a translation is a translation, hence, by (2.26), $\tau_2^{-1}\tau_1 = \iota$, i.e., $\tau_2 = \tau_1$.

If the symbols of the points defining a vector are composite, we shall write for clarity $[\![A,B]\!]$; for example, $[\![M(\sigma_p Q, \sigma_r S), \tau_{[\![AB]\!]} T]\!]$.

We proceed to define an algebraic structure on the set of vectors. In this we follow the procedure used for oriented angles.

(2.30)(i) $c = a + b$ _means_ $\tau_c = \tau_b \tau_a$
(ii) $c = -a$ _means_ $\tau_c = \tau_a^{-1}$
(iii) $c = 0$ _means_ $\tau_c = \iota$
(iv) $c = na$ _means_ $\tau_c = (\tau_a)^n$ _for integer n._

The definitions immediately imply

(2.30)(v) $0 + a = a + 0 = a$
(vi) $a + (-a) = 0.$

For $a + (-b)$ we write $a - b$. The associative law

(2.30)(vii) $(a + b) + c = a + (b + c) = a + b + c$

again is a consequence of the associativity of the composition of functions. The commutative law is proved by an argument which imitates the proof of (2.11)(vi). In fact, (2.27) implies that any two translations may be represented as products of reflections involving only three points. For any two vectors a and b we may write

$$\tau_a = \sigma_B \sigma_A = \sigma_{C'} \sigma_{B'} \qquad \tau_b = \sigma_C \sigma_B = \sigma_{B'} \sigma_A,$$

hence

$$\tau_{b+a} = \sigma_{C'} \sigma_A = \sigma_B \sigma_A \sigma_{B'} \sigma_A = \sigma_B \sigma_A \sigma_C \sigma_B$$
$$= \sigma_{B'} \sigma_B \sigma_C \sigma_A = \sigma_C \sigma_A = \tau_{a+b}.$$

The formula of the commutative law

(2.30)(viii) $\qquad a + b = b + a$

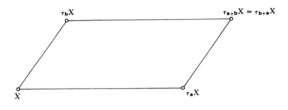

Fig. 2–11

is also known as the *parallelogram law* of vector addition. We justify our previous definition of a parallelogram by showing:

(2.31) For any X, a, and b, the four points X, $\tau_a X$, $\tau_{a+b} X$, $\tau_b X$ form a parallelogram.

For the proof we use the notations introduced for the proof of the commutative law.

$$\sigma_{\tau_b X} \sigma_{\tau_{a+b} X} \sigma_{\tau_a X} \sigma_X X = (\sigma_C \sigma_B \sigma_X \sigma_B \sigma_C)(\sigma_C \sigma_A \sigma_X \sigma_A \sigma_C)(\sigma_B \sigma_A \sigma_X \sigma_A \sigma_B)\sigma_X$$
$$= \sigma_C \sigma_B \sigma_X (\sigma_B \sigma_A \sigma_X)(\sigma_A \sigma_C \sigma_B)\sigma_A (\sigma_X \sigma_A \sigma_B)\sigma_X$$
$$= \sigma_C \sigma_B \sigma_X \sigma_X \sigma_A \sigma_B \sigma_B \sigma_C \sigma_A \sigma_A \sigma_B \sigma_A \sigma_X \sigma_X$$
$$= \sigma_C \sigma_B \sigma_A \sigma_C \sigma_B \sigma_A = \iota.$$

We may also note the useful formula which follows from (2.28):

(2.32) $\qquad [\![AB]\!] + [\![BC]\!] = [\![AC]\!].$

If we associate the segment (A,B) to the vector $[\![AB]\!]$, then all segments which correspond to one vector must be on parallel lines, and they must be congruent. More generally, vectors that are multiples of one another give rise to segments on parallels. Vectors that are negatives of one another correspond to parallel and congruent segments. Any product of an *even* number of point reflections equal to the identity

$$\sigma_{P_{2k}} \sigma_{P_{2k-1}} \cdots \sigma_{P_2} \sigma_{P_1} = \iota$$

is equivalent to a relation

$$2[\![P_1P_2]\!] + 2[\![P_3P_4]\!] + \cdots + 2[\![P_{2k-1}P_{2k}]\!] = \mathbf{0},$$

and hence also

$$[\![P_1P_2]\!] + [\![P_3P_4]\!] + \cdots + [\![P_{2k-1}P_{2k}]\!] = \mathbf{0}.$$

We apply this reasoning to polygons and triangles.

A finite ordered set of points $A_1, \ldots, A_n$ defines an *n*-gon. The points are the *vertices;* the segments (A_i, A_{i+1}) and (A_n, A_1) are the *edges* of the polygon. A quadrilateral (4-gon) naturally has two pairs of opposite edges (i.e., without common vertices).

The definition of a parallelogram

$$\sigma_D \sigma_C \sigma_B \sigma_A = \iota$$

is equivalent to either

$$[\![AB]\!] + [\![CD]\!] = \mathbf{0}$$

or

$$[\![BC]\!] + [\![DA]\!] = \mathbf{0}.$$

This proves:

(2.33)   *Opposite edges of a parallelogram are parallel and congruent.*

The midpoints of the edges of a polygon are $M_i = M(A_i, A_{i+1})$ and $M_n = M(A_n, A_1)$. For a quadrilateral we obtain

$$\sigma_{M_4} \sigma_{M_3} \sigma_{M_2} \sigma_{M_1} A_1 = A_1,$$

which implies by (2.28) and (2.26)

$$\sigma_{M_4} \sigma_{M_3} \sigma_{M_2} \sigma_{M_1} = \iota.$$

(2.34)   *The midpoints of the edges of a quadrilateral form a parallelogram.*

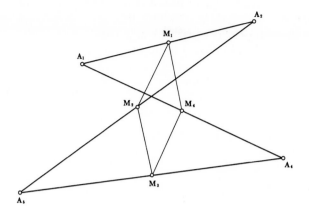

FIG. 2–12

The same reasoning can be applied to any polygon of an even number of vertices. For example, for a hexagon

$$\sigma_{M_6}\sigma_{M_5}\sigma_{M_4}\sigma_{M_3}\sigma_{M_2}\sigma_{M_1} = \iota,$$

which is the same as

$$\sigma_{M_5}\sigma_{M_4}\sigma_{M_3}\sigma_{M_2}\sigma_{M_1}\sigma_{M_6} = \iota$$

and, therefore, implies

$$[\![M_1M_2]\!] + [\![M_3M_4]\!] + [\![M_5M_6]\!] = \mathbf{0}$$

and

$$[\![M_6M_1]\!] + [\![M_2M_3]\!] + [\![M_4M_5]\!] = \mathbf{0},$$

which means

(2.35)   *The segments (M_1,M_2), (M_3,M_4), and (M_5,M_6), formed by the midpoints of the edges of a hexagon, form a triangle when brought together by translations so that the endpoint of one segment is the starting point of the next one. The same holds for the other three segments.*

The last two results can be considered as conditions which a set of $2n$ points must fulfill in order to be the set of midpoints of a $2n$-gon. In contrast, any odd number of points are the midpoints of a polygon with an odd number of vertices (see exercise 2–3, problems 11, 12).

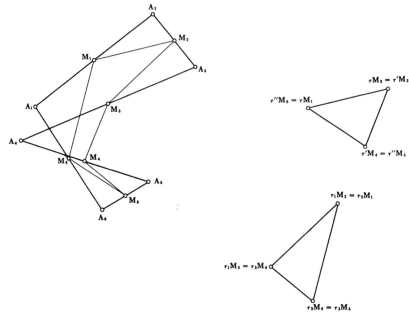

FIG. 2–13

For the triangle, we use the standard notations introduced in chapter I, sec. 5. By definition of the circumcenter,

$$[\![OB]\!] = [\![OM_a]\!] + [\![M_aB]\!]$$
$$[\![OC]\!] = [\![OM_a]\!] + [\![M_aC]\!] = [\![OM_a]\!] - [\![M_aB]\!].$$

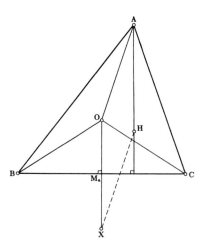

FIG. 2–14

We define a point X by

$$[\![OX]\!] = 2[\![OM_a]\!] = [\![OB]\!] + [\![OC]\!].$$

By construction, $l(O,X) = m_a$. If we define H by

$$[\![OH]\!] = [\![OX]\!] + [\![OA]\!] = [\![OA]\!] + [\![OB]\!] + [\![OC]\!],$$

then the four points O, X, H, and A form a parallelogram since

$$[\![OX]\!] + [\![HA]\!] = [\![OX]\!] + [\![HO]\!] + [\![OA]\!] = \mathbf{0}.$$

By (2.32), $l(A,H)$ is the parallel to m_a through A; it is the altitude h_a. The choice of names is arbitrary, and the definition of H is symmetric in A, B, and C. Therefore, H is on all three altitudes:

(2.36)   *The three altitudes of a triangle are concurrent at a point H, the orthocenter of the triangle, defined by*

$$[\![OH]\!] = [\![OA]\!] + [\![OB]\!] + [\![OC]\!].$$

The next main result will be proved in three steps.

(2.37)   *The diagonals of a parallelogram bisect each other.*

The diagonals of a polygon are the segments defined by vertices which are not edges. It can be seen from Fig. 2–15 [using (2.19)] that

$$\sigma_{M(A,C)}\Delta(A,B,C) = \Delta(C,D,A).$$

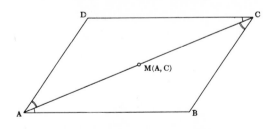

FIG. 2–15

In particular, $D = \sigma_{M(A,C)}B$, hence $M(A,C) = M(B,D)$.

(2.38)   *The line through a midpoint of an edge of a triangle parallel to a side meets the third edge at its midpoint.*

Let X be the intersection with c of the parallel to a through M_b. Define Y by

$$\triangle(M_b, Y, C) = \sigma_{M_b} \triangle(M_b, X, A).$$

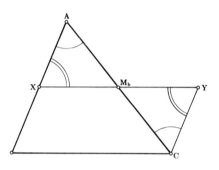

FIG. 2–16

B, C, Y, and X form a quadrilateral whose opposite edges are parallel. This condition uniquely defines the fourth point out of three, so does (2.21). Therefore, the four points form a parallelogram by (2.33). This means that opposite edges are also congruent,

$$(B,X) \cong (Y,C) \cong (X,A)$$

and $X = M_c$. The proposition is equivalent to the statement

$$l(M_b, M_c) \parallel a.$$

(2.39)   *The medians of a triangle are concurrent at the centroid G.*

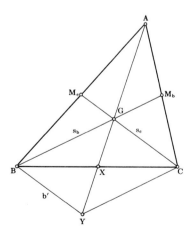

FIG. 2–17

Define $G = s_b \cap s_c$. Draw $b' \parallel s_c$ through B and put $Y = b' \cap l(A,G)$, $X = a \cap l(A,G)$. By (2.38), $G = M(A,Y)$. Hence also $s_b \parallel l(Y,C)$ by the same theorem applied to $\triangle(A,Y,C)$. The same argument as that one used in the proof of (2.38) shows that B,Y,C,G define a parallelogram. X is the intersection of the diagonals in that parallelogram, hence $X = M_a$ and $l(A,G) = s_a$ by (2.37).

The equation

$$[\![GB]\!] + [\![BY]\!] + [\![YG]\!] = 0$$

by the definition of G is equivalent to

(2.40) $[\![GA]\!] + [\![GB]\!] + [\![GC]\!] = 0,$

or, (Fig. 2–18),

$$\sigma_C \sigma_G \sigma_B \sigma_G \sigma_A \sigma_G = \iota.$$

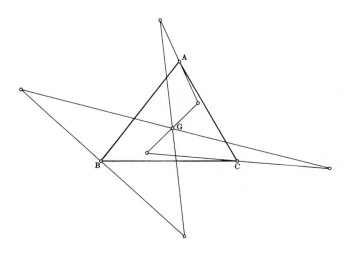

FIG. 2–18

If we combine (2.40) with the defining equation of H, we obtain

$$
\begin{aligned}
[\![OH]\!] &= [\![OA]\!] + [\![OB]\!] + [\![OC]\!] \\
&= [\![OG]\!] + [\![GA]\!] + [\![OG]\!] + [\![GB]\!] + [\![OG]\!] + [\![GC]\!] \\
&= 3[\![OG]\!].
\end{aligned}
$$

(2.41)   *The circumcenter O, centroid G, and orthocenter H of a triangle are collinear and $[\![GH]\!] = 2[\![OG]\!]$.*

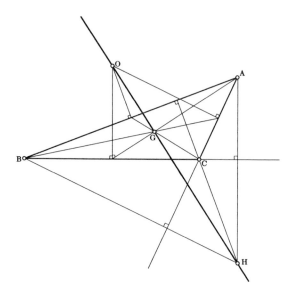

FIG. 2–19

The line which contains the three remarkable points O, G, and H is the *Euler line* of the triangle.

A special case of vector addition is the addition of vectors on one line. This can be used to define *length* of segments. On a fixed line l we choose a point O and designate one of the rays of O as the positive one. A point $A \in l$ defines both a vector $[\![OA]\!]$ and a segment (O,A). As long as we deal with segments on one line only, we usually drop the symbol $[\![\ \ ]\!]$ and define the vector $a = OA$, A in the positive ray, as the *length* of any segment (X,Y) congruent to (O,A) (or $[O,A]$). The same length is also denoted by XY. The length XY is distinct from the vector $[\![X,Y]\!]$; it is a vector realized by a segment (O,A) in some fixed ray, subject to $(X,Y) \cong (O,A)$. Since lengths are vectors, the rules (2.30) show that lengths may be added by the formal rules of addition of numbers. As long as we stay on one line, we may even define vectors OY, Y not in the positive ray, as the negative of the length $O\sigma_O Y$. In this way we are able to subtract lengths. It must be remarked that this is only possible if we restrict our attention to one line only. It is not possible to define a positive ray on each line so that rotations and translations always map positive rays onto positive rays. In fact, σ_O maps the positive onto the negative ray of l itself. But if we remember this limitation, the introduction of positive rays on arbitrary lines is an important tool, as we shall see in chapter V.

The comparison of segments induces a comparison of length by the definition

$$OA > OB \text{ if and only if } (O,A) > (O,B).$$

This means that $[[OA]] = [[OB]] + [[BA]]$, where $[[BA]] = [[OC]]$ and C is in the positive ray of O. This can be reformulated without reference to segments:

(2.42)   *If a and b are lengths, then $a > b$ if and only if the vector $a - b$ is equal to a length.*

For any other length c, the difference vector $(a + c) - (b + c)$ is equal to $a - b$:

(2.43) $a > b$ *implies* $a + c > b + c$.

   Products of lengths will be defined in chapter V. We shall also see in that chapter that our axioms guarantee the existence of a length a/n for all length a and all natural numbers n. Since the choice of l was arbitrary, this implies the existence of a vector $(1/n)v$ for all vectors v, in contrast to the situation found for oriented angles.

   The numbers of the real number system have the following property, which is known as the *axiom of Archimedes:*

axiom (A)   *If $a \geqslant 0$, $b > 0$, and $a < (1/n)b$ for all natural numbers n, then $a = 0$.*

Our axioms do not imply the axiom of Archimedes for lengths. An example of a geometry which satisfies our axioms I to XIII, but in which axiom (A) does not hold, is given in the appendix. The axiom of Archimedes is of an analytical, computational character and is not of fundamental importance in geometry. We shall need it only in secs. 3–3 and 8–1 to show that in an archimedean plane [i.e., a plane for which axiom (A) holds] certain configurations or maps are possible only in finitely many cases. The importance of the axiom of Archimedes in geometry is restricted to such counting problems. Therefore, we do not want to assume it, in general, and do not try to identify the lengths of segments with a subset of the positive real numbers.

Exercise 2–4

1. Find admissible a and b for given A and B in

$$\sigma_B \sigma_A = \sigma_b \sigma_a.$$

2. Find B if A, a, b are given in $\sigma_B \sigma_A = \sigma_b \sigma_a$.

3. Prove that $[[AB]] = 2[[A, M(A,B)]]$.

4. Which relation between AB and CB is expressed by

$$\sigma_A \sigma_B \sigma_C \sigma_B \sigma_C \sigma_B = \iota?$$

5. If $a \parallel b$, prove that for any point P in the plane

$$(\sigma_a \sigma_b \sigma_P)^2 = \iota.$$

6. If $a > b$ for two segments on a line, prove that $na > nb$ for all natural numbers n.

7. Given a parallelogram, show that for any point in the plane distinct from the points of the parallelogram there exists a quadrilateral for which the given point is the vertex A_1 and the parallelogram the set of midpoints of the edges (in contrast to exercise 2–3, problems 11 and 12).

8. Find the set of all points for which the sum of the distances (lengths of the segments on the perpendicular) from two given lines is a given length.

9. Prove that $\sigma_a\sigma_b\sigma_P\sigma_Q\sigma_b\sigma_a\sigma_Q\sigma_P = \iota$ implies either $Q = P$ or $(\sigma_a\sigma_b\sigma_Q)^2 = \iota$.

10. Prove that $\tau_v\sigma_A$ is a point reflection σ_Q and find Q.

11. Show that the sum of the lengths of the perpendiculars from any point of the base of an isosceles triangle to the legs is equal to the length of the perpendicular from one base vertex to the opposite leg.

12. If the point G is defined by $[\![AG]\!] = 2[\![GM_a]\!]$, then also $[\![CG]\!] = 2[\![GM_c]\!]$.

13. Deduce from the result of problem 12 a proof of the existence of the centroid, and a proof that the length of the segment between vertex and centroid is twice the length of the segment between centroid and opposite midpoint.

14. A and B are points in the strip between two parallel lines p and q. Find a light ray which is issued from A and reflected twice in each of p and q (first reflection at p) and passes through B.

15. Given four points in the plane. Find a square such that each point, in given order, is on one side of the square.

16. Given three points A, P, Q. Find a square of vertex A such that those of its sides which do not contain A pass through Q, P, respectively.

17. The parallel to a through I meets b at M and c at N. Prove that $MN = CM + BN$. How would the corresponding statement read for the parallel to c through the intersection of the external bisectors of $\hat{B}$ and $\hat{C}$?

18. Three concurrent lines are given and a point A on one of them. Prove that, in general, there exists a triangle:

  (a) of vertex A for which the lines are altitudes (one exceptional case),
  (b) such that A is a midpoint of an edge and the lines are the perpendicular bisectors,
  (c) of vertex A for which the lines are medians.

19. Prove that $(a,b) = (c,d)$ if and only if $\sigma_c\sigma_d\sigma_b\sigma_a$ is a translation.

20. Show that $(a,b) = (c,d)$ if and only if the same holds for the angles formed by the perpendiculars through a fixed point: $(p(a,X),p(b,X)) = (p(c,X),p(d,X))$.

21. Prove that O and H are isotomic images of one another in the triangle $\triangle(M_a,M_b,M_c)$.

22. Prove: if the quadrilateral $ABCP$ has right angles at A and C, then the orthocenter H of $\triangle(A,B,C)$ is $M(\sigma_A P,\sigma_C P)$.

5. Glide Reflections

We now turn to a discussion of products of three reflections. If the three lines a, b, and c are in a pencil, the product is equal to one reflection.

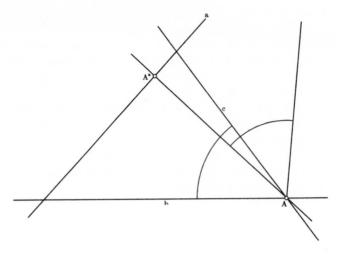

FIG. 2–20

Therefore, we have to discuss here the cases (a) the three lines are the sides of a complete triangle, and (b) two of the lines are parallel, the third is a transversal. For definiteness, let us assume that $A = b \cap c$ does exist. By (2.9) there exists d such that $\sigma_c \sigma_b = \sigma_d \sigma_{p(a,A)}$. Hence

$$\sigma_c \sigma_b \sigma_a = \sigma_d \sigma_{A^a}.$$

By the same argument, there exists a d' such that

$$\sigma_c \sigma_b \sigma_a = \sigma_{(a \cap b)^c} \sigma_{d'}$$

unless $a \parallel b$. But even in this case, we may replace $\sigma_c \sigma_b$ by some $\sigma_{c'} \sigma_{p(a,b \cap c)}$. Then we are back in the case $a \cap b \neq \emptyset$ and can obtain the desired representation.

(2.44)   *The product of three reflections in lines that do not form a pencil is equal to the product of a point reflection and a line reflection (in either order).*

For any such product $\sigma_l \sigma_P$ we may represent the point reflection by the product of the parallel m and the perpendicular n to l through P. If d is the vector which brings P into $n \cap l$, then

$$\sigma_l \sigma_P = \sigma_l \sigma_m \sigma_n = \tau_{2d} \sigma_n.$$

The product of a translation of vector v and a reflection in a line g parallel to v is called a *glide reflection* $\gamma_{v,g}$.

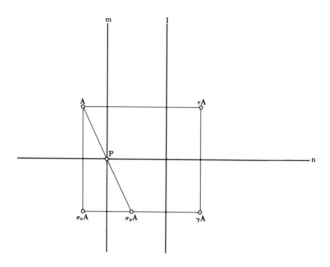

FIG. 2–21

(2.45)   *The product of three reflections in lines that do not form a pencil is a glide reflection.*

If the three lines are in a pencil, their product still can be considered as a glide reflection, namely of vector $v = 0$.

Since n is perpendicular to both l and m, we may also write

$$\gamma_{2d,n} = \sigma_n \tau_{2d}.$$

Therefore,

$$\gamma_{2d,n}^2 = \tau_{4d}.$$

This result contains the converse of theorem (2.3):

(2.46)   *For any three lines, $(\sigma_c \sigma_b \sigma_a)^2$ is a translation. It is the identity if and only if the lines form a pencil.*

It is now possible to reformulate theorem (2.1) in a more specific way:

(2.47)   *A motion is equal to one of the following:*

     (a) *line reflection σ_l*   (d) *translation τ_d*

     (b) *point reflection σ_P*   (e) *glide reflection $\gamma_{d,l}$.*

     (c) *rotation $\rho_{P,\alpha}$*

Each of these operations is the product of at most two involutions.

Theorem (2.46) has a curious consequence. Since translations are commutative, it is true that

$$(\sigma_a\sigma_b\sigma_c)^2(\sigma_b\sigma_c\sigma_a)^2 = (\sigma_b\sigma_c\sigma_a)^2(\sigma_a\sigma_b\sigma_c)^2,$$

and three arbitrary point reflections in the plane are always connected by a relation. If we multiply out and bring everything to one side, we obtain *Thomsen's relation:*

(2.48)   *Any three line reflections are connected by*

$$\sigma_a\sigma_b\sigma_c\sigma_a\sigma_b\sigma_c\sigma_b\sigma_c\sigma_a\sigma_b\sigma_c\sigma_a\sigma_c\sigma_b\sigma_a\sigma_c\sigma_b\sigma_c\sigma_b\sigma_a\sigma_c\sigma_b = \iota.$$

Exercise 2–5

1. Prove: if a glide reflection has a fixed point, it is a line reflection.

2. Prove: a point P is on a line l if and only if $\sigma_P\sigma_l$ is an involution.

3. Prove: if $\sigma_a\sigma_b\sigma_c\sigma_R\sigma_c\sigma_b\sigma_a\sigma_R = \iota$ for some point R, then the three lines form a pencil.

4. If $A \neq B$, prove that $g \perp l(A,B)$ if and only if $\sigma_A\sigma_g\sigma_B$ is an involution and $g \neq l(A,B)$.

5. If three lines form a complete triangle, prove that

$$\sigma_a(\sigma_b\sigma_a\sigma_c)^2\sigma_a(\sigma_c\sigma_a\sigma_b)^2 = \iota$$

implies that the triangle is isosceles of vertex A.

6. Prove: the isotomic image of a point P for $\triangle(A,B,C)$ is the circumcenter of $\triangle(\sigma_AP, \sigma_BP, \sigma_CP)$.

7. Prove: if three points on the sides of a complete triangle are collinear, so are their isotomic images for the triangle.

6.   Products of Rotations

We look for a formula for the product of two rotations about different centers. Two such rotations can always be written as

$$\rho_{A,\alpha} = \sigma_c\sigma_b \qquad \rho_{B,\beta} = \sigma_a\sigma_c,$$

where $c = l(A,B)$. Then

$$\rho_{B,\beta}\rho_{A,\alpha} = \sigma_a\sigma_b.$$

If a and b are not parallel, we obtain by (2.20) (see Fig. 2–22)

(2.49) $\rho_{B,\beta}\rho_{A,\alpha} = \rho_{C,\alpha+\beta},$

where $C = \rho_{B,\beta/2}l(A,B) \cap \rho_{A,-\alpha/2}l(A,B).$

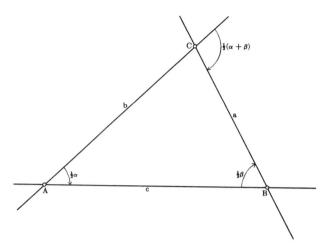

FIG. 2–22

If $b \parallel a$, $\alpha + \beta$ is an integer multiple of 360°, and the product of the two reflections is a translation [see the remark after (2.11)(ix)]:

$$(2.50) \qquad \rho_{B,\beta}\rho_{A,\alpha} = \tau \; if \; \alpha + \beta = k \cdot 360°.$$

By (2.26),

(2.51)   *If the sum of the angles in a product of rotations is an integer multiple of 360° and if the product admits a fixed point, it is the identity.*

We give some illustrations and applications of these results.

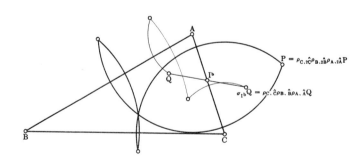

FIG. 2–23

The product of the rotations about the vertices of a triangle by twice the angles at the vertices is the identity:

$$(2.52) \qquad \rho_{C,2\hat{C}}\rho_{B,2\hat{B}}\rho_{A,2\hat{A}} = \sigma_a\sigma_b\sigma_b\sigma_c\sigma_c\sigma_a = \iota.$$

The product of the rotations about the vertices by the angles of the triangle must be a point reflection, since the angle sum is 180°. In the computation we use (1.16) and the formula of Fig. 2–1:

$$(2.53) \qquad \begin{aligned} \rho_{C,\hat{C}}\rho_{B,\hat{B}}\rho_{A,\hat{A}} &= \sigma_b\sigma_{t_c}\sigma_{t_b}\sigma_c\sigma_{t_a}\sigma_b \\ &= \sigma_b\sigma_{t_c}\sigma_{t_b}\sigma_{t_a} \\ &= \sigma_b\sigma_{p(b,I)} = \sigma_{I^b}. \end{aligned}$$

A triangle is *equilateral* if its three edges are of equal length. The existence of equilateral triangles for any length of edges will be established in chapter V For an equilateral triangle, perpendicular bisectors, altitudes, angle bisectors, and medians coincide. The incenter is identical to the circumcenter, the orthocenter, and the centroid. If m is any perpendicular bisector of the equilateral triangle, then $\sigma_m\triangle = \triangle$. Hence all angles are congruent, and also

$$\angle AOB \cong \angle BOC \cong \angle COA.$$

In oriented angles,

$$(2.54) \qquad \rho_{O,120°}A = B.$$

On the edges of an arbitrary triangle $\triangle(A,B,C)$ we construct equilateral triangles in the exterior of the triangle. The circumcenters of these triangles, in cyclic order, are O_a, O_b, and O_c. By (2.54),

$$\rho_{O_b,120°}\rho_{O_a,120°}\rho_{O_c,120°}A = A,$$

hence, by (2.51),

$$\rho_{O_b,120°}\rho_{O_a,120°}\rho_{O_c,120°} = \iota.$$

Let X be the third vertex of the equilateral triangle constructed over the edge $[O_c,O_a]$ in the halfplane of O_b. By (2.52),

$$\rho_{X,120°}\rho_{O_a,120°}\rho_{O_c,120°} = \iota.$$

The last two equations together imply

$$\rho_{O_b,120°} = \rho_{X,120°}.$$

This is possible only for $O_b = X$.

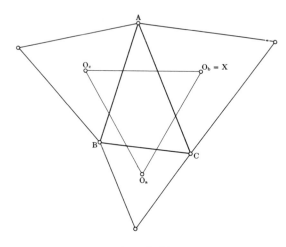

FIG. 2–24

(2.55)   *The circumcenters of the equilateral triangles constructed on the edges of an arbitrary triangle in the exterior of the triangle form an equilateral triangle.*

Exercise 2–6

1. Given ρ_1 and ρ_2. Find a point A such that

$$\rho_1 A = \rho_2 A.$$

Discuss the existence of such a point.

2. Prove that the center of $\rho_1\rho_2\rho_1^{-1}$ is on the line defined by the centers of ρ_1 and ρ_2.

3. For any two rotations, prove that the center of $\rho_1\rho_2$ and that of $\rho_2\rho_1$ are images of one another in the reflection in the line which joins the centers of ρ_1 and ρ_2.

4. Given three points A_1, A_2, A_3 and three angles α_1, α_2, α_3. Find a triangle such that the given points are the vertices of isosceles triangles for which the edges of the desired triangles are bases, and the α_i are the vertical angles of the isosceles triangles. In particular, discuss the case $\alpha_1 + \alpha_2 + \alpha_3 = k \cdot 360°$.

5. Find a formula for

$$\rho_{B,-\beta}\rho_{A,-\alpha}\rho_{B,\beta}\rho_{A,\alpha}.$$

Chapter III

GROUPS

1. Groups and Homomorphisms

The theory of reflections and of classification of motions is part of *group theory*, a discipline in abstract algebra. The main topic of group theory is the study of the properties common to all sets on which a reasonable multiplication (composition) is defined. We shall start with an abstract discussion of groups; this will help us to better understand the structure of plane geometry. We shall also discuss some examples from the theory of numbers.

A *group* is a set G such that to any ordered pair (a,b) of elements of G there exists a unique element $c \in G$, denoted by ab, for which the following properties hold:

(i) $(ab)c = a(bc)$ for any three elements in G

(ii)   there exists an element ι (the unit) in G such that $a\iota = \iota a = a$ for all $a \in G$

(iii)   for any $a \in G$ there exists an element $a^{-1} \in G$ such that $a^{-1}a = aa^{-1} = \iota$.

Condition (i) is the associative law which we have met in the composition of functions. If it holds, the product of three elements is independent of the order in which the multiplications are executed (but naturally in general not independent of the order of the elements). As a consequence, parentheses may be dropped for the multiplication in groups,

$$(ab)c = a(bc) = abc,$$

just as for the composition of transformations.

We note some immediate consequences of the definitions.

(3.1)   *A group contains only one unit.*

59

If ι^* is another unit in G, then, by definition, $\iota = \iota^*$. But also, by the definition of ι, $\iota^* = \iota^*$. Hence $\iota = \iota^*$.

(3.2)   *The inverse a^{-1} of any element a is unique.*

The proof contains an application of the associative law (i). If both a^{-1} and a_*^{-1} are elements which satisfy the condition (iii), then

$$a_*^{-1} = \iota a_*^{-1} = (a^{-1}a)a_*^{-1} = a^{-1}(aa_*^{-1}) = a^{-1}\iota = a^{-1}.$$

As a consequence, if we have found *an* inverse of some element a, we know that it is *the* inverse. As an application of this remark, we prove that

(3.3) $(a^{-1})^{-1} = a.$

The inverse x of a^{-1} is an element of G which satisfies $xa^{-1} = a^{-1}x = \iota$. The element a fits that description by definition (iii).

We now list some examples of groups.

All products of reflections form the group $\mathfrak{M}$ of *motions* in the plane. The group property follows from the associative law for reflections, the existence of the identity mapping in the plane as unit, and the existence of an inverse by (1.11).

The products of an *even* number of reflections (rotations and translations) form the group $\mathfrak{M}^+$ of *proper motions* in the plane. Since every proper motion is a motion, the associative law holds. Also, the product of two proper motions is a proper motion. The identity is a proper motion by axiom VIII. The inverse of a proper motion is a proper motion by (1.11).

The products of an *odd* number of reflections do not form a group.

The rotations about a fixed point P form a group $\mathfrak{R}_P$. The proof of the group property is left as an exercise. Equation (2.50) shows that the set of *all* rotations is not a group since the product of two rotations is not necessarily a rotation. The proof of (2.50) shows that every translation can be obtained as the product of two rotations. Therefore, $\mathfrak{M}^+$ is the smallest group which contains all rotations. The smallest group which contains a given set of elements is uniquely defined by that set. The technical term is that the smallest group is *generated* by the set.

(3.4) $\mathfrak{M}^+$ *is generated by the rotations.*

The set of all translations is a group $\mathfrak{J}$. The group property can be derived from (2.28) and (2.32). The set of vectors on one line (i.e., the set of lengths and their negatives) forms a group $\mathfrak{L}$.

All motions which leave a point P fixed form a group $\mathfrak{g}_P$. The elements of $\mathfrak{g}_P$ are the rotations of center P and the reflections in lines containing P.

For a fixed natural number n, the rotations about a point P of angles

$(k/n) \cdot 360°$, $0 \leqslant k < n$, k an integer, form a group $\mathcal{Z}_{P,n}$ if a rotation of angle $360°/n$ exists in the geometry. This group can be visualized as the set of rotations about P which bring a regular n-gon of center P onto itself.

The real numbers with the operation $+$ and the unit $\iota = 0$ form a group **R**. This means that we define "ab" in the group as the $a + b$ of ordinary arithmetic. The operation "times" does not define a group on the real numbers since 0 has no inverse. But the *positive* real numbers with multiplication as the group operation and $\iota = 1$ as unit define a group **R***.

Similarly, the integers under addition form a group **Z**. The positive integers do not form a group under multiplication since the inverse of an integer is not an integer unless it is 1.

Another type of arithmetic group can be defined by remainders in division. For any natural number $n > 0$ we define a group structure on the set of integers $0, 1, \ldots, n - 1$, by

$$a + b = \begin{array}{ll} a + b & \text{if } a + b < n \\ a + b - n & \text{if } a + b \geqslant n. \end{array}$$

In accordance with the additive notation, the inverse will be written as $-a$. By the definitions, $-a = n - a$. The identity is 0. An alternative description of this group $\mathbf{Z}_n$ is the following: The result of the operation $+$ is obtained from $a + b$ if we replace each number by its smallest non-negative remainder in division by n. [In number theory, one usually retains $+$ as sign for the operation we have named $+$, but then changes $=$ into $\equiv$, or $\equiv$ (mod n). These notations are based on the theory of rings, rather than that of groups.]

In the same way, we can define a group $\mathbf{R}_{2\pi}$ on the real numbers $0 \leqslant r < 2\pi$ if we replace the sum of any two such numbers by its remainder in division with 2π.

In addition to the group properties (i), (ii), and (iii), the groups $\mathcal{R}_P$, $\mathcal{Z}_{P,n}$, $\mathfrak{I}$, $\mathfrak{L}$, and all the groups defined on numbers have the property that

(c) $$ab = ba$$

for all couples of elements. The property (c) is the *commutative* law. If it holds, the group is called *commutative*, or *abelian*. For abelian groups, the notation $a + b$ for the group operation is preferred over the multiplicative notation ab. Naturally, this is done only if it is possible without complications. For example, the rotations about a fixed point are both elements of the abelian group $\mathcal{R}_P$ and the non-abelian group $\mathfrak{M}$. Since we consider rotations as motions, their composition must be written as a product. But if we use the language of oriented angles, we sever the relation with those motions that are not rotations, and, therefore, we may use the additive notation. A similar remark applies to translations and vectors.

The group $\mathcal{Z}_{P,n}$ contains an element x [the rotation about P of angle

$(360/n)°]$ such that all elements of the group can be written as x^k. Such a group is called *cyclic.* Since

$$x^k x^m = x^{k+m} = x^{m+k} = x^m x^k \qquad (m,k \text{ integer}),$$

a cyclic group is abelian. If we use the additive notation, as for vectors and oriented angles, we have to write kx instead of x^k. Here the integer k is not an element of the group; it is an operation symbol defined by

$$kx = x + x + \cdots + x \qquad (k \text{ times}).$$

For instance, $\mathbf{Z}_n$ is a cyclic group written in additive notation. Its elements are all multiples (additive powers) for the element $x = 1$. Both for $\mathcal{Z}_{P,n}$ and $\mathbf{Z}_n$ the number n is the smallest positive integer m such that $x^m = \iota$. This smallest positive integer is the *order* of the cyclic group. $\mathcal{Z}_{P,n}$ and $\mathbf{Z}_n$ are cyclic groups of order n. If a cyclic group has no order, it is *infinite*. $\mathbf{Z}$ is an infinite cyclic group; its elements are the multiples of 1.

A collection H of elements of a group G, which itself is a group under the multiplication of G, is called a *subgroup* of G. In our examples, e.g., $\mathfrak{M}^+$, $\mathcal{R}_P$, $\mathfrak{Z}$, $\mathcal{I}_P$, $\mathcal{Z}_{P,n}$ are subgroups of $\mathfrak{M}$, $\mathcal{L}$ is a subgroup of $\mathfrak{J}$ which itself is a subgroup of $\mathfrak{M}^+$, and $\mathbf{Z}$ is a subgroup of $\mathbf{R}$.

Since the multiplication in H is that in G, the associative law for H is a consequence of that for G; it does not need to be checked again.

(3.5)   *A subset H of a group G is a subgroup if and only if the product of any two elements of H is in H, and the inverse of any element of H is in H.*

Condition (ii) is satisfied since $aa^{-1} = \iota \in H$ if the two conditions hold.

If H and K are two subsets of a group G, we denote by HK the set of all elements hk, $h \in H$, $k \in K$, and by H^{-1} the set of all elements h^{-1}, $h \in H$. With this notation, the two conditions of (3.5) can be reformulated:

A subset H of a group G is a subgroup if and only if

$$HH = H \qquad H^{-1} = H.$$

We are allowed to write $H^{-1} = H$ instead of $H^{-1} \subset H$ because of (3.3).

In many cases, group theory is concerned not with the concrete properties of the elements of a group, but with the relations defined by the group multiplication. These relations are studied by means of *homomorphisms.* A homomorphism of a group G into a group G' is a function $g' = f(g)$, defined on the whole of G with values in G', which makes products in G correspond to products in G':

$$f(g_1 g_2) = f(g_1) f(g_2).$$

If a homomorphism is a one-to-one function, it is called a *monomorphism*. If every element of G' is the image, for f, of an element of G, we say that f is a mapping of G *onto* G', or an *epimorphism*. If f is both a monomorphism and an epimorphism, it is called an *isomorphism*. If there exists an isomorphism of G onto G', then G and G' are said to be *isomorphic*. The inverse mapping of an isomorphism exists and is an isomorphism of G' onto G. Isomorphic groups can be considered as different realizations of one abstract multiplication law since to each relation between the elements of G there exists uniquely one in G', and vice versa.

$\mathbf{R}^*$ is isomorphic to $\mathbf{R}$ under the isomorphism

$$r' = e^r.$$

In fact, this function is one-to-one, every positive real number is the exponential of some real number, and the exponential function maps the composition (addition) in $\mathbf{R}$ into the composition (multiplication) in $\mathbf{R}^*$:

$$e^{r+s} = e^r e^s.$$

The inverse isomorphism of $\mathbf{R}$ onto $\mathbf{R}^*$ is the logarithmic function. In the same way, the function

$$f\big[\rho_{P,(k/n)360°}\big] = k$$

is an isomorphism of $Z_{P,n}$ and $\mathbf{Z}_n$. The proof follows directly from the definitions (2.11). Also,

$$F(\rho_{P,\alpha}) = \rho_{Q,\alpha}$$

is an isomorphism of $\mathfrak{R}_P$ and $\mathfrak{R}_Q$.

An important theorem in the study of homomorphisms is

(3.6)   *If f is a homomorphism of a group G into a group G', then $f(G)$ is a subgroup of G'.*

$f(G)$ is the set of all elements $f(g)$, $g \in G$. By the definition of a homomorphism, the product of two elements of $f(G)$ is in $f(G)$. Let ι be the unit of G, and ι' that of G'. Since

$$f(g) = f(\iota g) = f(\iota)f(g)$$

for arbitrary $g \in G$, it follows that

$$\iota' = f(\iota).$$

Therefore, $gg^{-1} = \iota$ is translated into

$$f(g)f(g^{-1}) = \iota'$$

or

$$f(g)^{-1} = f(g^{-1}) \in f(G).$$

Hence $f(G)$ is a subgroup by (3.5).

Exercise 3–1

1. Prove the group property for   (a) $\Re_P$ (b) $\mathbf{Z}_n$ (c) $\mathbf{R}_{2\pi}$.

2. Show that $\mathfrak{J}$ is not a cyclic group.

3. Show that a subset H of a group G is a subgroup if and only if $HH^{-1} = H$.

4. Give an example to show that the condition $HH = H$ is not sufficient to guarantee that H is a subgroup. (Hint: look for subsets of $\mathbf{Z}$.)

5. Prove that isomorphism of groups is an equivalence relation.

6. What is -3 in $\mathbf{Z}_5$?

7. The *center* of a group G is the set C of the elements of G which commute with all elements of G: $c \in C$ means $ac = ca$ for all $a \in G$. Prove that C is a subgroup.

8. Prove: if all elements of a group are products of at most two involutions and if no involution is in the center, then C consists of the identity alone (definition in problem 7).

9. (Sequel to problem 8.) Prove that the center of $\mathfrak{M}$ contains only the identity.

10. What is the center of   (a) $\mathfrak{M}^+$ and   (b) $\mathfrak{J}$?

11. In analytic geometry, the expression for a rotation of angle α about the origin is

$$x' = x \cos \alpha + y \sin \alpha$$
$$y' = -x \sin \alpha + y \cos \alpha.$$

Show that the addition formulae for the sin and cos functions express the fact that these transformations $f(x,y) = (x',y')$ form a group isomorphic to $\Re_O$.

12. For $a \in G$ define a map f_a of G onto itself by

$$f_a(x) = axa^{-1}.$$

Show that f_a is an isomorphism of G onto itself (an *automorphism*). What is f_a in the group $\mathfrak{M}$?

13. Prove that $(a_1 a_2 \cdots a_n)^{-1} = a_n^{-1} \cdots a_2^{-1} a_1^{-1}$.

14. If G and G' are two cyclic groups of the same order n, prove that G and G' are isomorphic.

15. What is the number of elements of a cyclic group of order n?

16. Prove that the set of all isometric mappings of a plane set onto itself is a subgroup of $\mathfrak{M}$.

17. What is the group of all isometric mappings of an equilateral triangle onto itself?

18. Prove that if A and B are subgroups of G, so is $A \cap B$.

19. What is the group of all proper motions which map an equilateral triangle onto itself (problems 17 and 18)?

20. How many reflections are needed to generate the group of problem 17?

21. Solve problems 17, 19, and 20 for the square instead of the equilateral triangle.

2. Homogeneous Spaces

If H is a subgroup of the group G, the set xH (i.e., the set of all elements xh, $h \in H$) is the *left coset* of x. The *right* coset would be Hx. Then H is itself a coset since $H = \iota H$ and also $H = hH$ for all $h \in H$. This example shows that the label x of a coset xH is by no means unique. The ambiguity is harmless, however, since

(3.7)   *If two cosets have an element in common, they are identical.*

If the two cosets xH and yH have an element in common, then h_1 and h_2 exist in H such that

$$xh_1 = yh_2$$

or

$$x = yh_2h_1^{-1},$$

hence

$$xH = yh_2h_1^{-1}H = yH.$$

Of interest are also the sets xHx^{-1}.

(3.8)   *If H is a subgroup of G, then xHx^{-1} is a subgroup isomorphic to H.*

As before, x here is a fixed element of G. We define a function

$$f(h) = xhx^{-1}.$$

This is a homomorphism of G into itself since

$$f(hh') = xhh'x^{-1} = xhx^{-1}\,xh'x^{-1} = f(h)f(h').$$

By (3.6), $f(H) = xHx^{-1}$ is a subgroup of G. It remains to show that f is a monomorphism, i.e., that $f(h) = f(h')$ implies $h = h'$. This follows immediately from the definition:

$$xhx^{-1} = xh'x^{-1}$$

implies

$$h = x^{-1}xhx^{-1}x = x^{-1}xh'x^{-1}x = h'.$$

The groups xHx^{-1} are called *conjugate* to H. A subgroup N is called *normal* if it is identical with all its conjugate groups in G:

$$N = xNx^{-1} \hspace{3cm} \textit{for all } x \in G.$$

This does *not* mean that $f(n) = n$ for $n \in N$, only $f(n) \in N$. For a normal subgroup, left cosets are right cosets since the definition can also be written

$$Nx = xN.$$

As a consequence,

(3.9)   *All subgroups of an abelian group are normal.*

We give some examples from groups of motions. It follows from (2.14) and (1.15) that for any pair of points P and Q:

$$\rho_{Q,\alpha} = \sigma_{M(P,Q)} \rho_{P,\alpha} \sigma^{-1}_{M(P,Q)}.$$

This proves

(3.10)   *Any two rotation groups $\Re_P$ and $\Re_Q$ are conjugate both in $\mathfrak{M}^+$ and in $\mathfrak{M}$.*

All these rotation groups are isomorphic, but, since they are distinct, they are not normal subgroups of $\mathfrak{M}^+$ or $\mathfrak{M}$.

(3.11)   *$\mathfrak{J}$ is a normal subgroup of $\mathfrak{M}^+$ and of $\mathfrak{M}$.*

A translation is the product of two reflections at parallel lines. Parallel lines are mapped into parallel lines by any motion. Hence, by (1.15), $\Sigma\tau\Sigma^{-1}$ is a translation for any motion Σ and any translation τ.

The topic of the first two chapters was not abstract groups, but groups of transformations of a space onto itself. There is an intimate connection between transformation groups and cosets.

The collection of all the cosets $\{xH\}$ of a group G for a subgroup H is denoted by G/H and called a *homogeneous space*. (Remember that x is only an ambiguous label of the set xH.) The coset $xH = P$, when considered as an element of the homogeneous space G/H, is also called a *point*. G acts as a group of transformations in G/H: For any $g \in G$, define gP as the point gxH.

(3.12)   *The action of G on G/H defines a one-to-one map of G/H onto itself (a transformation) for all $g \in G$.*

By definition, the function gP is uniquely defined. If $gxH = gyH$, then we multiply from the left by g^{-1} and obtain $xH = yH$. Hence the action of g is a one-to-one function. It is a map onto G/H [i.e., $g(G/H) = G/H$] since any point in G/H can be written as an image under g:

$$xH = g(g^{-1}xH).$$

If N is a normal subgroup of G, it is possible to define a multiplication in the homogeneous space G/N. In this case, the set of all products of group elements in xN by elements in yN is just xyN since

$$xN\,yN = x\,Ny\,N = x\,yN\,N = xy\,NN = xyN.$$

(If H is not normal, $xHyH$ is not a coset.) For this multiplication of points

$$(xN)(yN) = xyN,$$

the associative law holds, since it holds in G. The point N is the unit element:

$$N(xN) = (\iota x)N = xN$$
$$(xN)N = xN,$$

and $x^{-1}N$ is the inverse of xN.

(3.13)   *If N is a normal subgroup of G, then G/N is a group.*

G/N is called the *factor group of G modulo N*. As an example, let us determine the group $\mathfrak{M}^+/\mathfrak{I}$. The elements of this group are the sets $\rho_{P,\alpha}\mathfrak{I}$ since the rotations are the only elements of $\mathfrak{M}^+$ which are not in $\mathfrak{I}$. Any translation τ may be written as the product of reflections in two lines, the second of which passes through P. The rotation then may be given by two lines, the first of which is identical with the second line of the translation (Fig. 3–1). From

$$\tau = \sigma_m \sigma_l, \quad \rho_{P,\alpha} = \sigma_n \sigma_m,$$

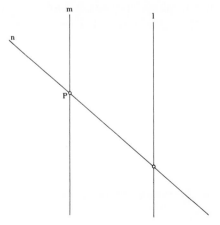

Fig. 3–1

it follows that

$$\rho_{P,\alpha}\tau = \sigma_n\sigma_l = \rho_n \cap l,\alpha.$$

The elements of the coset $\rho_{P,\alpha}\mathfrak{J}$, therefore, are all rotations of angle α about points of the plane. In particular,

$$\rho_{P,\alpha}\mathfrak{J} = \rho_{Q,\beta}\mathfrak{J} \text{ if and only if } \alpha = \beta.$$

(2.10) and (2.17) together with our result show

(3.14)   *The elements of the group* $\mathfrak{R} = \mathfrak{M}^+/\mathfrak{J}$ *are the oriented angles.*

We call $\mathfrak{R}$ *the* rotation group in the plane. It is independent of any particular center of rotation. It also follows from our proof that

(3.15)   *The map* $F(\rho_{P,\alpha}) = \rho_{P,\alpha}\mathfrak{J}$ *is an isomorphism of* $\mathfrak{R}_P$ *onto* $\mathfrak{R}$.

If we define a notion of positive orientation of an angle by, say, clockwise rotation about some point P, then the isomorphism F carries that definition over to $\mathfrak{R}$ and, therefore, to rotations and angles of arbitrary center. We may define positive orientation of $\alpha = (a_0,b(\alpha))$, for instance, by the condition that $b(\alpha)$ pass through a fixed quadrant defined by a_0 and $p(a_0,P)$.

The two preceding theorems explain the fact that oriented angles and vectors have properties that are largely parallel but not identical. Vectors are elements of an additive group isomorphic to a normal *subgroup*, oriented angles of an additive group isomorphic to a *factor group*, of $\mathfrak{M}^+$.

If a transformation group G acts on a space, the *isotropy group* $\mathfrak{J}_P$ of a point P is the subgroup of all elements $g \in G$ for which $gP = P$. For $\mathfrak{M}$ acting on the plane, this definition is identical with that given in section 1. If G acts on G/H, let $\mathfrak{J}_x$ be the isotropy group of xH. Its elements i are defined by

$$ixH = xH.$$

This means that for every $h \in H$ there exists an $h' \in H$ such that

$$ixh = xh'.$$

Hence

$$i = xh'h^{-1}x^{-1},$$

and since $h'h^{-1}$ is an element of the group H, i is an element of xHx^{-1}. Conversely,

$$xHx^{-1}xH = xHH = xH,$$

hence

$$\mathfrak{I}_x = xHx^{-1}.$$

(3.16)   *The isotropy groups of a homogeneous space are the subgroups conjugate to the subgroup which defines the space.*

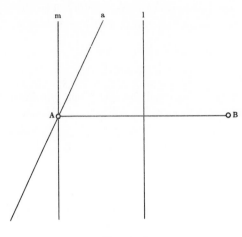

FIG. 3–2

As an illustration of the preceding theory, we determine the space $\mathfrak{M}/\mathfrak{I}_A$ in the plane. First we determine $\sigma_l\mathfrak{I}_A$ for an arbitrary line l in the plane. The elements of $\mathfrak{I}_A$ are the rotations of center A and the reflections at lines a containing A. Let m be the parallel to l through A, and define $B = \sigma_l A$. Then

$$\sigma_l\sigma_a = \sigma_l\sigma_m\sigma_m\sigma_a = \tau_{[\![AB]\!]}\rho_A(a,m).$$

Any rotation in $\mathfrak{I}_A$ can be written as $\rho_{A,\alpha} = \sigma_m\sigma_a$. Hence

$$\sigma_l\rho_{A,\alpha} = \sigma_l\sigma_m\sigma_a = \tau_{[\![AB]\!]}\sigma_a.$$

Both results taken together show that

(3.17) $\sigma_l\mathfrak{I}_A = \tau_{[\![AB]\!]}\mathfrak{I}_A.$

There are no other cosets. Any rotation (including point reflections) or translation in the plane can be given as $\sigma_l\sigma_a$, $A \in a$. Hence

$$\sigma_l\sigma_a\mathfrak{I}_A = \sigma_l\mathfrak{I}_A$$

is one of the sets described by (3.17). In the same way, any glide reflection can be written as $\sigma_P\sigma_a$, $A \in a$. Therefore,

$$\gamma_{v,l}\mathfrak{I}_A = \sigma_P\sigma_a\mathfrak{I}_A = \sigma_P\mathfrak{I}_A$$

again is one of the cosets generated by one line reflection. Since A is fixed, the mapping

$$F(B) = \tau_{[\![AB]\!]}\mathcal{G}_A$$

is a one-to-one correspondence between the points B of the plane and the cosets $\tau_{[\![AB]\!]}\mathcal{G}_A$ of the homogeneous space $\mathfrak{M}/\mathcal{G}_A$. The isotropy groups of the point B in the plane and of the coset $F(B)$ in $\mathfrak{M}/\mathcal{G}_A$ are identical since in both cases

$$\mathcal{G}_B = \tau_{[\![AB]\!]}\mathcal{G}_A\tau_{[\![BA]\!]}.$$

Therefore, no geometric fact will be lost if we consider B and $\tau_{[\![AB]\!]}\mathcal{G}_A$ as two names for the same geometric object.

(3.18)   *The plane can be identified with the homogeneous space $\mathfrak{M}/\mathcal{G}_A$.*

This is a special case of a general situation. If π is an arbitrary space, and G a group of transformations of π, we say that G is *transitive* if for any couple P and Q of points of π there exists a transformation g of G which maps P into Q, $gP = Q$. Two cosets of the isotropy group of P, $g\mathcal{G}_P$ and $g'\mathcal{G}_P$ are identical if and only if

$$g\mathcal{G}_Pg'^{-1} = \mathcal{G}_P,$$

i.e., $gP = g'P$. Therefore, the map $F(gP) = g\mathcal{G}_P$ is a one-to-one map of the set π onto the homogeneous space $G/\mathcal{G}_P$ such that the isotropy groups of gP in π and that of $F(gP)$ in $G/\mathcal{G}_P$ coincide.

(3.19)   *If a transitive group of transformations acts on a space, the space can be identified with the homogeneous space of the group modulo one of its isotropy groups.*

The theory of homomorphisms and factor spaces can also serve to elucidate the notion of angle which is used in trigonometry. Since this is not connected with any further development in this book, we give only a survey of the problem of trigonometric angles. Analytic geometry based on real numbers satisfies not only our axioms I to XIII and the archimedean axiom, but also an axiom of *completeness:* Every bounded increasing sequence of real numbers has a least upper bound. This implies that the length of arcs of circles can be measured by real numbers, *viz.*, the least upper bound of the lengths of unions of segments inscribed in the arc. (This is proved in every better text of calculus.) Angles can then be measured by the length of an arc cut off on a unit circle about the vertex of the angle. This gives an isomorphism i of $\mathbf{R}_{2\pi}$ onto $\mathfrak{R}$.

The group $\mathbf{R}_{2\pi}$ is a factor group of $\mathbf{R}$. Let Ω be the set of all numbers $n \cdot 2\pi$ for integer (positive and negative) n. The set Ω is a subgroup of $\mathbf{R}$, hence by (3.9) it is a normal subgroup. The cosets of $\mathbf{R}/\Omega$ are the sets of elements $r + n \cdot 2\pi$ since we use the additive notation for the group multiplication. Therefore, there is a one-to-one correspondence between the cosets of $\mathbf{R}/\Omega$ and the real numbers r between zero and 2π. It is easily seen that the map j defined by $j(r + n \cdot 2\pi) = r, 0 \leqslant r < 2\pi$ is an isomorphism $j(\mathbf{R}/\Omega) = \mathbf{R}_{2\pi}$. Then we may define: A real number x is a trigonometric angle of an oriented angle α if and only if $ij(x) = \alpha$. By definition, two trigonometric angles of one oriented angle differ by an integer multiple of 2π.

Exercise 3–2

1. Find all subgroups and all homogeneous spaces of the group of problem 17, exercise 3–1.

2. Let $n\mathbf{Z}$ be the additive group of multiples of the integer n. Prove that $\mathbf{Z}/n\mathbf{Z}$ is isomorphic to $\mathbf{Z}_n$.

3. For any homomorphism F of a group G into a group G' define the *kernel* ker F as the set of all $g \in G$ which are mapped into the unit element ι' of G': $g \in$ ker F if and only if $F(g) = \iota'$. Prove that ker F is a normal subgroup of G.

4. Show that the mapping $F^*(g) = g$ ker F of G into the cosets of $G/$ker F is in fact an isomorphism $F(G) = G/$ker F.

5. (Sequel to problem 4.) Find a function F which reduces the isomorphism of problem 2 to a special case of problem 4.

6. Solve the same problem as 5 for the isomorphism j.

7. Use problem 4 to find an isomorphism of $\mathbf{R}/\mathbf{Z}$ and $\mathbf{R}_{2\pi}$.

8. Prove that if G/H consists of two elements only, then H is a normal subgroup of G. In this case, G/H is isomorphic to $\mathbf{Z}_2$.

9. Show that $\mathfrak{M}/\mathfrak{M}^+$ consists of two elements only (cf. problem 8).

10. For any subgroup H of a group G, prove that the homogeneous spaces G/H and G/xHx^{-1} are identical.

11. Prove that the plane is in one-to-one correspondence with the cosets of $\mathfrak{M}^+/\mathfrak{R}_P$.

12. The *commutator* subgroup of a group is the smallest subgroup which contains all products $aba^{-1}b^{-1}$ formed by elements of the group. (For an abelian group, it is the group formed by ι alone.) What is the commutator subgroup of $\mathfrak{M}$? of $\mathfrak{M}^+$?

13. Prove: the greatest normal subgroup of a group G contained in a subgroup H is the intersection of H and all its conjugate subgroups.

14. (Sequel to 13.) What is the greatest normal subgroup of $\mathfrak{M}^+$ contained in $\mathfrak{R}_P$?

15. (Sequel to 13.) The action of G on G/H is *faithful* if no element of G leaves all points of G/H fixed. Prove that the action of G on G/H is faithful if and only if the only normal subgroup of G contained in H is the group formed by the single element ι.

16. (Sequel to 13.) The action of G on G/H is *asystatic* if no two distinct points have identical isotropy groups (i.e., there does not exist a $g \notin H$ such that $gHg^{-1} = H$). Prove the following.

(a) If the action of G on G/H is asystatic, then H is not a normal subgroup of some bigger subgroup of G.

(b) If the action of G on G/H is not asystatic, then the set of all elements $g^k H$, g as defined above, is a subgroup H' of G, and H is a normal subgroup of H'.

17. Is the action of $\mathfrak{M}$ ($\mathfrak{M}^+$) on the plane asystatic? What is the implication for $\mathcal{I}_P$ ($\mathfrak{R}_P$)?

18. Prove that the center of a group (exercise 3–1, problem 7) is a normal subgroup.

19. Prove that a subgroup of an abelian group is abelian.

20. If G is a finite group of g elements, then all cosets of a subgroup H of h elements also have h elements. Prove this statement and deduce from it that h must divide g.

21. (Sequel to problem 20.) Prove that the only subgroups of a finite group of a prime number of elements are the group itself and the group $\{\iota\}$.

3. Crystallographic Groups

An interesting application of group theory is the determination of the possible forms of crystals in solid geometry and the possible schemes of ornaments in the plane. Here we solve the plane problem for an *archimedean* plane.

An *ornament* is a pattern whose regular repetition fills the plane (see Fig. 3–5). Our first task is to make this statement definite.

We have defined the interior only for convex polygons. In general, a polygon does not need to have an interior (see Fig. 2–13). However, if the edges of the polygon intersect only at the vertices, then the polygon can be decomposed into a finite number of triangles by segments which appear as

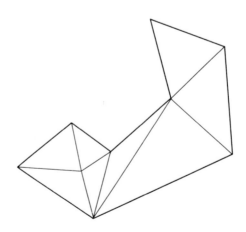

FIG. 3–3

edges of two triangles each. The interior of the polygon is the union of the interiors of the triangles and of the edges which have been added. If in the remainder of this section we speak of a polygon, it will be a polygon with an interior.

A *crystallographic group* is a subgroup $\mathcal{G}$ of $\mathfrak{M}$ for which there exists a polygon Π such that

> (1) every point in the plane is the image, by some element of $\mathcal{G}$, of a point of Π or its interior, and
>
> (2) if $g_1\Pi$ and $g_2\Pi$ have an interior point in common ($g_1,g_2 \in \mathcal{G}$), then $g_1\Pi = g_2\Pi$.

The two conditions say that the whole plane can be covered by Π and its images under $\mathcal{G}$ without holes or double coverings. For this reason the ornament of the polygons $g\Pi$, $g \in \mathcal{G}$ is also called a *tiling*. Π is the *fundamental domain* of the ornament, or tiling. The illustrations given later show that for a given group $\mathcal{G}$ there are infinitely many possible fundamental domains Π, and that it is not necessary to restrict Π to be a polygon. On the other hand, the possibilities for crystallographic groups are rather restricted.

(3.20)   *There are seventeen classes of non-isomorphic crystallographic groups in an archimedean plane.*

The job of an artist in creating an ornament is to choose a pleasing fundamental domain as one of the infinitely many realizations of the seventeen basic possibilities.

The proof of (3.20) is by explicit construction of the groups $\mathcal{G}$ as *lattice groups* and their subgroups. A *lattice* is the set of all points $\tau_{mv_1+nv_2}X$, where X is a fixed point, v_1 and v_2 are two fixed, non-parallel vectors, and m, n are arbitrary integers. Any point of a lattice can be taken as *base point X*. The *group of the lattice* is the greatest subgroup of $\mathfrak{M}$, which is a transformation group of the lattice (i.e., for which the lattice is a homogeneous space).

We choose a point X in the interior of a fundamental domain Π of a given ornament of group $\mathcal{G}$ and consider the set L of all points gX, $g \in \mathcal{G}$. The next theorem shows that instead of looking for crystallographic groups we may hunt for groups that admit a lattice as a homogeneous space $\mathcal{G}/H$:

(3.21)   *L is a lattice.*

By condition (1) of crystallographic groups, $\mathcal{G}$ contains an infinity of elements. Hence $\mathcal{G}$ contains products of two reflections. We prove first that $\mathcal{G}$ contains two translations whose vectors are not parallel, i.e., that L contains a lattice.

If all products of two reflections in $\mathcal{G}$ are translations, the vectors cannot all be parallel since, then, the images $g\Pi$ would cover only a strip, not the whole plane. In this case, then, the statement would be true.

If $\mathcal{G}$ contains $\rho_{A,\alpha}$, it also contains its inverse $\rho_{A,-\alpha}$. Both rotations are elements of the isotropy group of $\mathcal{G}$ at A. Hence for $B = gA$ the isotropy group contains $\rho_{B,-\alpha}$. Hence $\mathcal{G}$ contains the translation $\rho_{B,-\alpha}\rho_{A,\alpha}$. By condition (1) there certainly exists a point C such that the vector of the translation $\rho_{C,-\alpha}\rho_{A,\alpha}$ is not parallel to that defined by B. It follows that $\mathcal{G}$ contains two translations whose vectors are not on parallel lines. Hence it contains all sums of multiples of these vectors, and L contains a lattice. It also follows that $A, B \in L$ implies $2[\![AB]\!] \in \mathcal{G}$.

Next we have to show that all points of L are lattice points or, equivalently, that the subgroup of the translations of $\mathcal{G}$ is identical to the group of vectors $m_1\mathbf{v}_1 + m_2\mathbf{v}_2$, where m_1, m_2 are arbitrary integers and $\mathbf{v}_1, \mathbf{v}_2$ are two fixed non-parallel vectors. The proof depends essentially on the axiom of Archimedes. That axiom is computational, not geometric. Therefore, it is to be expected that the proof will be computational, not geometric. Unfortunately, this cannot be changed. The proof is characteristic for the messy way the axiom of Archimedes usually appears in geometry.

If X is an interior point of a fundamental domain, then it follows from condition (2) of a crystallographic group that on any line through X there exists an interval about X in which there is no point gX other than X. By the axiom of Archimedes this means that for any length l there exists a positive integer N such that $XgX < l/N$ implies $gX = X$. We have to show that this condition implies that $\mathcal{G}$ is a vector group. In fact, this is an arithmetical theorem valid in any dimension. In order to simplify the proof we discuss first the case of a crystallographic group in one dimension, i.e., a group $\mathcal{G}$ of translations in a line for which there exists a closed interval Π such that: (1) every point in the line is the image, by some element of $\mathcal{G}$, of a point of Π, and (2) two distinct images of Π do not have an interior point in common. With any vector $\mathbf{v}$, $\mathcal{G}$ contains the group of all multiples $m\mathbf{v}$, m integer. Either $\mathcal{G}$ is identical to the latter group or it contains a vector $\mathbf{w}$ that is not a multiple of $\mathbf{v}$. Two cases are possible.

It may be that there exist nonzero integers m_1 and m_2 such that $m_1\mathbf{v} + m_2\mathbf{w} = \mathbf{0}$. In this case we prove that there exists a vector $\mathbf{v}^* \in \mathcal{G}$ such that both $\mathbf{v}$ and $\mathbf{w}$ are in the cyclic group of the elements $m\mathbf{v}^*$. The method of proof is known as the euclidean algorithm. For definiteness, let us assume that $|m_1| > |m_2|$. We divide m_2 by m_1 in order to obtain a smallest remainder in integers:

$$m_2 = q_2 m_1 + r_2 \qquad |r_2| < |m_1|.$$

The vector $\mathbf{v}' = \mathbf{v} + q_2\mathbf{w}$ satisfies

$$m_1\mathbf{v}' + r_1\mathbf{w} = \mathbf{0}$$

and is an element of $\mathcal{G}$. In this process the coefficient m_2 has been reduced from a value $> |m_1|$ to one $< |m_1|$. We can start the same process again and divide m_1 by r_2. Since an integer can be reduced in absolute value only a finite number of times, it follows that after a finite number of steps:

$$\mathbf{v}' = \mathbf{v} + q_2\mathbf{w}$$
$$\mathbf{w}' = \mathbf{w} + q_3\mathbf{v}'$$
$$\mathbf{v}'' = \mathbf{v}' + q_4\mathbf{w}',$$
$$\cdot \quad \cdot \quad \cdot$$

one of the remainders must become zero, and we obtain a relation either of the form $\mathbf{v}^* + q_n\mathbf{w}^* = \mathbf{0}$ or $\mathbf{w}^* + q_n\mathbf{v}^* = \mathbf{0}$. This means that one of the vectors $\mathbf{v}^*$, $\mathbf{w}^*$ is in the cyclic group generated by the other. Retracing our steps, we see that all vectors $\mathbf{v}^{(k)}$, $\mathbf{w}^{(k)}$ are in that group as well as $\mathbf{v}$ and $\mathbf{w}$.

If no integers exist such that $m_1\mathbf{v} + m_2\mathbf{w} = \mathbf{0}$, we assume for definiteness that $|\mathbf{v}| < |\mathbf{w}|$. For each $m_i\mathbf{w}$ we define $[m_i\mathbf{w}]$ as the unique element $m_i\mathbf{w} + n\mathbf{v} \in \mathcal{G}$ for which

$$0 < [m_i\mathbf{w}] < |\mathbf{v}|.$$

Two distinct elements $m_i\mathbf{w}$ and $m_j\mathbf{w}$ will induce distinct vectors $[m_i\mathbf{w}]$ and $[m_j\mathbf{w}]$ since we would otherwise have a linear relation with integer coefficients between $\mathbf{v}$ and $\mathbf{w}$.

Let N be an arbitrary natural number. We divide the interval $[0, |\mathbf{v}|]$ into N intervals of length $|\mathbf{v}|/N$. Since the infinitely many distinct vectors $[m_i\mathbf{w}]$ are all in the interval $[0, |\mathbf{v}|]$, there exists a small interval which contains at least two of these vectors. (This reasoning is known as the pigeonhole principle.) Hence, for arbitrary N there exists in $\mathcal{G}$ a vector

$$m_i\mathbf{w} - m_j\mathbf{w} = (m_i - m_j)\mathbf{w} + (n_i - n_j)\mathbf{v}$$

of length $|\mathbf{v}|/N$. This is impossible by the axiom of Archimedes.

(3.22)　　*A one-dimensional group of translations without arbitrarily small elements in an archimedean plane is a cyclic group.*

Now we come back to the two-dimensional case. Through any point $P \in L$ we draw the parallel to $\mathbf{v}_2$ and intersect it with the line through X which carries the vector $\mathbf{v}_1$. Let P' be the point of intersection. The map

$$h_1([\![XP]\!]) = [\![XP']\!]$$

is a homomorphism of the group of translations of $\mathcal{G}$ into the group of translations of a line. If P is not on the line through X in the direction of $\mathbf{v}_2$, then it is not in the interior of any polygon $\tau_{m\mathbf{v}_2}\Pi$, and, therefore, XP' cannot be arbitrarily small. By (3.22), the group of vectors $[\![XP']\!]$ is cyclic. A change of names proves the same result for the projection $h_2([\![XP]\!])$ into the group of vectors on the line in direction $\mathbf{v}_2$.

If $\mathcal{G}$ contains a vector $\mathbf{v}$ not in the group of vectors $m_1\mathbf{v}_1 + m_2\mathbf{v}_2$, then $\mathbf{v}_1$ and $h_1(\mathbf{v})$ are integer multiples of a vector $\mathbf{w}_1$. Then $\mathbf{v}_2$ and $h_2(\mathbf{v})$ are integer multiples of a vector $\mathbf{w}_2$. Since

$$\mathbf{v} = h_1(\mathbf{v}) + h_2(\mathbf{v}),$$

it follows that there exist integers m_i $(i = 1,2,3)$ such that

$$m_1\mathbf{v}_1 + m_2\mathbf{v}_2 + m_3\mathbf{v} = \mathbf{0}.$$

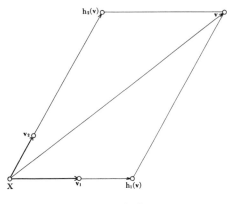

FIG. 3–4

By the homomorphism h_1,

$$h_1(m_1\mathbf{v}_1 + m_2\mathbf{v}_2 + m_3\mathbf{v}_3) = m_1 h_1(\mathbf{v}_1) + m_2 h_1(\mathbf{v}_2) + m_3 h_1(\mathbf{v})$$
$$= m_1\mathbf{v}_1 + m_3 h_1(\mathbf{v}) = \mathbf{0},$$

and the proof of (3.22) shows that $\mathbf{w}_1$ belongs to $\mathcal{G}$. By the same argument for h_2, $\mathbf{w}_2$ belongs to $\mathcal{G}$, and the group generated by $\mathbf{v}_1$, $\mathbf{v}_2$, $\mathbf{v}$ is identical to the lattice group of the linear combinations of $\mathbf{w}_1$ and $\mathbf{w}_2$. Hence the maximal group of translations which is the subgroup of a crystallographic group is a lattice group, and L is a lattice.

The remainder of the determination of the crystallographic groups is geometry. By (3.21) we have to find the maximal group of isometric transformations of a lattice and all those subgroups which contain the group of all translations defined by two points of the lattice. Then we have to find examples to show that all these groups in fact are crystallographic groups. The examples are collected in Fig. 3–6, which is due to Professor G. Pòlya. In his terminology, the names of the crystallographic groups are chosen mainly with reference to their isotropy groups. If the isotropy group is a rotation group $\mathcal{Z}_{X,n}$, the crystallographic group is called C_n. If the isotropy group contains n reflections or there are n axes of glide reflections, the crystallographic group is denoted D_n. If several crystallographic groups exist for a given isotropy group, they are distinguished by a symbol k for each parallel pencil of axes of reflection, and g for each parallel pencil of axes of glide reflection, or otherwise by distinguishing signs.

In the drawings which illustrate the full lattice groups, the lattice points are given by small black discs. Small circles denote centers of rotations or point reflections in the group which are not lattice points. Axes of reflection are shown by heavy lines, axes of glide reflection by light lines (unless they coincide with axes of reflection). A glide reflection will be called *trivial* if it is the product of a reflection and a translation in $\mathcal{G}$.

In some of Professor Pòlya's drawings, the lines bound unions of fundamental domains rather than fundamental domains in order to obtain a more pleasing picture. The same classification, based on another principle and accompanied by beautiful pictures, is given in the book by Fejes-Tóth (reference 12). An arithmetical determination of all the groups is given in reference 5. The proof that no two groups are isomorphic has been given by Nowacki; see references 8 and 12.

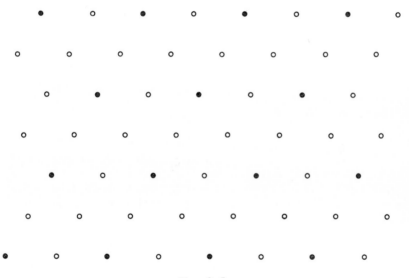

Fig. 3–5

First we study the lattice generated by two vectors $\mathbf{v}_1$ and $\mathbf{v}_2$ that do not span a right angle (Fig. 3–5). The maximal group of motions which transforms this lattice into itself certainly contains the group of the translations

$$\tau_{m_1\mathbf{v}_1 + m_2\mathbf{v}_2}.$$

However, since

$$\tau_{-m_1\mathbf{v}_1 - m_2\mathbf{v}_2} X = \sigma_X \tau_{m_1\mathbf{v}_1 + m_2\mathbf{v}_2} X,$$

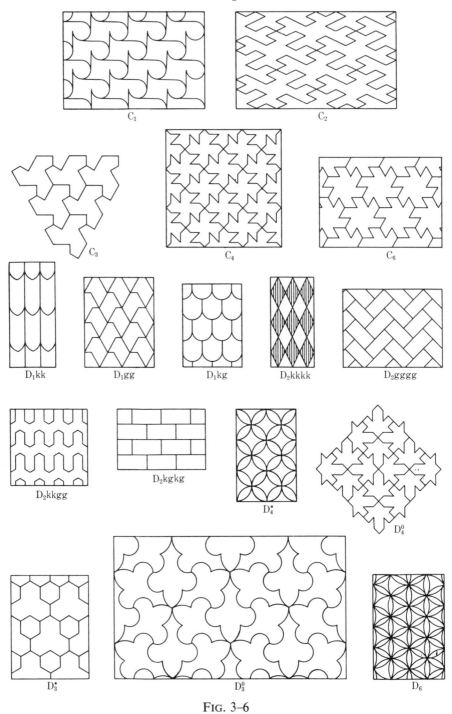

FIG. 3-6

it also contains the reflections in the lattice points. In addition, it contains the reflections in the midpoints of the edges and diagonals of the parallelograms of the lattice since with σ_X and $\tau_{[XY]}$ it must contain

$$\sigma_X \tau_{[XY]} = \sigma_X \sigma_X \sigma_{M(X,Y)} = \sigma_{M(X,Y)}.$$

The maximal group C_2 contains these translations and point reflections. The only admissible subgroup is the group C_1 of just the translations. In fact, C_2 is generated by C_1 and a single point reflection.

Before we proceed, we want to justify the expression "*the* group C_1." In fact, there are infinitely many distinct translation groups of lattices. However, the group $\{m_1 \mathbf{v}_1 + m_2 \mathbf{v}_2\}$ is isomorphic to the group $\{m_1 \mathbf{w}_1 + m_2 \mathbf{w}_2\}$ by the homomorphism

$$h(m_1 \mathbf{v}_1 + m_2 \mathbf{v}_2) = m_1 \mathbf{w}_1 + m_2 \mathbf{w}_2.$$

This map, however, cannot in general be extended to an isomorphism of the group $\mathfrak{M}$ onto itself. This is possible only if the fundamental parallelograms for two lattices are congruent. In that case, the lattice groups are conjugate subgroups of $\mathfrak{M}$. (For the visual impression, shape is more important than size; we are inclined to identify lattices whose groups are conjugate not in the group $\mathfrak{M}$ of motions but in the group $\mathfrak{S}$ of similitudes defined in chapter VI.) The first choice in the construction of an ornament is the choice of a class of conjugate subgroups of $\mathfrak{M}$.

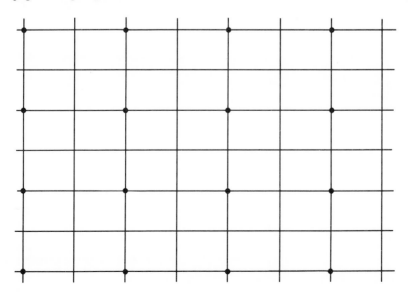

FIG. 3–7

If the isotropy group of the lattice contains no rotations other than point reflections, but the group $\mathcal{G}$ of the lattice is different from C_2, then $\mathcal{G}$ must contain reflections or glide reflections. The axes must meet at right angles; we obtain a rectangular lattice. In addition to the operations of C_2, the lattice admits as transformations the reflections in the two families of mutually perpendicular lines defining the rectangles and the two pencils of midlines of the rectangles. Its symbol, therefore, is D_2kkkk. If a lattice admits a reflection in a line l, and if $\mathbf{v}$ is a vector of the lattice, then the line $\tau_{\mathbf{v}}l$ also is an axis of reflection by (1.15). Therefore, we have to count as essentially different those pencils of parallel axes of reflection that do not result from one another by a translation in the lattice group.

The group of the rectangular lattice does not admit non-trivial glide reflections. Since the vector of any trivial glide reflection is a lattice vector, and $\gamma_{l,\mathbf{v}\tau-\mathbf{v}} = \sigma_l$, it follows that a crystallographic subgroup of D_2kkkk which contains a glide reflection must also contain the reflection in the axis of the glide reflection. Therefore, the only crystallographic subgroup of D_2kkkk, which is distinct from the groups of the parallelogram lattice, is the group D_1kk containing only the reflections in one direction. (The group D_1k is isomorphic to D_1kk. We simply must delete every second lattice point.)

The set of midpoints of the rectangular lattice is invariant for all automorphisms of that lattice. If we add the set to the lattice, we obtain the *rhombic* lattice (Fig. 3–8). Its group contains the group of the rectangular lattice and, in addition, the motions which exchange vertices and midpoints of the rectangles. These are two families of non-trivial glide reflections. The description of the maximal group is D_2kgkg. Its subgroups which are distinct from

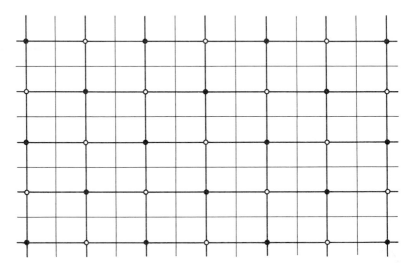

FIG. 3–8

those of the rectangular lattice must contain non-trivial glide reflections. In a systematic way, the groups must be one of the following:

    a. alternating axes of reflection and glide reflection
        1. in both directions: D_2kgkg
        2. in one direction: D_1kg
    b. axes of reflection in one direction, of glide reflections in the other: D_2kkgg
    c. glide reflections only
        1. in both directions: D_2gggg
        2. in one direction: D_1gg.

The translation group of the rhombic lattice is generated by two vectors on the sides of the fundamental rhombus.

    Next we look for lattices which admit groups with more than two axes of reflections passing through one point. The isotropy group then will contain a group $Z_{X,n}$. But σ_X must be an element of this group, hence $n = 2m$ is even.

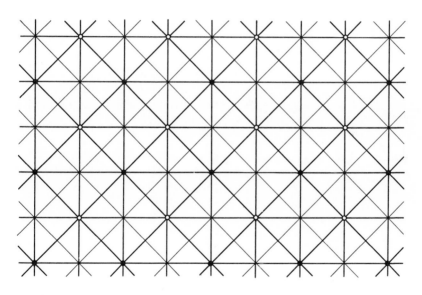

FIG. 3–9

    For $m = 2$ we have the square lattice given by the black discs in Fig. 3–9. Its rotations are generated by reflections in the sides and the diagonals of the squares, as well as in the midlines. Centers of rotation, therefore, are not only the vertices of the squares (which are lattice points), but also the centers of the squares (which do not belong to the lattice). In addition, there are two families of non-trivial glide reflections. The symbol of the group in Fig. 3–5 is D_4^*. The rhombic lattice associated with the square lattice is again a square lattice.

All the admissible subgroups of D_4^* which are not isomorphic to rectangular groups must contain $\zeta_{X,4}$ in the isotropy group. If it is a proper subgroup (not equal to D_4^*), it cannot contain the reflections in lines passing through the lattice points. Otherwise, by composition with the rotations, the isotropy group would be that of D_4^* both at the vertices and at the centers, and the group itself would be D_4^*. Therefore, the isotropy group either at the lattice points or at the centers must be $\zeta_{X,4}$. We may assume that it is the isotropy group at the lattice points. Then the group either contains the reflections through the centers (D_4^0) or all isotropy groups are rotation groups (C_4).

If $m = 3$, the two generating vectors are of equal length and make angles of 60°. The lattice is built up of equilateral triangles. In addition to the translation group and the cyclic groups of order six of rotations about the vertices, the lattice allows rotation groups of order three about the centers of the

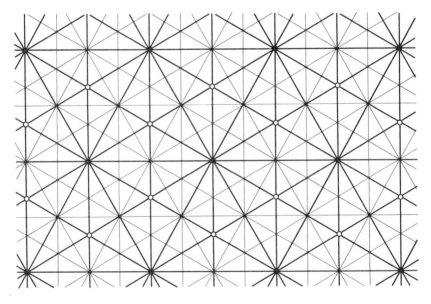

FIG. 3–10

equilateral triangles. The sides of the triangles and the perpendicular bisectors are axes of reflections. The midlines of both systems of axes of reflection are non-trivial axes of glide reflection. However, these glide reflections are trivial in another sense. The existence of glide reflections and rotations in a crystallographic group implies the existence of certain reflections. For instance, let X and Y be two adjoining lattice points. Let Z be the third vertex of an equilateral triangle $\triangle(X,Z,Y)$, and let γ be the glide reflection of axis $p(l(X,Z),M(X,Y))$ and minimal vector $[\![M(X,Z),Y]\!]$. Then

$$\tau_{YX}\gamma\rho_{X,60°} = \sigma_{l(X,Y)}.$$

Hence we may disregard the glide reflections in our classification. Also, with one axis of reflection not only all its translates by lattice vectors appear, but also its images in the rotations.

As in the case of the square lattice, a proper crystallographic subgroup of the full lattice group D_6 may contain at most one family of reflections. If the isotropy group at the lattice points contains the cyclic group of order six and the group admits reflections, then the composition of reflections and rotations generates the second family of reflections and, therefore, the whole group D_6. As a consequence, the only possibilities are:

    a. isotropy group $\mathcal{Z}_{X,6}$, no reflections: C_6
    b. isotropy group containing the cyclic group of order 3
        1. no reflections: C_3
        2. reflections in sides of triangles: D_3°
        3. reflections in altitudes: D_3^{*}.

There are no lattices with $m > 3$. If a lattice admits an isotropy group which contains $\mathcal{Z}_{X,2m}$, then any lattice point is the center of a regular $2m$-gon, i.e., a convex polygon transformed into itself by the action of $\mathcal{Z}_{X,2m}$. If $m > 3$, then the angle at the center for any triangle formed by the center X and two consecutive vertices P_1 and P_2 is smaller than for the hexagon. For the hexagon we obtain a regular triangle (equilateral triangle), hence $P_1P_2 < XP_1$ by (1.33). If a lattice is given, choose X as point of minimal distance from P_1 in the lattice. We assume that this is a geometry in which the rotations of angle $180/m°$ do exist. If the isotropy group of the lattice contains a rotation group of order $2m$, the point

$$P_2 = \rho_{X,180/m°}P_1$$

is a point of the lattice. However, by our previous result,

$$P_1P_2 < P_1X,$$

which contradicts the definition of X. Therefore,

(3.23)   *No lattice admits rotations by angles which are not multiples of 60° or 90°.*

A count of the cases shows that we have found seventeen groups for tilings. Our axioms postulate the existence of right angles. In chapter V we shall prove that the axioms imply the existence of the angle of 60°. Therefore, all groups can be realized in every plane which satisfies our axioms, and they are the only ones (up to isomorphisms) if the axiom of Archimedes holds.

Exercise 3–3

1. The ornaments which illustrate the groups C_2, C_3, C_4, C_6, D_2kkgg are made up of sets which are unions of several fundamental domains. Identify a fundamental domain in each of these drawings.

2. Find lattices in all the drawings of Fig. 3–5.

3. Find illustrations of the groups C_1, D_1kg, D_4^*, D_3^o, and D_6 for which the fundamental domain is a polygon.

4. Why do we not count a group D_1k in our list? (or the same problem for D_1g)?

5. Identify the group generated by the non-trivial glide reflections in the square lattice with one of the groups obtained earlier (rectangle or rhombus).

6. If G is a crystallographic group and G_0 its isotropy group at some lattice point, what is G/G_0?

7. Prove that the rhombic lattice associated to a square lattice is a square lattice.

8. Identify by name the group generated by the non-trivial glide reflections of the hexagonal lattice.

9. If a group of transformations of the square lattice has isotropy group $Z_{X,4}$ at the vertices of the square, find the movements necessarily contained in the isotropy group of the centers of the square.

10. If the isotropy group of a vertex of a square contains $Z_{X,4}$ and a reflection in a line through X, prove that the group is D_4^*.

11. If the isotropy group of a vertex in the hexagonal lattice contains $Z_{X,6}$ and a reflection in a line through X, prove that the group is D_6.

12. A regular polygon is a polygon which admits a cyclic group of rotations as transformation group of the polygon onto itself, where the order of the group is equal to the number of the vertices of the polygon. The set of vertices is defined by the center of the rotations and one vertex. For given center and vertex, draw all regular seven-gons (heptagons). (Convexity is not part of our definition.)

13. If a group of motions contains only the multiples of one translation, it is also called the transformation group of a band-ornament, or a ribbon. Draw such a ribbon which admits an axis of glide reflections.

14. What is the homogeneous space $C_6/Z_{M,3}$?

15. Find the centers of symmetry of the hexagonal lattice which are neither lattice points nor centers of rotation.

Chapter IV

CIRCLES

1. Circles

The circle $O(r)$ of *center* O and *radius* r is defined as the set of all points X such that $OX = r$. The name *radius* is used not only for the length r but also for any segment $[O,X]$, $X \in O(r)$. A line through the center of a circle is a *diameter* of the circle.

If g is a diameter, then $[O,X] \cong [O,\sigma_g X]$, hence $\sigma_g O(r) = O(r)$:

(4.1)   *Any diameter is an axis of symmetry of the circle. $O(r)$ is mapped onto itself by the groups $\mathcal{S}_0$ and $\mathcal{R}_0$.*

Now (1.38) can be reformulated to read:

(4.2)   *No line can have more than two points in common with a circle.*

By (1.30) there exists a segment of length r on any ray of vertex O, hence

(4.3)   *A diameter has two points of intersection with a circle, one on each ray defined by the center.*

The *tangent* to the circle $O(r)$ at one of its points X is the perpendicular $p[l(O,X),X]$ at X to the radius $[O,X]$. The notion of tangent used here has nothing to do with any limit process. Instead, we describe the tangent as the *line of support* of the circle at X. A *line of support* of a set S at a point $X \in S$ is a line l through X such that all points of S which are not on l are in one halfplane only of l. We show that the tangent at X is the *unique* line of support of the circle at X. The proof is based on some lemmas which are useful in themselves.

(4.4)   *A line is a tangent to a circle if and only if it has exactly one point of intersection with the circle.*

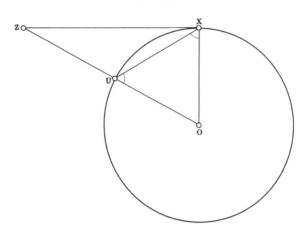

FIG. 4–1

If the tangent through X would have a second point Y ($\neq X$) in common with the circle $O(r)$, then, by (4.1), it also would meet the circle at the third point $Z = \sigma_{l(O,X)} Y$. This is impossible by (4.2). All other lines g through X have two points in common with $O(r)$, namely, both X and $\sigma_{p(g,O)} X$.

Let Z ($\neq X$) be a point on the tangent to $O(r)$ at X and put

$$U = O(r) \cap O[Z].$$

Then $\triangle(X,O,U)$ is isosceles; hence $\hat{X} = 90° - \frac{1}{2}\hat{C}$. This means that $X[U]$ is in the interior of the right angle $\angle OXZ$. By (1.33), this implies $OZ > OU = r$.

(4.5)   *The segment cut off on the perpendicular is the shortest among all segments defined by a fixed point and the points on a line.*

The length of the shortest segment is the *distance* of the point from the line.
     It follows from (4.5) that for any line g through a point $X \in O(r)$ all the points whose distance from O is $< r$ will be in the halfplane of O if and only if g is the tangent.

(4.6)   *The tangent is the unique line of support at any point of the circle.*

     If a set S has lines of support at all its points, its *interior* is the intersection of all the halfplanes belonging to lines of support and containing points of S. By (1.4) the interior then is convex.

(4.7)   *The interior of a circle $O(r)$ is a convex set. It is the set of all points Y, $OY < r$.*

If two circles $O_1(r_1)$ and $O_2(r_2)$ have a point X in common, they also intersect at $Y = \sigma_{l(O_1,O_2)}X$. The two points coincide if and only if X is a point of the *central* $l(O_1,O_2)$ of the two circles. If the two circles have a third point Z in common, then, by (sss), the triangle $\triangle(O_1,O_2,Z)$ is congruent to both $\triangle(O_1,O_2,X)$ and $\triangle(O_1,O_2,Y)$. Since all three triangles have the edge $[O_1,O_2]$ in common, either the circles coincide or Z is one of the points X or Y.

(4.8)   *Two non-identical circles intersect in at most two points. If two circles have only one point of intersection, their tangents at the common point coincide.*

It follows from here that three non-collinear points belong to at most one circle. On the other hand, we know that the vertices of a triangle are on the circle $O(OA)$, where O is the circumcenter. This unique circle is the *circumcircle* of the triangle.

(4.9)   *Three non-collinear points A, B, C define a unique circle $\Gamma(A,B,C)$.*

By the definition of the incenter, the circle $I(II^a)$ is tangent to all three edges of the triangle. It is called the *incircle* of $\triangle(A,B,C)$. There are three other circles, the *excircles,* which are tangent to the three sides of the complete

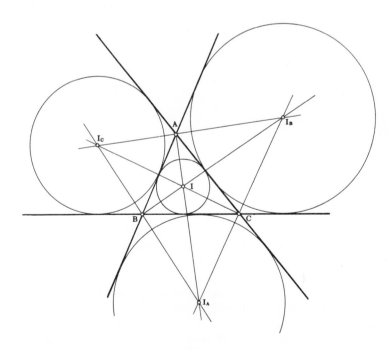

Fig. 4–2

triangle. Their centers, the *excenters* I_A, I_B, I_C, are the intersections of one angle bisector of the triangle with two bisectors of external angles of the triangle.

Theorem (4.3) is a re-statement of axiom X. In fact, if g is a diameter and X any point on the circle, the intersections of g and the circle are the images of X in a reflection at the angle bisectors of $l(O,X)$ and the rays of g at O. We have been able to prove that a diameter always intersects a circle, and that a line which has one point in common with a circle either is a tangent or else meets the circle at a second point. It turns out that our axioms are not strong enough to guarantee the validity of the following statement:

axiom X*.   *If a line has a point in the interior of a circle, it meets the circle in two points.*

We shall see in sec. 5–3 that X* implies not only axioms X and XI, but also that two circles intersect in two points if one has points in the interior of the other circle. After the algebraic discussion in chapter V, we shall assume X* as our axiom instead of axiom X. As a matter of fact, there are not too many theorems that really need the stronger axiom X*.

Exercise 4–1

1. Show that all points of a triangle are on lines of support. What are the points which admit only one line of support?

2. What are the lines of support of a segment?

3. Prove that if a set S admits two distinct lines of support through a point $X \in S$, then it admits an infinity.

4. Prove: a polygon admits a line of support at all of its points if and only if it is convex.

5. The angle bisectors of a triangle are the altitudes in the triangle of the excenters.

6. Given two circles Γ_1 and Γ_2 and a line g. Find a square having two opposite vertices on g and one vertex each on Γ_1 and Γ_2. How must the circles be situated that the problem have a solution?

7. Given two circles Γ_1, Γ_2, and a vector **v**. Find $A \in \Gamma_1$, $B \in \Gamma_2$ such that $[\![AB]\!] = \mathbf{v}$. What is the condition for existence?

8. Prove: every regular polygon admits a circumscribed circle.

9. Given two circles Γ_1 and Γ_2, find a line on which the two circles cut off chords of equal length. Find the possible directions for such a line.

10. Prove that the image of a circle in any isometry is a circle.

11. Let d be a diameter of a circle $O(r)$, and $C \in d$ a point in the exterior of $O(r)$. Let g be a line through C which meets the circle in D and E, D being between C and E. Prove that if $DC = r$, then $(d, l(O,E)) = 3(d,g)$.

12. A *chord* of a circle is the segment defined by two points of the circle. Prove that two chords of equal length are images of one another in a reflection in a diameter.

13. Given two circles, a line, and a length, find a second line parallel to the given one such that the segment between the two circles cut off on the second line is of the length given.

14. Prove that the line joining the centers of two intersecting circles is the perpendicular bisector of their common chord.

15. It will be shown in the next chapter that from a point in the exterior of a circle there always exists a tangent to the circle. Prove that there are then two tangents, and the segments defined by the point and the point of contact are congruent.

16. Two circles are *concentric* if their centers coincide. Prove that if two circles are concentric, all chords cut off by the larger circle on the tangents to the smaller are congruent.

17. A *tangential quadrilateral* is formed by four tangents to a circle. Prove that a quadrilateral is tangential to some circle if and only if the sum of the lengths of two opposite edges is equal to half the perimeter. (See problem 15.)

2.   The Fundamental Theorem

The main theorem of the elementary theory of circles is about angles subtended by an arc.

Two points A and B on a circle define their segment, the *chord* of the circle, as well as the *center angle* $\angle AOB$, the oriented center angle $(l(O,A),l(O,B))$, and the arc AB, which is the intersection of the circle with the interior of $\angle AOB$. For reasons that will appear soon we prefer to work with $(l(O,A),l(O,B))$, instead of $\frac{1}{2}(l(O,A),l(O,B))$. For notational convenience, we shall write angle (A,B) for $(l(O,A),l(O,B))$. If X is a third point on the circle, the angle subtended by the arc AB, or the chord $[A,B]$, at X shall be the oriented angle $(l(X,A),l(X,B))$ rather than one half of that angle. These definitions are chosen to obtain a nicer theorem:

(4.10)   *All angles subtended at the circle by an arc of the circle are equal.*

If we had stayed with the elementary definitions, the theorem would have read: All angles subtended at points of the arc are equal; all angles subtended at the complementary of the arc are supplementary to the angle subtended at the arc (Fig. 4–3). The proof of (4.10) is based on two simple lemmas.

(4.11)   angle $(A,B) = -$angle (C,D) *if and only if* $l(A,C) \parallel l(B,D)$.

The two angles must be images of one another in a product of an odd number of reflections. But the center O is fixed, so it must be a reflection in a line through O. This line, then, is the common perpendicular to $l(A,C)$ and $l(B,D)$. Conversely, if A,B,C,D are on a circle $O(r)$ and the two lines mentioned are both perpendiculars to one line l through O, then angle $(C,D) = \sigma_l$ angle (A,B).

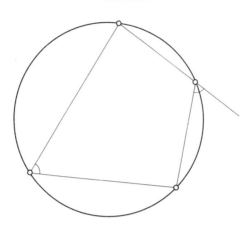

Fig. 4–3

(4.12)   *Two angles whose vertices are on a circle and whose legs are pairwise parallel are subtended by arcs of equal center angles.*

The proof is based on (4.11) and can be read from Fig. 4–4. If the angle of vertex A is subtended by the arc $A'A''$ and the arc of vertex B is subtended by arc $B'B''$, then

$$\begin{aligned}
\text{angle } (A',A'') &= \text{angle } (A',B') + \text{angle } (B',A'') \\
&= -\text{angle } (A,B) + \text{angle } (B',A'') \\
&= \text{angle } (B',A'') + \text{angle } (A'',B'') \\
&= \text{angle } (B',B'').
\end{aligned}$$

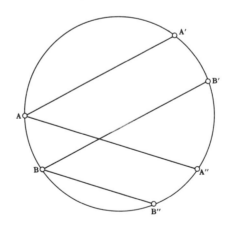

Fig. 4–4

Since the condition of lemma (4.11) is necessary and sufficient, the lemma has a converse: *If two angles on a circle are subtended by arcs of equal center angle and if one pair of legs is parallel, then so is the other pair.* The proof of (4.10) follows from this statement: Let C and D be vertices, on the circle,

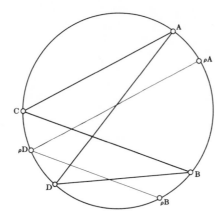

FIG. 4–5

of angles subtended by arc AB. Let ρ be the rotation of center O and angle $(p[l(B,D),O],p[l(B,C),O])$. By definition, the perpendiculars to $l(B,C)$ and $\rho l(B,D)$ coincide. Therefore, the image of the angle of vertex D is an angle subtended by an arc of center angle

$$\text{angle } (\rho A, \rho B) = \text{angle } (A,B),$$

for which one leg is parallel to the corresponding leg of the angle subtended at C. By the converse to (4.12), the other pair of legs is also parallel, and the two oriented angles are equal by (2.17).

By our theorem, we may compute the angle at the circumference for some special case in order to obtain the general result. If we choose the leg $l(C,A)$ to be a diameter, $\triangle(B,O,C)$ is isosceles and

$$(l(O,A),l(O,B)) = 2\hat{B} + 2\hat{C} = 4\hat{C} = 2(l(C,A),l(C,B)).$$

(4.13)   *The angle subtended at the circle is half the center angle.*

An immediate corollary is

(4.14)   *Arcs of equal center angle subtend equal angles at the circle.*

If one lets C "tend" to A on the circle, the angle subtended by arc AB at C would "tend" to the angle between the tangent to the circle at A and

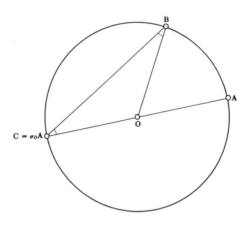

FIG. 4–6

the chord $l(A,B)$. Therefore, we expect the latter angle to be half the center angle. This is indeed the case. If t is the tangent, then, by definition,

$$
\begin{aligned}
(t,l(A,B)) &= 180° - (l(A,B),l(A,O)) \\
&= (l(A,O),m(A,B)) \\
&= \tfrac{1}{2} \text{ angle } (A,B).
\end{aligned}
$$

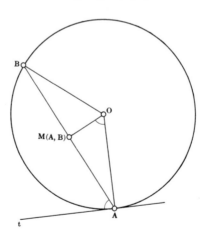

FIG. 4–7

(4.15)   *The angle subtended at the circle by an arc AB is equal to the angle between the tangent at A and the chord $l(A,B)$.*

For the remainder of this chapter we shall discuss consequences of the preceding propositions.

The center angle belonging to a half circle is the straight angle (180°) of the corresponding diameter. The oriented angle is the identity. Therefore,

(4.16)   *The elementary angles subtended by a diameter at the circle are right angles.*

The main theorem allows a converse. (This converse becomes very clumsy for elementary angles.) A subset of a circle is also called a set of *concyclic* points. The statement of the converse is contained in:

(4.17)   *Four points A, B, C, and D are concyclic if and only if*

$$(l(C,A),l(C,B)) = (l(D,A),l(D,B)).$$

The condition is necessary by (4.10). We have to prove that it implies $D \in \Gamma(A,B,C)$. If $l(A,D)$ is not the tangent to $\Gamma(A,B,C)$ at A, let D' be its second intersection with the circle. Then

$$(l(D,A),l(D,B)) = (l(D',A),l(D',B)).$$

Hence either $D = D'$ or

$$D = \sigma_{p[l(A,D),B]}D'$$

from the elementary angles. But the angle defined by the second point is the negative of that defined by the first, hence $D = D'$ is the only possibility. In a similar way one may exclude the case of D being on the tangent at A to $\Gamma(A,B,C)$ since the angle $(l(O,A),l(O,B))$ would be the negative of that defined by C (Fig. 4–8).

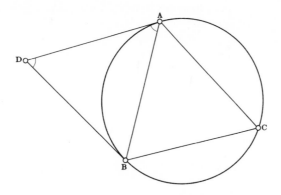

FIG. 4–8

For elementary angles we have to distinguish between angles subtended at points of the arc AC and at points of the complementary set, as exemplified in Fig. 4–3. An application is the following theorem which is very useful in construction problems:

(4.18)   *The set of the points at which a given segment subtends a given elementary angle is the union of two arcs of circle which are reflections of one another in the line of the segment.*

The construction is shown in Fig. 4–9.

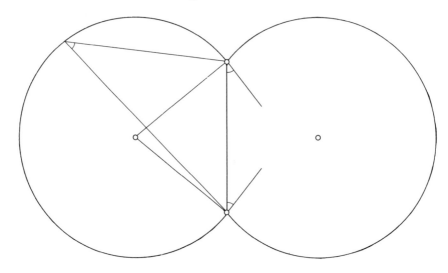

FIG. 4–9

Next, we use the main theorem to study some properties of the triangle. Let X_a be the second intersection of t_A with the circumcircle $\Gamma(A,B,C)$. By (4.14), angle BX_a = angle X_aC, hence $BX_a = X_aC$ and $\triangle(B,X_a,C)$ is isosceles:

(4.19)   *Corresponding angle bisectors and perpendicular bisectors meet at the circumcircle:* $t_A \cap m_a \in \Gamma(A,B,C)$.

The second intersection of the altitude h_a with the circumcircle is denoted by S_a, that of the circumdiameter $l(A,O)$ by T_a. By construction, $\triangle(S_a,C,F_a)$ is a right triangle. Hence

$$\tfrac{1}{2}(l(S_a,C),a) = 90° - \tfrac{1}{2}(h_a,l(S_a,C));$$

$\triangle(B,C,F_c)$ also is a right triangle:

$$\tfrac{1}{2}(a,h_c) = 90° - \hat{B}.$$

But

$$2\hat{B} = (h_a,l(S_a,C))$$

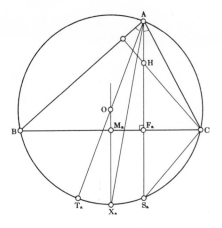

Fig. 4–10

since both are angles at the circle subtended by AC. The previous equations therefore imply that $\triangle(H,C,S_a)$ is isosceles, hence

(4.20) $S_a = \sigma_a H.$

Also $(h_a,t_A) = (m_a,t_A)$ as alternating angles at parallels. $\triangle(A,O,X_a)$ is isosceles, hence $(m_a,t_A) = (t_A,l(A,O))$. The two equations together mean

$$t_A = t[h_a,l(A,O)].$$

Previously (exercise 2–1, problem 4) a point Q was defined as the *isogonal* image of a point P if $l(A,Q) = \sigma_{t_A}l(A,P)$ and similarly for B and C. With this definition, our result implies

(4.21)   *Circumcenter and orthocenter are isogonal images of one another.*

Finally, since $H = \sigma_a \sigma_{m_a} T_a$, it follows that

(4.22) $M_a = a \cap m_a = M(H,T_a).$

These results will be used in chapter VI, sec. 3.
    The next theorem will be needed in chapter VIII.

(4.23)   *If points P, Q, and R are taken on the sides of a (complete) triangle $\triangle(A,B,C)$, the circles $\Gamma(A,Q,R)$, $\Gamma(B,R,P)$, and $\Gamma(C,P,Q)$ pass through a common point.*

The proof consists in a multiple application of (4.17). Let D be the second point of intersection of the first two circles. [The two circles might be tangent

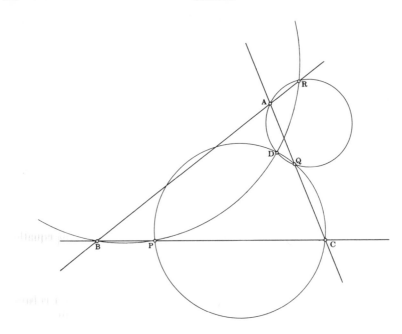

Fig. 4–11

to one another at R. In this case the proof still holds if we put $D = R$ and $l(D,R)$ the common tangent. The verification is left to the reader.] Then

$$
\begin{aligned}
(l(D,Q),l(D,P)) &= (l(D,Q),l(D,R)) + (l(D,R),l(D,P)) \\
&= 2\hat{A} + 2\hat{B} = 360° - 2\hat{C} = -2\hat{C} \\
&= (l(C,Q),l(C,P)),
\end{aligned}
$$

hence C, D, P, and Q are concyclic.

Exercise 4–2

1. Prove: the circle over one edge as diameter intersects the other two sides of the triangle in the feet of the altitudes.

2. Let A, B, C, D be the vertices of a quadrilateral. Prove that

$$(l(D,A),l(B,A)) = (l(D,C),l(B,C))$$

implies

$$(l(D,A),l(C,A)) = (l(D,B),l(C,B))$$

and

$$(l(D,B),l(A,B)) = (l(D,C),l(A,C)).$$

3. Prove: the feet of the perpendiculars drawn from the feet of the altitudes to the sides of the triangle (i.e., the points F_a^b, F_a^c, F_b^c, F_b^a, F_c^b, F_c^a) are six concyclic points.

4. Four lines, no three of which are concurrent, define four triangles. Prove that the four circumcircles are concurrent.

5. Prove that X_a is the center of $\Gamma(B,I,C)$ and that, therefore, the excenter I_a on t_A is $I_a = \sigma_{X_a} I$.

6. Let $\triangle(A,B,C)$ be a right triangle, $\hat{B} = 90°$, and g,h a pair of perpendicular lines. Let Σ be any motion such that $\Sigma A \in g$, $\Sigma C \in h$. What is the set of all points ΣB?

7. In a *convex* cyclic quadrilateral, the angle bisectors of the two pairs of opposite sides are perpendicular, if they exist. Prove the statement and formulate it in the cases where at least one pair of sides are parallel.

8. Let Y_a be the second intersection of $l(X_a,O)$ with $\Gamma(A,B,C)$. Identify $l(A,Y_a)$ to one of the lines joining A to one or more remarkable points of the triangle.

9. An arc of circle subtends elementary angles at the points of the plane. Prove that they are smaller than the angle at the circumference if the point is in the exterior, greater if the point is in the interior, of the circle.

10. Let A_1, A_2, A_3 be three collinear points and P a point not on the line of the A_i. Let u_i be the tangent at P to $\Gamma(P,A_j,A_k)$, $i \neq j \neq k$, $i,j,k = 1,2,3$. Show that

$$t[u_1, l(P,A_1)] = t[u_2, l(P,A_2)] = t[u_3, l(P,A_3)].$$

Use problem 3, exercise 2–2.

11. The sides of a convex pentagon form five triangles external to the pentagon. Prove that their circumcircles intersect in another five points which are concyclic.

12. The theorem of problem 11 is a special case of a theorem about circumcircles of triangles formed by five lines of which no three are in a pencil. Formulate and prove that theorem.

13. Let P be a point of intersection of two circles Γ_1 and Γ_2. On Γ_1 choose a fixed point Q, on Γ_2 a point R. Prove that for any line through P which intersects Γ_1 at A_1, Γ_2 at A_2, the angle $\big(l(A_1,Q),l(A_2,R)\big)$ is independent of the line chosen.

14. Prove that A, F_b, H, F_c are concyclic.

15. Let P be a point on a circle Γ and Q a point in the exterior of Γ. Denote by T_1, T_2 the points of contact of the tangents to Γ through Q. Let x be the parallel through Q to the tangent to Γ at P, and put $Y_1 = x \cap l(P,T_1)$, $Y_2 = x \cap l(P,T_2)$. Prove that Y_1 and Y_2 are on $Q(QT_1)$.

16. Let G be a group of proper motions such that there exists a point P and a line a which satisfy $P \in \Sigma a$ for all $\Sigma \in$ G. Prove the following.

(a) The centers of all rotations of G are concyclic.

(b) For any line g, either all $\Sigma g(\Sigma \in$ G) are concurrent or they are tangents of a circle.

17. In the configuration of Fig. 4–11, compute the angles of the lines joining D to A, B, C as functions of the angles of $\triangle(A,B,C)$ and $\triangle(P,Q,R)$.

18. (Sequel to problem 17.) If the points P,Q,R in (4.23) are collinear, prove that the point of intersection D is on the circumcircle $\Gamma(A,B,C)$.

19. Find a point at which two given segments subtend two given angles, respectively.

20. Prove: all triangles with the same base a and congruent angles $\hat{A}$ have the same circumcircle.

21. Two points P and Q are taken on a circle Γ. For any other point $X \in \Gamma$ define Y by the condition that $XPYQ$ be a parallelogram. What is the set of the points Y?

22. Prove that $\Gamma(B,H,C) \cong \Gamma(A,B,C)$.

23. Let D be a point of the base $l(A,C)$ of an isosceles triangle $\triangle(A,B,C)$ of vertex B. Prove that $\Gamma(A,D,B) \cong \Gamma(C,D,B)$.

24. Through B draw the parallel p to the tangent at A to $\Gamma(A,B,C)$. Prove that c is the tangent at B to $\Gamma(B,C,p \cap b)$.

25. In the interior of a triangle, find a point at which the three edges subtend equal angles.

26. Through the vertices of an equilateral triangle one draws lines x_A, x_B, x_C such that the three lines $t(h_a, x_A)$, $t(h_b, x_B)$, $t(h_c, x_C)$ are parallel. Prove that the lines are concurrent at a point of the circumcircle.

The problems 27 to 33 form a whole.

27. Prove: the isogonal image of a point of the circumcircle is a pencil of parallel lines. The feet of the perpendiculars from the point to the sides of the triangle are collinear, the line being perpendicular to the isogonal pencil. (This line is called the *Simson* line without historical justification.)

28. Prove: if the isogonal image of a point is a pencil of parallel lines, then the point is on the circumcircle.

29. Prove: the six projections of two isogonal conjugate points upon the sides of the triangle are concyclic.

30. The angle subtended on the circumcircle by one of its chords is equal to the angle of the Simson lines of the endpoints of the chord. Prove this statement and formulate the theorem obtained in the special case of the endpoints of a diameter.

31. If $X \in \Gamma(A,B,C)$, then, for any rotation ρ, prove that the points ρX^a, ρX^b, and ρX^c are collinear.

32. In theorem (4.23), let O_1, O_2, O_3 be the centers of the three circles. If P, Q, R are collinear, prove that the lines $l(A,O_1)$, $l(B,O_2)$, $l(C,O_3)$ are concurrent at a point of $\Gamma(A,B,C)$.

33. For a given triangle $\triangle(A,B,C)$ find the set of points M such that $p[l(A,M),A]$, $p[l(B,M),B]$, $p[l(C,M),C]$ are concurrent.

34. On a given circle find an arc of given center angle such that the lines from its endpoints to two fixed points in the plane are parallel.

3.   Theorems of Pappus, Desargues, and Pascal

The first two theorems discussed in this section are quite important for the modern research in the foundations of geometry. The third theorem is equally important in the history of projective geometry. Some indications of these applications are given in the exercises. It is for their importance for a general education in geometry that we take time out for proofs and discussion even though these theorems will not be needed in further developments.

For the first theorem we need a lemma which in content and proof is similar to (4.23).

(4.24)   *If triples of points are given on two lines, $A_i \in a$, $B_i \in b$, $i = 1,2,3$ such that*

$$l(A_1,B_2) \parallel l(A_2,B_1) \qquad l(A_1,B_3) \parallel l(A_3,B_1),$$

then the three circles $\Gamma(A_1,A_2,B_3)$, $\Gamma(A_2,A_3,B_1)$ and $\Gamma(A_3,A_1,B_2)$ pass through a common point $C \in b$.

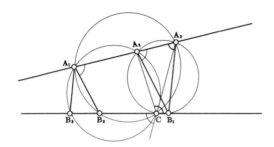

FIG. 4–12

Let C be the second point of intersection of $\Gamma(A_1,A_2,B_3)$ and b, or $C = B_3$ if the circle is tangent to b. We show that both A_2,C, B_1,A_3 and A_3,C, B_2,A_1 are concyclic sets. This follows from (4.17) since

$$
\begin{aligned}
\left(l(C,B_1),l(C,A_2)\right) &= \left(l(C,B_3),l(C,A_2)\right) && \text{by identity}\\
&= \left(l(A_1,B_3),l(A_1,A_2)\right) && \text{by (4.10)}\\
&= \left(l(A_3,B_1),l(A_3,A_2)\right) && \text{by hypothesis}
\end{aligned}
$$

and, similarly,

$$
\begin{aligned}
\left(l(C,B_2),l(C,A_3)\right) &= \left(l(C,B_1),l(C,A_3)\right) && \text{by identity}\\
&= \left(l(A_2,B_1),l(A_2,A_3)\right) && \text{by (4.10)}\\
&= \left(l(A_1,B_2),l(A_1,A_3)\right) && \text{by hypothesis.}
\end{aligned}
$$

In keeping with our terminology for polygons, we call *hexagon* the figure formed by six points, the vertices, in cyclic order and by the lines, the sides, which join adjacent vertices. The six points will be denoted by the numbers 1 to 6. *Opposite* pairs of sides are

$$l(1,2) \text{ and } l(4,5) \qquad l(2,3) \text{ and } l(5,6) \qquad l(3,4) \text{ and } l(6,1).$$

The points of intersection of opposite pairs of sides, if they exist, are called *diagonal points* and are denoted by

$$L = l(1,2) \cap l(4,5)$$
$$M = l(2,3) \cap l(5,6)$$
$$N = l(3,4) \cap l(6,1).$$

The next theorem is known as the *affine theorem of Pappus*.

(4.25)   *If the vertices of a hexagon are alternatingly on two straight lines (excluding their intersection), and if two pairs of opposite sides are parallel, so is the third pair.*

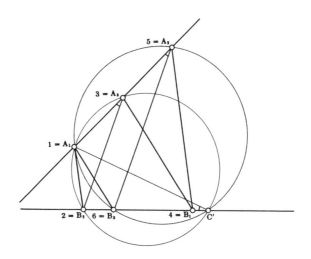

FIG. 4–13

We shall use (4.24). To this effect we put $1 = A_1$, $3 = A_3$, $5 = A_2$ and $2 = B_2$, $4 = B_1$, $6 = B_3$. The hypotheses of (4.24) then are

$$l(1,2) \parallel l(4,5) \qquad l(3,4) \parallel l(6,1).$$

The point C is defined in the statement of (4.24). We have

$$(l(2,3),a) = (l(A_3,B_2),l(A_3,A_1))$$
$$= (l(C,B_2),l(C,A_1))$$
$$= (l(C,B_3),l(C,A_1))$$
$$= (l(A_2,B_3),l(A_2,A_1)) = (l(5,6),a),$$

hence

$$l(2,3) \parallel l(5,6).$$

Any two pairs of opposite sides can be made to correspond to our assumptions by an adequate choice of the names of the points. Therefore, the theorem is proved in general.

On the other hand, five points of the hexagon and the condition of parallelism of pairs of opposite sides uniquely define the sixth point. Therefore, it is impossible that the converse of the Pappus theorem should be false:

(4.26)   *If opposite sides of a hexagon are parallel and the points 1,3,5 are collinear, then also 2,4,6 are collinear.*

For a convenient formulation of the next result, the *affine theorem of Desargues*, we define two triangles $\triangle(A_1,A_2,A_3)$ and $\triangle(B_1,B_2,B_3)$ to be *perspective* if the lines joining the vertices, $l(A_1,B_1)$, $l(A_2,B_2)$, and $l(A_3,B_3)$, form a pencil of three distinct lines.

(4.27)   *If in perspective triangles two pairs of corresponding sides are parallel, so is the third pair.*

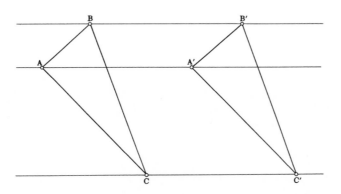

Fig. 4–14

If the lines joining the vertices are parallel, the theorem is known as the *little Desargues theorem*. It follows from

$$\triangle(B_1,B_2,B_3) = \tau_{[\![A_1B_1]\!]}\triangle(A_1,A_2,A_3).$$

Next we consider two perspective triangles $\triangle(A_1,A_2,A_3)$ and $\triangle(B_1,B_2,B_3)$, for which the lines joining the vertices are concurrent at a point V. We denote the lines $l(A_i,B_i)$ by g_i. About $\triangle(A_1,A_2,A_3)$ we circumscribe a triangle $\triangle(P_1,P_2,P_3)$ subject to $A_i \in p_i$ and

$$2\hat{P}_i = (p_j,p_k) = (g_j,g_k) \qquad\qquad i \neq j \neq k.$$

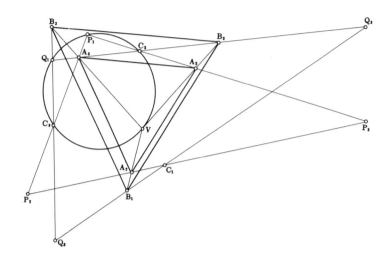

FIG. 4–15

This means that all quadruples V, A_i, P_j, A_k are concyclic, and, therefore, for the lines $p'_i = l(V, P_i)$ one obtains

(*) $(g_i, a_j) = (p'_j, p_k).$

The same construction is done for the second triangle $\triangle(B_1, B_2, B_3)$, for which we obtain a circumscribed triangle $\triangle(Q_1, Q_2, Q_3)$ and lines q_i, q'_i. We choose q_1 not parallel to p_1. This means that the points $C_i = q_i \cap p_i$ do exist for $i = 1, 2, 3$. Let h_i denote the line $l(V, C_i)$. Desargues's theorem now is proved in three steps.

(1) $a_i \parallel b_i$ *implies* $(h_j, h_k) = (g_j, g_k)$ $(i \neq j \neq k)$. For the argument we choose $i = 1, j = 2, k = 3$. Let the line h'_2 through V be defined by $(h'_2, h_3) = (g_2, g_3)$, and also

$$c'_1 = l(C_3, p_2 \cap h'_2)   \qquad c''_1 = l(C_3, q_2 \cap h'_2).$$

By construction, P_1, $p_2 \cap h'_2$, V, C_3 are concyclic. Hence

$$(p_2, p'_1) = (c'_1, h_3).$$

For the same reason also

$$(q_2, q'_1) = (c''_1, h_3).$$

The hypothesis $a_1 \parallel b_1$ implies by (*) that

$$(p_2, p'_1) = (q_2, q'_1),$$

i.e., $c'_1 = c''_1$ and $p_2 \cap h'_2 = q_2 \cap h'_2 = C_2$, or $h'_2 = h_2$.

(2) $(h_j, h_k) = (g_j, g_k)$ *implies* $a_i \parallel b_i$. We use the same notations as before. By hypothesis, both P_1, C_2, V, C_3 and Q_1, C_2, V, C_3 are concyclic. This implies

$$\big(l(C_2, C_3), h_3\big) = (p_2, p_1') = (a_1, g_1)$$
$$\big(l(C_2, C_3), h_3)\big) = (q_2, q_1') = (b_1, g_1),$$

hence $a_1 \parallel b_1$.

(3) *Proof of (4.27).* If both $a_1 \parallel b_1$ and $a_2 \parallel b_2$, then by (1),

$$(h_2, h_3) = (g_2, g_3) \text{ and } (h_3, h_1) = (g_3, g_1),$$

hence, by addition, $(h_2, h_1) = (g_2, g_1)$ and, by (2), $a_3 \parallel b_3$. Desargues's theorem also has a converse:

(4.28)   *If the sides of two complete triangles are pairwise parallel, then the lines which connect corresponding vertices form a pencil.*

If $l(A_1, B_1) \parallel l(A_2, B_2)$, then $\triangle(B_1, B_2, B_3) = \tau_{\llbracket A_1 B_1 \rrbracket} \triangle(A_1, A_2, A_3)$, hence $l(A_1, B_1) \parallel l(A_3, B_3)$. If $V = l(A_1, B_1) \cap l(A_2, B_2)$ does exist, so does the point $B_3^* = l(V, A_3) \cap b_1$. By the Desargues theorem, $a_2 \parallel l(B_1, B_3^*)$. By hypothesis, $a_2 \parallel b_2$. By the uniqueness of parallels, $b_2 = l(B_1, B_3^*)$ and $B_3^* = B_3$.

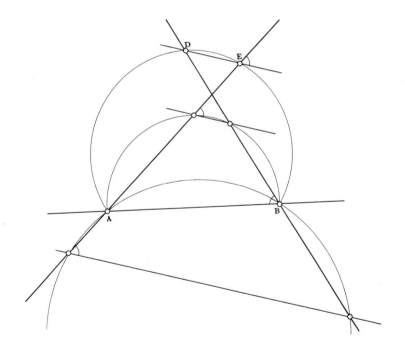

FIG. 4–16

For the next theorem we need another lemma about circles.

(4.29)   *All circles which have one edge of a triangle as a chord meet the other two sides in points which define the lines of a pencil of parallel lines.*

A circle through A and B meets a again at D, b at E. Then

$$(l(E,D),b) = (a,c) = -2\hat{B}$$

is independent of the circle. Hence the angle is the same for all circles; the lines are parallel.

This lemma will now be used to prove *Pascal's theorem:*

(4.30)   *If the vertices of a hexagon are concyclic, then the three diagonal points (if they exist) are collinear.*

Let Γ be the circle which contains the vertices of the hexagon. We draw the auxiliary circle $\Gamma^* = \Gamma(1,4,L)$ and introduce the auxiliary points

$$R = l(1,2) \cap l(3,4) \qquad \text{and} \qquad S = l(4,5) \cap l(1,6).$$

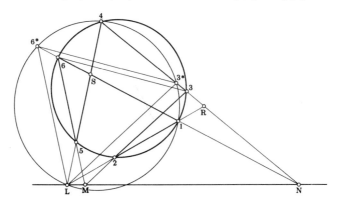

FIG. 4–17

[If one of these points should fail to exist, a line through it shall be a line in the corresponding pencil of parallel lines. Lemma (4.29) holds also if $a \parallel b$.] Now we use the lemma (4.29) three times. The two circles, drawn over $[1,4]$, meet

$$\triangle(1,4,N) \text{ in } l(3,6) \parallel l(3^*,6^*)$$
$$\triangle(1,4,R) \text{ in } l(3,M) \parallel l(3^*,L)$$
$$\triangle(1,4,S) \text{ in } l(6,M) \parallel l(6^*,L),$$

where the points 3* and 6* are defined by the intersections. The two triangles $\triangle(6,3,M)$ and $\triangle(6^*,3^*,L)$ satisfy the hypotheses of the converse Desargues theorem (4.28), hence the lines $l(L,M)$, $l(6,6^*) = l(6,1)$, and $l(3,3^*) = l(3,4)$ are concurrent at N.

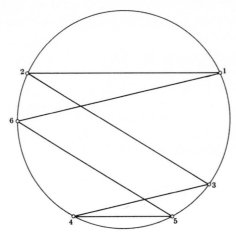

FIG. 4–18

The proof shows that, if L exists but N does not, then $\triangle(6,3,M) \cong \triangle(6^*,3^*,L)$, hence M exists. The existence of one diagonal point implies that of a second one:

(4.31)   *If two pairs of opposite sides of a concyclic hexagon are parallel, so is the third pair.*

If L and M do exist but N does not, the line $l(L,M)$ is in the pencil of the ideal point N. The proof may be read from Fig. 4–19.

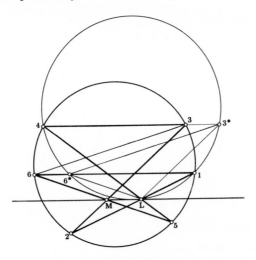

FIG. 4–19

Exercise 4–3

1. If the two lines which carry the hexagon in the Pappus theorem are parallel, the statement (4.25) is known as the *little Pappus* theorem. Prove the little Pappus theorem by the method of chapter 2, without using circles.

2. Prove the statement following (4.31).

3. Prove the Pascal theorem in the case that 1 and 2 coincide and $l(1,2)$ is the tangent to the circle at $1 = 2$.

4. Prove the Pascal theorem in case $1 = 2$, $4 = 5$, and both lines $l(1,2)$ and $l(4,5)$ are tangents.

5. Prove the Desargues theorem in case $V = A_1$.

6. In the configuration of the Desargues theorem draw the parallel d through A_1 to $l(V,A_2)$ and define the points $P = d \cap b_2$, $Q = d \cap l(V,A_3)$, $R = l(P,B_2) \cap a_3$. If the three points exist, prove that (V,B_2,B_1,P,A_1,R), (V,A_2,A_3,A_1,Q,R), and (V,B_2,B_3,P,Q,R) are Pappus hexagons.

7. Derive from problem 6 a proof of the Desargues theorem in the case that P exists. Can the proof be saved if P does not exist?

8. Prove the converse of Pascal's theorem: if five points of a hexagon are concyclic and the diagonal points collinear, then all six points are concyclic.

9. Through a point O draw two lines a and b. On a mark a point E and through E draw the parallel e to b. An addition of points on b is then defined as follows: Given points A and B, draw the parallel x to a through A and the line $y = l(E,B)$. Through $e \cap x$ draw the parallel z to y. Then we define $A + B = z \cap b$. Show that the little Pappus theorem implies

    (a) $A + B = B + A$

    (b) $(A + B) + C = A + (B + C)$.

10. A multiplication of points on a line can be defined as follows: Through a point O one draws two lines, g and g^*. On g one marks a point E, on g^* a point E^*, both distinct from O. For $A \in g$ let A^* be the intersection with a^* of the parallel to $l(E,E^*)$ through A. The point AB is the intersection with a of the parallel through A^* to $l(B,E^*)$. Prove that the Pappus theorem implies that $AB = BA$.

The remaining problems all refer to the following two constructions: On a circle we choose three points P_0, P_1, and P_∞. Let a be the tangent to the circle at P_∞ and $m = l(P_0,P_\infty)$. A line joining two coinciding points of the circle means the tangent to the circle at the point. For any two points A and B, distinct from P_∞, the sum $A + B$ is defined as the second intersection with the circle of $l[P_0,a \cap l(A,B)]$. The product AB is defined as the second intersection with the circle of $l[P_1,m \cap l(A,B)]$. Since the definitions are symmetric in A and B, it is clear that $A + B = B + A$ and $AB = BA$.

11. Show that the points of the circle distinct from P_∞ form an abelian group under addition.

12. Show that the points of the circle distinct from P_∞ and P_0 form an abelian group under multiplication.

Chapter V

METRIC GEOMETRY

1. Area

We define the multiplication of segments through the notion of area. Only the area of polygons will be treated. The definition of the area of domains bounded by curves uses limit processes and therefore is properly studied in calculus.

All polygons considered in this section are assumed to have an interior as defined in sec. 3–3. This fact has to be added to all stated hypotheses. (The area function for arbitrary polygons is studied in some of the exercises for this section.) To each polygon P we want to define a length $\alpha(P)$ as its *area*. $\alpha(P)$ is a function whose domain are the polygons with interior and whose range are the lengths. It is defined by four conditions. The first three are:

A1. $\alpha(P) > 0$.
A2. *If* $P \cong Q$, *then* $\alpha(P) = \alpha(Q)$.
A3. *If* P *and* Q *have no interior points in common, then*

$$\alpha(P \cup Q) = \alpha(P) + \alpha(Q).$$

The developments of this chapter are all based on (5.1) which, as *theorem of the gnomon*, is the principal tool of Euclid's books II and VI.

Through a point E of a diagonal of the parallelogram of vertices A,B,C,D we draw the parallels to the edges which intersect the other edges at points F,G and H,I, as indicated in Fig. 5–1. In this way we obtain four triangles (which form two parallelograms, see Fig. 2–15) and two parallelograms ① and ②, which are the *complementary parallelograms* defined by the point E.

(5.1) *Complementary parallelograms have equal area.*

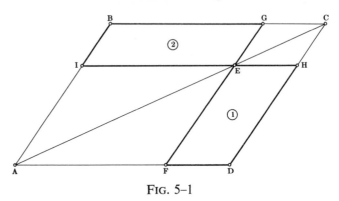

$$\text{Fig. 5-1}$$

The proof of (2.37) shows that the diagonal of a parallelogram divides the parallelogram into two congruent triangles. In our case, this means, by A2,

$$\alpha[\text{①} \cup \triangle(A,F,E) \cup \triangle(E,H,C)] = \alpha[\text{②} \cup \triangle(A,I,E) \cup \triangle(E,G,C)]$$

or, by A3,

$$\alpha(\text{①}) + \alpha[\triangle(A,F,E)] + \alpha[\triangle(E,H,C)] = \alpha(\text{②}) + \alpha[\triangle(A,I,E)] + \alpha[\triangle(E,G,C)].$$

But, again by A2,

$$\alpha[\triangle(A,F,E)] = \alpha[\triangle(A,I,E)]$$
$$\alpha[\triangle(E,H,C)] = \alpha[\triangle(E,G,C)],$$

hence

$$\alpha(\text{①}) = \alpha(\text{②}).$$

The theorem admits a converse. The parallels to the edges through an interior point of the parallelogram divide the parallelogram into four smaller parallelograms. Two of them are *opposite* if their intersection reduces to the given point.

(5.2)   *If two opposite parallelograms are of equal area, the point of inter-section is on a diagonal.*

If the point E is not on the diagonal which joins the two vertices of the original parallelogram that are not vertices of one of the opposite parallelograms, then let E^* be the intersection of that diagonal with one of the parallels to the edges through E. If we draw the parallel to the other edge through E^*, we obtain four smaller parallelograms ①, ②, ③, ④ as indicated in Fig. 5–2. The hypothesis is

$$\alpha(\text{①}) = \alpha(\text{③} \cup \text{④}) = \alpha(\text{③}) + \alpha(\text{④}).$$

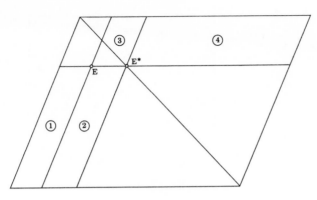

FIG. 5–2

The gnomon theorem (5.1) reads in our case

$$\alpha(① \cup ②) = \alpha(①) + \alpha(②) = \alpha(④),$$

hence, by A1,

$$\alpha(1) < \alpha(1) + \alpha(2) = \alpha(4) < \alpha(3) + \alpha(4)$$

against the hypothesis.

We now choose a certain segment and assign it the length *one*. This choice is arbitrary, but once the unit length is chosen it should not be changed again. In chapter II we had defined addition of lengths as a special case of vector addition. The gnomon theorem and the choice of a unit length now let us define a multiplication of lengths. This is obtained from the last condition we impose on the area function:

A4. *The area of a rectangle of edges a and 1 is a.*

We also need

(5.3)   *Every rectangle is equal in area to some rectangle, one of whose edges is of unit length.*

This is a consequence of the gnomon theorem. A comparison of Figs. 5–3 and 5–4 shows that the second edge of the desired rectangle can be found without explicit reference to the gnomon configuration. The edge $[D,H]$ of length b of the rectangle is produced by a segment $[H,C]$ of unit length. The second edge of the rectangle is of length FA, $A = l(D,F) \cap l(C,E)$.

If two rectangles both have one edge of length 1 and they are complementary in a bigger rectangle, then either the common point is the midpoint

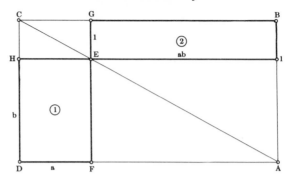

FIG. 5–3

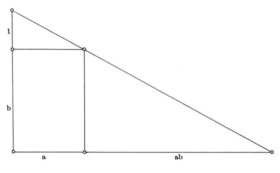

FIG. 5–4

of the diagonal [Fig. 5–5 (a)], or the diagonal makes 45° angles with the edges and, therefore, is the diagonal of a square [Fig. 5–5 (b)]. In both cases the two remaining edges also are of equal length. On the other hand, it follows from the proof of (5.2) that two rectangles of equal area, if moved into the position of complementary rectangles, are indeed complementary rectangles in a bigger rectangle.

(5.4)   *The area of rectangles is uniquely defined.*

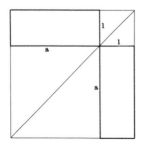

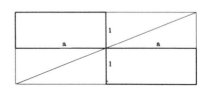

FIG. 5–5

This lets us put our final definition: *The product ab of two lengths a and b is the area of the rectangle of edge lengths a and b.*

By (5.4) the multiplication is well defined. We have to show that it satisfies the usual rules of computations with numbers. The definition is independent of the order of *a* and *b*:

(5.5) $ab = ba.$

The proof of the distributive law

(5.6) $a(b + c) = ab + ac$

can be read from Fig. 5–6; the verbal formulation of the proof is left to the reader. Also, by definition A4,

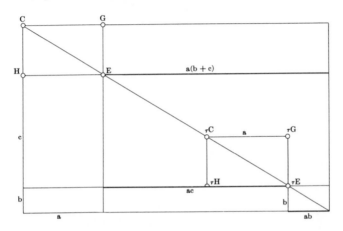

FIG. 5–6

(5.7) $a \cdot 1 = a$ for all length *a*.

Figure 5–7 shows the construction of an *x* such that $ax = b$ for given *a* and *b*. Hence we may not only multiply, but also divide, nonzero lengths by $x = b/a$.

The associative law

(5.8) $a(bc) = (ab)c$

is proved by Fig. 5–8. By construction, *A* is on the diagonal of the rectangle defined by the two complementary rectangles of areas $(ab)c$ and $a(bc)$. The result follows from (5.1).

We may identify the integers with the multiples of the unit length by $2 = 1 + 1$, $3 = 1 + 2$, etc. The multiplication of a segment by an integer as

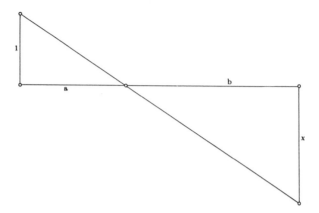

FIG. 5–7

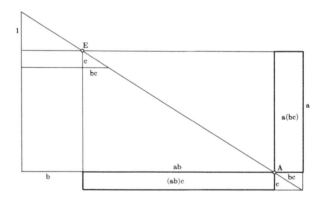

FIG. 5–8

defined in sec. 2–4 then appears as a special case of the multiplication defined on segments.

Next we turn to the actual determination of areas.

(5.9)   *The area of a triangle of base b and h is $\frac{1}{2}bh$.*

The proof must consider three cases.

(a) If $\hat{C} = 90°$, then, by the definitions,

$$BC \cdot CA = \alpha[\triangle(A,B,C)] + \alpha[\triangle(B,A,\sigma_{M_c}C)] = 2\alpha[\triangle(A,B,C)].$$

BC is the length of the base, CA the height, i.e., the length of the altitude.

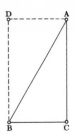 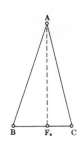 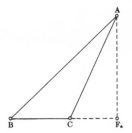

Fig. 5–9

(b) If both angles at the base are acute, the altitude divides the triangle into two right triangles. By (a),

$$\alpha[\triangle(A,B,C)] = \tfrac{1}{2}BF_a \cdot AF_a + \tfrac{1}{2}F_aC \cdot AF_a = \tfrac{1}{2}(BF_a + F_aC)AF_a$$
$$= \tfrac{1}{2}BC \cdot AF_a.$$

(c) If $\hat{C}$ is obtuse, the right triangle $\triangle(B,F_a,C)$ is the union of $\triangle(A,B,C)$ and $\triangle(A,C,F_a)$. Hence

$$\alpha[\triangle(A,B,C)] + \alpha[\triangle(A,C,F_a)] = \tfrac{1}{2}BF_a \cdot AF_a = \tfrac{1}{2}(BC + CF_a)AF_a$$
$$\alpha[\triangle(A,C,F_a)] \qquad\qquad = \qquad \tfrac{1}{2}CF_a \cdot AF_a,$$

and the result follows.

We have used before the fact that a diagonal splits a parallelogram into two congruent triangles. If one edge is called the base and the distance of the parallel edge the height, then

(5.10)   *The area of a parallelogram is base times height.*

Of general results we prove only

(5.11)   *The area function is uniquely determined for all polygons that have an interior.*

By (5.9), the area of a triangle is half the area of the rectangle formed by base and height. Hence it is uniquely determined by (5.4). By definition, our polygons are unions of triangles without common interior points. By condition A3, the area of the polygon is the sum of the areas of the triangles. Let us assume now that a polygon has been dissected into triangles in two different ways (Fig. 5–10). The intersections of the triangles of decompositions are a finite number of *convex* polygons which, in turn, are unions of triangles. In both cases, the area of the original polygon appears as the sum of the areas of the smaller triangles which make up the convex polygons. Only the

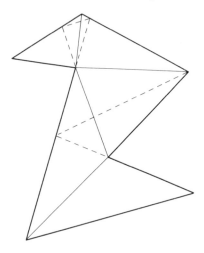

Fig. 5-10

order of summation distinguishes between the computations of the area according to the two decompositions. Since addition of segments is commutative and associative, the result does not depend on the decomposition.

The multiplication of segments extends naturally to oriented segments, i.e., parallel vectors. If $[\![OA]\!]$ is a vector in the positive ray of its line, we write

$$[\![OA]\!] > 0 \qquad [\![-OA]\!] = [\![AO]\!] < 0.$$

Alternatively, we define the *sign* of an oriented segment by

$$\text{sgn } AB = 1 \ if \ [\![AB]\!] > 0$$
$$\text{sgn } AB = -1 \ if \ [\![AB]\!] < 0$$

and define *for parallel vectors*

$$[\![AB]\!] \cdot [\![CD]\!] = \text{sgn } AB \cdot \text{sgn } CD \cdot AB \cdot CD.$$

We also define multiplication by the zero vector:

$$a \cdot 0 = 0 \qquad for \ all \ a.$$

This is the only possible definition if we want to preserve the distributive law for our multiplication, since

$$ab = a(b + 0) = ab + a \cdot 0.$$

It is easily checked that the rules of computation, (5.5) to (5.8), are preserved for the new definitions. The zero length may stand for the area of polygons defined by collinear vertices. The use of negative areas is discussed in calculus.

Products are not defined for vectors which are not parallel. The orientation depends on an arbitrary choice of a direction for each line. As has been pointed out in sec. 2–4, no such choice can be compatible with all operations of the group $\mathfrak{M}^+$ since point reflections reverse the orientation of any line through the center of the reflection!

If the orientation is fixed on a line, lengths, and hence vectors, have an inverse. If two points A and B are fixed on a line, any other point $C \in l(A,B)$ is uniquely determined by the *ratio of division*

$$\lambda = \frac{[\![AC]\!]}{[\![CB]\!]}$$

since

(5.12) $[\![AC]\!] = \dfrac{\lambda}{(1+\lambda)} [\![AB]\!].$

λ is positive if and only if $C \in (A,B)$. The two complementary segments are characterized by $\lambda < -1$ and $-1 < \lambda < 0$.

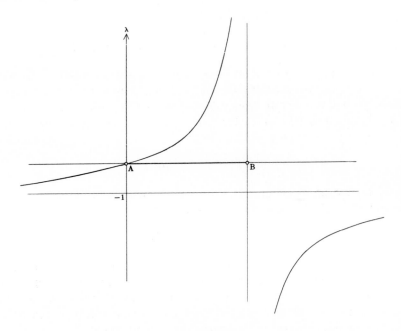

FIG. 5–11

Ratios of division depend only on the ratio of the signs of two parallel vectors, not on their value. Therefore, they are independent of the choice of the positive ray on any line. In fact, $a = -b$ implies $\Sigma a = -\Sigma b$ for all

$\Sigma \in \mathfrak{M}$. Therefore, it is possible to compute these ratios all on the one line which serves to define lengths. *Ratios of division are defined only for parallel vectors, but sum and product are defined for any two such ratios.*

The constructions of this section have some importance in algebra. A set *F* is a *field* if:

> (a) it is an abelian group with unit 0 for an operation $+$;
> (b) its nonzero elements form an abelian group for an operation $\cdot$;
> (c) the operations $+$ and $\cdot$ are connected by the distributive law (5.6).

The field is *ordered* if on it there is defined a relation $>$ subject to

$$a > b \text{ implies } b \not> a$$
$$a > b \text{ and } b > c \text{ implies } a > c$$
$$a \not> a \text{ for all } a,$$

and the algebraic conditions

$$a > b \text{ implies } a + c > b + c$$
$$a > 0 \text{ and } b > 0 \text{ implies } ab > 0.$$

Then we can sum up the algebraic part of our construction by

(5.13)   *The lengths of oriented segments form an ordered field.*

Through a point *O* we choose two perpendicular lines *a* and *b*. On each line we fix a positive ray. For each line there is a one-to-one correspondence between its points *X* and the elements *x* of the ordered field of the geometry by $x = [\![OX]\!]$. Any point *P* in the plane is uniquely determined by its two projections P^a and P^b since

$$P = p(a, P^a) \cap p(b, P^b).$$

Therefore, the points of the plane are in one-to-one correspondence with the ordered couples of elements of the field of the geometry by

$$x = [\![OP^a]\!], \qquad y = [\![OP^b]\!].$$

Our geometry then becomes an analytic geometry whose coordinates (x, y) have values in some ordered field *F*. Such a geometry can be developed just as the usual analytic geometry based on the real number line. We are not really interested in analytic geometry; its development will be restricted to some occasional remarks. In particular, the proportionality theorem of sec. 5–3 will imply that the coordinates (x, y) of the points on a line through the *origin O* must satisfy a linear equation $y = cx$. The theorems of sec. 5–3 will also imply that the usual proof, that a straight line has a linear equation, still holds in our more general setting. This proof is given in any book on analytic geometry.

Some further analytic developments of our geometry, in particular formulae for σ_l, are contained in the appendix. These formulae show that the set of ordered couples of any ordered field F can be turned into a geometry which satisfies our axioms I to IX, XI to XIII. The algebraic equivalent for axioms X and X* will be discussed in sec. 5–3.

A field is an algebraic system in which addition, subtraction, multiplication, and division are possible according to the usual rules. If the field is ordered, magnitudes can be compared in the usual way. The most simple example of such a field is that of the rational numbers. This example shows that, in general, it is not possible to find roots or logarithms of elements of the field. A more detailed study of fields can be found in any book on modern algebra. A non-archimedean field is described in the appendix. Some exercises on fields are given in sec. 5–3.

Exercise 5–1

1. Write down a formal proof of (5.6).

2. Prove the gnomon theorem for rectangles by cutting one of the complementary rectangles into pieces and rearranging the areas so as to produce the other rectangle.

3. Dissect a triangle into convex polygons so that the pieces may be rearranged to form a rectangle over the base of a triangle.

4. Use problems 2 and 3 to prove: two polygons have equal area if and only if one can be cut into convex polygons which may be rearranged to give the second polygon.

5. Prove: the two triangles defined by the diagonals of a trapezoid over the base have equal area.

6. For a given triangle find a triangle of equal area, equal base, and satisfying one of the following conditions. Find the conditions for the existence of a solution of the problem, if any.

    (a) resulting triangle isosceles
    (b) resulting triangle of given circumradius R
    (c) resulting triangle of given length of midline s_a.

7. For a given convex quadrilateral find a triangle of equal area by drawing a minimum number of lines.

8. Dissect two squares into convex polygons that may be put together to form a single square. Try to use a minimal number of cuts.

9. The vertices A_i of a square are given in a cyclic order. The lines $l[A_{i+1}, M(A_i, A_{i-1})]$ define a smaller square. What is the ratio of the area of the new square to that of the given one?

10. A *tangential polygon* is a convex polygon all of whose edges are tangents to a fixed circle. The area of a tangential polygon is half its perimeter times the radius of the circle. Prove this statement and use it to obtain a formula for the inradius of a triangle.

11. Find the area of a trapezoid of height h and parallel edges b_1 and b_2.

12. Through a point in the interior of an angle draw a line which from the angle cuts off the triangle of minimal area.

13. Prove: for any four collinear points,

$$[\![DA]\!][\![BC]\!] + [\![DB]\!][\![CA]\!] + [\![DC]\!][\![AB]\!] = 0.$$

14. Prove: if the points A,B,C,A',B',C' are collinear, then the function

$$f(P) = [\![PA]\!][\![PA']\!][\![M(B,B')M(C,C')]\!] + [\![PB]\!][\![PB']\!][\![M(C,C')M(A,A')]\!]$$
$$+ [\![PC]\!][\![PC']\!][\![M(A,A')M(B,B')]\!]$$

is a constant for P on the line of the given points (using problem 13).

15. For a triangle $\triangle(A,B,C)$ and a point P define $E = a \cap l(A,P)$. If E exists, prove that

$$\frac{PE}{AE} = \frac{\alpha[\triangle(B,P,C)]}{\alpha[\triangle(A,B,C)]}.$$

We have seen in sec. 3-2 that in the plane the notion of a positive (anti-clockwise) rotation can be defined. This may be used to define signed areas. For a triangle, we define

$$\alpha^\circ(A,B,C) = \alpha[\triangle(A,B,C)] \text{ if } A \to B \to C \text{ in positive sense on } \Gamma(A,B,C)$$
$$= 0 \text{ if } A,B,C \text{ are collinear}$$
$$= -\alpha[\triangle(A,B,C)] \text{ if } A \to B \to C \text{ in negative sense on } \Gamma(A,B,C).$$

The function α° might be extended to ordered sets of k points $A_1,\ldots,A_k$, by putting

$$\alpha^\circ(A_1,\ldots,A_k) = \sum_{i=1}^{k} \alpha^\circ(P,A_i,A_{i+1}),$$

where P is an arbitrary point in the plane and $k + 1$ is identified to 1.

16. Prove that the definition of $\alpha^\circ(A_1,A_2,\ldots,A_k)$ is independent of the choice of the point P.

17. If A,B,C,D form a parallelogram, prove that for arbitrary P:
    (a) $\alpha^\circ(P,A,B) + \alpha^\circ(P,C,D) = \alpha^\circ(A,B,C)$
    (b) $\alpha^\circ(P,A,B) + \alpha^\circ(P,A,D) = \alpha^\circ(P,A,C)$.

18. If $[\![AB]\!] = [\![AC_1]\!] + [\![AC_2]\!] + \cdots + [\![AC_n]\!]$, prove that

$$\alpha^\circ(P,A,B) = \alpha^\circ(P,A,C_1) + \cdots + \alpha^\circ(P,A,C_n).$$

19. Define $\mathbf{v} = [\![A_1A_2]\!] + [\![A_3A_4]\!] + \cdots + [\![A_{2n-1}A_{2n}]\!]$.
    (a) If $\mathbf{v} \neq 0$, prove that the function

$$f(P) = \alpha^\circ(P,A_1,A_2) + \alpha^\circ(P,A_3,A_4) + \cdots + \alpha^\circ(P,A_{2n-1},A_{2n})$$

is constant on any line parallel to the direction of $\mathbf{v}$.
    (b) If $\mathbf{v} = 0$, prove that either $f(P)$ is constant in the plane or it is not constant on any line.

20. If A,B,B',A' is not a parallelogram, prove that

$$\alpha°(P,A,B) + \alpha°(P,A',B) + \alpha°(P,A,B') + \alpha°(P,A',B') = 0$$

for all points $P \in l[M(A,A'),M(B,B')]$. Use problem 19(a).

21. Prove: if A, B, and C are collinear, then $\alpha°(P,A,B)/\alpha°(P,A,C) = [\![AB]\!]/[\![AC]\!]$.

22. Prove: if $l(A,B) \parallel l(C,D)$, then for arbitrary Q and R

$$\alpha°(C,Q,R) - \alpha°(D,Q,R) = [\![CD]\!]/[\![AB]\!][\alpha°(A,Q,R) - \alpha°(B,Q,R)].$$

23. Prove: if A, B, and C are collinear, then for any Q and R

$$[\![AC]\!]\alpha°(B,Q,R) + [\![CB]\!]\alpha°(A,Q,R) = [\![AB]\!]\alpha°(C,Q,R).$$

24. Prove: for any six points A,B,C and P,Q,R,

$$\alpha°(P,B,C)\alpha°(A,Q,R) + \alpha°(A,P,C)\alpha°(B,Q,R) + \alpha°(A,B,P)\alpha°(C,Q,R)$$
$$= \alpha°(A,B,C)\alpha°(P,Q,R).$$

25. Prove: for any five points A, B, C, D, and E,

$$\alpha°(A,B,E)\alpha°(C,D,E) + \alpha°(B,C,E)\alpha°(A,D,E) + \alpha°(C,A,E)\alpha°(B,D,E) = 0.$$

26. Prove: $\alpha°(A_1,A_2,A_3,A_4) = 0$ if and only if $l(A_1,A_3) \parallel l(A_2,A_4)$.

27. Prove: if the diagonals of two parallelograms are pairwise parallel, then the ratio of the areas of the parallelograms is equal to the ratio of the products of the lengths of the diagonals.

28. Given six points A, B, C, P, Q, R and three points P', Q', R' such that $[\![PP']\!] = [\![QQ']\!] = [\![RR']\!]$, prove that

$$\alpha°(P,B,C) + \alpha°(Q,C,A) + \alpha°(R,A,B) = \alpha°(P',B,C) + \alpha°(Q',C,A) + \alpha°(R',A,B).$$

29. If the four lines a_i $(i = 1,2,3,4)$ are concurrent at P, prove that the expression

$$\frac{\alpha°(A_1,A_2,P)\alpha°(A_3,A_4,P)}{\alpha°(A_2,A_3,P)\alpha°(A_4,A_1,P)}$$

is independent of the choice of the points $A_i \in a_i$. (The expression is the *cross ratio* of the four lines.)

30. If a line g intersects four concurrent lines a_i in points G_i, prove that the cross ratio of the four lines is

$$\frac{[\![G_1G_2]\!] \cdot [\![G_3G_4]\!]}{[\![G_2G_3]\!] \cdot [\![G_4G_1]\!]}.$$

2.   The Pythagorean Theorem

The theorem of Pythagoras is so important that we give three proofs in this section and a fourth in the next.

As a matter of convention, all the names of lines connected with a triangle also stand for the length of the segment which is the intersection of

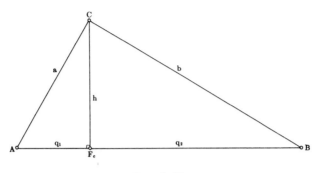

Fig. 5–12

the line with the interior and the boundary of the triangle. In the standard notation for a right triangle, one puts the right angle at C. The height h_c is written simply h. The length of the hypotenuse is c; the lengths of the legs are a and b. The projections of the legs onto the hypotenuse are $q_1 = BF_c$, $q_2 = AF_c$.

(5.14)   *In a right triangle the square over the hypotenuse is equal to the sum of the squares over the legs.*

The first proof is algebraic (Fig. 5–13): We construct the square of edge $(a + b)$ and cut off four times the given triangle, as indicated in the figure.

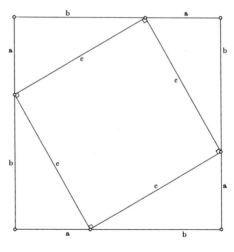

Fig. 5–13

The remaining area is an equilateral quadrilateral of edge c. The angles at the vertices are all congruent since the figure admits the rotation group of order four about the intersection of the diagonals of the square. Hence all angles are right angles; the quadrilateral is the square of area c^2. The figure, therefore, shows

$$(a + b)^2 = c^2 + 4 \cdot \tfrac{1}{2}ab = c^2 + 2ab.$$

By the distributive and associative laws,

$$(a + b)^2 = a^2 + b^2 + 2ab,$$

hence

$$c^2 = a^2 + b^2.$$

The next proof, by An-Nairizi, is a direct one. We cut the squares a^2 and b^2 into pieces and put them together again to form c^2. The details can be seen in Fig. 5–14, where congruent pieces are given identical shading.

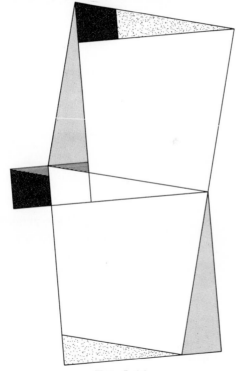

FIG. 5–14

The proof is remarkable in that the pieces need to be moved by translations only. In general it is impossible to transform a polygon into another one of equal area by cutting and gluing if we move the pieces by translations only. (This problem is investigated in the booklet by Boltyanskii quoted in the references.)

The third proof, given by Euclid, shows a little more, namely,

(5.15) $a^2 = q_1 c.$

We draw the square a^2 and the rectangle of edges q_1 and c over the segment q_1. Let G be the end point of the second edge of the square attached to B.

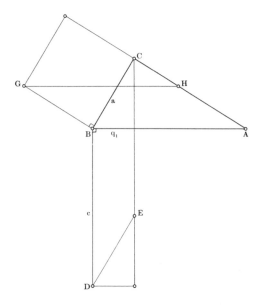

FIG. 5–15

Through G we draw the parallel to the edge c. The parallelogram $(GHAB)$ obtained in this way has area a^2 by (5.10). In the rectangle, let D be the end point of the second edge attached to B. Through D we draw the parallel to the edge a. The parallelogram $(DECB)$ obtained in this way has area $q_1 c$ by (5.10). But $(GHAB) = \rho_{B,90°}(CEDB)$. Equation (5.15) follows by A2.

The altitude h divides the right triangle into two smaller right triangles. Therefore,

$$a^2 = q_1^2 + h^2$$
$$b^2 = q_2^2 + h^2.$$

Since

$$c^2 = q_1^2 + 2q_1 q_2 + q_2^2 = a^2 + b^2,$$

it follows that

(5.16) $h^2 = q_1 q_2.$

Using oriented segments we can formulate an extension of Pythagoras's theorem, known as *Stewart's formula*, which, in principle, solves all computational problems in plane geometry.

(5.17)   *If A, B, and C are collinear, then for any point P in the plane*
$$PA^2 \cdot [\![BC]\!] + PB^2 \cdot [\![CA]\!] + PC^2 \cdot [\![AB]\!] + [\![AB]\!] \cdot [\![BC]\!] \cdot [\![CA]\!] = 0.$$

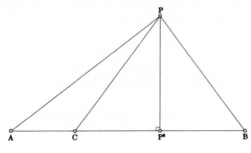

Fig. 5–16

In order to use the pythagorean theorem, we introduce the projection P^g, $g = l(A,B)$. Then

$$PA^2 = AP^{g\,2} + P^g P^2$$
$$PB^2 = BP^{g\,2} + P^g P^2.$$

Also

$$AP^{g\,2} = [\![P^g A]\!]^2 = ([\![P^g C]\!] + [\![CA]\!])^2$$
$$= P^g C^2 + 2[\![P^g C]\!] \cdot [\![CA]\!] + CA^2,$$

hence

$$PA^2[\![BC]\!] + PB^2[\![CA]\!] + PC^2[\![AB]\!]$$
$$= AP^{g^2}[\![BC]\!] + BP^{g^2}[\![CA]\!] + CP^{g^2}[\![AB]\!] + P^g P^2([\![BC]\!] + [\![CA]\!] + [\![AB]\!])$$
$$= (P^g C^2 + 2[\![P^g C]\!] \cdot [\![CA]\!] + CA^2)[\![BC]\!]$$
$$+ (P^g C^2 + 2[\![P^g C]\!] \cdot [\![CB]\!] + CB^2)[\![CA]\!] + P^g C^2 \cdot [\![AB]\!]$$
$$= [\![CA]\!] \cdot [\![BC]\!]([\![CA]\!] + [\![BC]\!]) = -[\![AB]\!] \cdot [\![BC]\!] \cdot [\![CA]\!].$$

We give two applications of Stewart's formula. In a triangle $\triangle(A,B,C)$ we take one vertex as the point P and the other two vertices with their midpoint as the three collinear points. In our standard notation, (5.17) becomes

$$c^2 \cdot \frac{a}{2} - S_a^2 \cdot a + b \cdot \frac{a}{2} - \frac{a}{2} a \frac{a}{2} = 0,$$

or

(5.18) $S_a^2 = \frac{1}{2}(b^2 + c^2) - \frac{1}{4}a^2.$

Next we want to compute the area of a triangle as function of the lengths of its edges. In addition to the notations introduced in sec. 1–5, we use the semi-perimeter

$$p = \frac{a+b+c}{2}$$

and $q_1 = [\![BF_a]\!]$, $q_2 = [\![F_aC]\!]$. By definition, $q_1 + q_2 = a$. We have two formulas of Pythagoras and one of Stewart:

$$q_1^2 + h_a^2 = c^2$$
$$q_2^2 + h_a^2 = b^2$$
$$c^2 q_2 - h_a^2 a + b^2 q_1 - q_1 q_2 a = 0.$$

If we eliminate q_1 and h_a from the formulas, we obtain

$$q_2 = \frac{a^2 + b^2 - c^2}{2a}.$$

Stewart's formula then lets us compute h_a:

$$h_a^2 = \frac{1}{4a^2}(2a^2b^2 + 2a^2c^2 + 2b^2c^2 - a^4 - b^4 - c^4).$$

For the area we obtain finally

$$\alpha^2 = \tfrac{1}{16}(2a^2b^2 + 2b^2c^2 + 2c^2a^2 - a^4 - b^4 - c^4).$$

A simple check shows that this formula can be written either as

(5.19a) $\qquad \alpha^2 = p(p-a)(p-b)(p-c),$

or in the form of a determinant

(5.19b)
$$-16\alpha^2 = \begin{vmatrix} 0 & c^2 & b^2 & 1 \\ c^2 & 0 & a^2 & 1 \\ b^2 & a^2 & 0 & 1 \\ 1 & 1 & 1 & 0 \end{vmatrix}.$$

Exercise 5–2

1. On two edges b,c of a triangle as bases draw arbitrary parallelograms. The sides parallel to the bases intersect at a point P. On a as base draw the parallelogram whose second edge, as a vector, is equal to $[\![PA]\!]$. Prove that the area of this parallelogram is the sum of the areas of the first two.

2. Give a proof of Pythagoras's theorem based on problem 1.

3. For the right triangle $\triangle(A,B,C)$ draw the rectangle of sides c, $p_{C,90°}c$, $p_{C,90°}\tau[\![c_A]\!]h_a$, and $p(c,B)$. Prove (5.16) as a direct consequence of the gnomon theorem.

4. For a given rectangle of edges x and y construct a square of equal area.

5. For given *positive* lengths q_1,q_2 prove that

$$\frac{q_1 + q_2}{2} \geqslant \sqrt{q_1 q_2} \geqslant \frac{2q_1 q_2}{q_1 + q_2}.$$

6. Three points E,F,G on the sides of a triangle (in order) are the feet of the perpendiculars from one point in the plane if and only if

$$BE^2 - CE^2 + CF^2 - AF^2 + AG^2 - BG^2 = 0.$$

7. For a triangle $\triangle(A_1,A_2,A_3)$ and a line h define $g_i = p(a_i,\sigma_h A_i)$, $(i = 1,2,3)$. Prove that the lines g_i are concurrent (using problem 6).

8. From a point P draw the perpendiculars to the three sides of a triangle. The circle $\Gamma(P^a,P^b,P^c)$ intersects the sides in a second triple of points. Show that the perpendiculars at these points to the corresponding sides are concurrent. (Use problem 6.)

9. On the sides of a triangle take three points E, F, G defined by ratios of division λ, μ, ν from the vertices in cyclic order. Let $\tilde{\Delta}$ be the triangle whose edges are congruent to (A,E), (B,F), (C,G). Compute $\alpha(\tilde{\Delta})/\alpha(\Delta)$ as a function of λ, μ, ν.

10. In a scalene triangle show that

$$c^2 = a^2 + b^2 - 2b \cdot CF_b.$$

11. Squares are drawn on the edges of a triangle in the exterior of the triangle. Prove that the sum of the squares of the segments which join adjacent vertices of different squares is three times the sum of the squares of the edges of the triangle. (Use problem 10.)

12. Prove that $AB^2 + CH^2 = 4R^2$, where R is the circumradius of the $\triangle(A,B,C)$.

13. With the same notations as problem 12, prove that

$$AH^2 + BH^2 + CH^2 = 3R^2 + OH^2.$$

14. Prove that the sum of the squares of the distances of a point from the vertices of a triangle is equal to three times the square of the distance of the point from the centroid plus the sum of the squares of the distances of the centroid from the vertices.

15. Prove that A, B, C are collinear, if and only if

$$AB^4 + BC^4 + CA^4 - 2AB^2BC^2 - 2BC^2CA^2 - 2CA^2AB^2 = 0.$$

16. If A,B,C are collinear, then for any point P prove that

$$\alpha°(A,B,P)^2CP^2 + \alpha°(A,B,P)\alpha°(B,C,P)AP^2 + \alpha°(A,B,P)\alpha°(C,A,P)BP^2 \\ + \alpha°(B,C,P)\alpha°(C,A,P)AB^2 = 0.$$

17. For any four points in the plane, prove that

$$\alpha°(A,B,D)^2CD^2 + [\alpha°(A,B,D) - \alpha°(A,B,C)]\alpha°(B,C,D)AD^2 \\ + [\alpha°(A,B,D) - \alpha°(A,B,C)]\alpha°(C,A,D)BD^2 + \alpha°(B,C,D)\alpha°(C,A,D)AB^2 = 0.$$

18. For any four points in the plane, prove that

$\alpha°(A,C,D)\alpha°(B,C,D)AB^2 + \alpha°(B,A,D)\alpha°(C,A,D)BC^2 + \alpha°(C,B,D)\alpha°(A,B,D)CA^2$
$+ \alpha°(A,B,C)\alpha°(D,B,C)AD^2 + \alpha°(B,C,A)\alpha°(D,C,A)BD^2 + \alpha°(C,A,B)\alpha°(D,A,B)CD^2$
$$= 0.$$

19. For any four points in the plane, prove that

$$\begin{vmatrix} 0 & AB^2 & AC^2 & AD^2 & 1 \\ BA^2 & 0 & BC^2 & BD^2 & 1 \\ CA^2 & CB^2 & 0 & CD^2 & 1 \\ DA^2 & DB^2 & DC^2 & 0 & 1 \\ 1 & 1 & 1 & 1 & 0 \end{vmatrix} = 0.$$

3.   The Proportionality Theorem

The next theorem is the basis of the theory of similitude. In Euclid, it also serves to develop a theory of "magnitudes" parallel to that of real numbers.

(5.20)   *If the legs a and b of an angle of vertex O are intersected by two parallel lines g_1 and g_2, respectively, at $A_1, A_2 \in a$ and $B_1, B_2 \in b$, then*

$$\frac{[\![OA_1]\!]}{[\![OA_2]\!]} = \frac{[\![OB_1]\!]}{[\![OB_2]\!]} = \frac{[\![A_1B_1]\!]}{[\![A_2B_2]\!]}.$$

All ratios are defined since they refer to parallel vectors. We suppose first that g_1 and g_2 both intersect the legs of the same elementary angle defined by rays of a and b at O. We choose the names so that $A_1 \in [O,A_2]$. Let h be the height from B_1 common to $\triangle(O,B_1,A_1)$ and $\triangle(O,B_1,A_2)$. Then

$$\frac{OA_1}{OA_2} = \frac{\frac{1}{2}OA_1 \cdot h}{\frac{1}{2}OA_2 \cdot h} = \frac{\alpha[\triangle(O,B_1,A_1)]}{\alpha[\triangle(O,B_1,A_2)]}.$$

By a similar computation

$$\frac{OB_1}{OB_2} = \frac{\alpha[\triangle(O,A_1,B_1)]}{\alpha[\triangle(O,A_1,B_2)]}.$$

The numerators of both fractions are identical. For the denominators we obtain

$$\begin{aligned} \alpha[\triangle(O,B_1,A_2)] &= \alpha[\triangle(O,B_1,A_1)] + \alpha[\triangle(B_1,A_1,A_2)] \\ &= \alpha[\triangle(O,B_1,A_1)] + \alpha[\triangle(B_1,A_1,B_2)] \\ &= \alpha[\triangle(O,A_1,B_2)] \end{aligned}$$

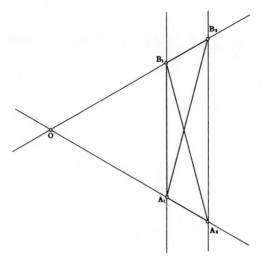

FIG. 5–17

since the two smaller triangles have equal base and height. This proves

$$\frac{OA_1}{OA_2} = \frac{OB_1}{OB_2}.$$

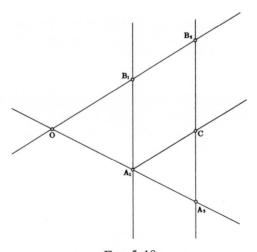

FIG. 5–18

Through A_1 we draw the parallel to b. It intersects g_2 at C. The relation just proved means for the angle of vertex A_2:

$$\frac{A_2C}{A_2B_2} = \frac{A_2A_1}{A_2O}.$$

But

$$\frac{A_2C}{A_2B_2} = \frac{A_2B_2 - CB_2}{A_2B_2} = 1 - \frac{CB_2}{A_2B_2} = 1 - \frac{A_1B_1}{A_2B_2}$$

and

$$\frac{A_2A_1}{A_2O} = \frac{A_2O - A_1O}{A_2O} = 1 - \frac{OA_1}{OA_2};$$

hence also

$$\frac{OA_1}{OA_2} = \frac{A_1B_1}{A_2B_2}.$$

If g_1 and g_2 meet different rays of a and b, then $\sigma_O g_1$ and g_2 satisfy the hypotheses of the preceding proof. In this case we have to multiply all ratios by -1 to obtain the form stated in the theorem.

Theorem (5.20) has a converse:

(5.21)   *If one of the equations (5.20) holds for the points of intersection of two transversals with two concurrent lines, then the transversals are parallel.*

In fact, if A_1, B_1, and A_2 are given, B_2 is uniquely determined by its ratio of division on b with respect to O and B_1. By (5.20), the same ratio, hence the same point of intersection, is obtained for the parallel to g_1 through A_2. Therefore, the second transversal must be identical to that parallel.

We discuss some consequences of the proportionality theorems.

(5.22)   *Corresponding edges in equiangular triangles have equal ratios.*

If the angles of $\triangle(A,B,C)$ and $\triangle(A',B',C')$ are pairwise congruent, then there exists a motion Σ which maps B' onto B, $B'[C']$ onto $B[C]$, and $B'[A']$ onto $B[A]$. By (2.19), $\Sigma l(C',A') \parallel l(C,A)$, hence, by (5.20), $a'/a = b'/b = c'/c$. By (5.21), the theorem has a converse:

(5.23)   *If corresponding edges have equal ratios in two triangles, the triangles must have congruent angles.*

In fact, the ratios and a', b' uniquely determine c'. By (sss), the second triangle is congruent to the one determined by segments of length a', b' on the legs of $\hat{C}$.

Theorem (5.22) yields a very short proof of Euclid's formula (5.15). With the notations of Fig. 5–12, the triangles $\triangle(A,B,C)$ and $\triangle(C,B,F_c)$ have pairwise congruent angles. Hence $a/q_1 = c/a$.

(5.24)   *The internal and external angle bisectors at a vertex of a triangle meet the opposite side at points which divide the base in the ratio of the adjacent edges and its negative.*

Proof: Through C we draw the parallel q to c. It intersects the internal bisector t_A at D, the external bisector t'_A at E. The points of intersection of

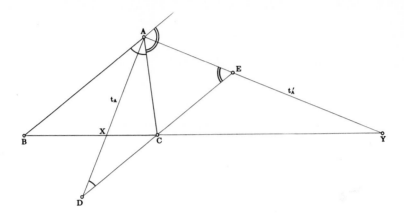

FIG. 5–19

the bisectors with the base are X and Y. Thus $(c,t_A) = (q,t_A)$ and $(c,t'_A) = (q,t'_A)$ as alternating angles at parallels. Therefore, both $\triangle(A,D,C)$ and $\triangle(A,E,C)$ are isosceles, $DC = CE = b$. Theorem (5.20), applied to the angles of vertices X and Y, gives

$$\frac{[\![BX]\!]}{[\![XC]\!]} = \frac{[\![BA]\!]}{[\![DC]\!]} = \frac{c}{b}$$

$$\frac{[\![BY]\!]}{[\![YX]\!]} = \frac{[\![BA]\!]}{[\![EC]\!]} = -\frac{c}{b}.$$

The point X exists always. By the definition of the ratio of division, Y exists unless the given triangle is isosceles. In this case, t'_A is parallel to a. Therefore, it will be an acceptable abuse of language to say: If in a formula there appears an expression BY/YC where $Y = g \cap l(B,C)$ for some line g, then $BY/YC = -1$ will stand for $g \parallel l(B,C)$, i.e., g belongs to the ideal point of lines parallel to $l(B,C)$. This language eliminates the special cases from (5.24) and the theorems we are going to prove in the next section.

If two points X,Y divide a segment (B,C) in opposite ratios, the quadruple of points $(B,C;X,Y)$ is a *harmonic range*. With this notion, (5.24) can be reformulated:

(5.24a)   *The internal and external bisectors of a vertex of a triangle meet
the base in points which together with the end points of the base
form a harmonic range.*

The angle formed by the internal and external bisectors at A is one
half of 180°. By (4.15), A is on the circle of diameter $[X,Y]$.

(5.25)   *The set of all points A for which the ratio of the distances from
two fixed points B and C is constant $(= \lambda)$ is the circle of diameter
$[X,Y]$, where X and Y divide $[B,C]$ in the ratios λ and $-\lambda$.*

This circle is known as the *circle of Apollonius*. Its construction is shown in
Fig. 5–20.

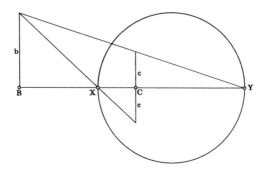

FIG. 5–20

A final remark on a matter of principle. Theorem (5.22) is the basis of
trigonometry since it shows that the ratios of the legs of a right triangle are
functions of one of the angles. It also yields the formula (Fig. 5–21)

$$\cos 2\alpha = \cos^2 \alpha - \sin^2 \alpha$$

and the other formulae for the functions of the double angle. (We assume
known the definitions of the trigonometric functions. They will not be used
formally elsewhere in the book.) By our axioms a right triangle can be constructed for which the ratio of the lengths is an arbitrary length. This means
that for $a > 0$ there exists α such that $\tan \alpha = a$. Axiom X says that to $\tan \alpha$
there exists $\tan \alpha/2$. From the identity

$$\tan \alpha = \frac{2 \tan \alpha/2}{1 - \tan^2 \alpha/2},$$

it follows that $x = \tan \alpha/2$ is a solution of $ax^2 + 2x - a = 0$, and this is an
element of our field if and only if the discriminant $2(1 + a^2)^{\frac{1}{2}}$ is an element

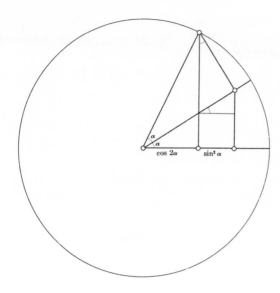

FIG. 5–21

of the field. By the pythagorean theorem, $2 = 1^2 + 1^2$ is a square. (By induction, $n = (n - 1) + 1^2$ is a square for natural n; see Fig. 5–22.) The product of two squares is a square. Therefore, we see that our geometry satisfies axiom X if and only if $(1 + a^2)^{\frac{1}{2}}$ is a length for every length a. For example, if we would take only the points with rational coordinates in the plane of analytic geometry, the resulting geometry does not satisfy axiom X.

We said before that (4.3) is another expression for axiom X. To see this, we introduce rectangular coordinates as discussed in sec. 5–1. Theorem (5.20) implies that the equation of a line through the origin is $y = cx$. Here c

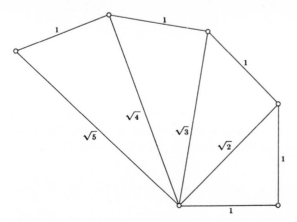

FIG. 5–22

is the tangent of the angle formed by the *x*-axis and line, hence it may be an arbitrary element of the field of the geometry. By the pythagorean theorem, the equation of a circle of radius *r* about the origin is $r^2 = x^2 + y^2$. The points of intersection of the line and the circle may be computed from

$$r^2 = (1 + c^2)x^2,$$

and we see that *x* exists if and only if it is possible to find an element *a* in the field such that $a^2 = 1 + c^2$. This is the same condition as that obtained for the existence of an angle bisector.

For example, we see from Fig. 5–22 that $\sqrt{3}$ always is a length in our geometry. In an equilateral triangle, the height is $\sqrt{3}/2a$ if the edge is *a*. Hence tan 60° = $\sqrt{3}$.

(5.26)   *There exists an equilateral triangle.*

Next we turn to axiom X*. It was stated in sec. 4–1 that the axioms I to XIII do not imply the statement of X*. In fact, it follows from (5.16) that for each *a* > 0 there exists an *x* such that $a = x^2$ if every line through the interior of a circle meets the circle (Fig. 5–23). Since it is not always true that all positive elements of an ordered field can be written as $(1 + c^2)^{\pm 1}$, this condition definitely is stronger than the one which corresponds to axiom X.

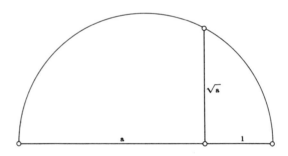

FIG. 5–23

(5.27)   *An ordered field is the field of lengths of a geometry if and only if* $1 + c^2$ *has a square root in the field for every c in the field. An ordered field is the field of lengths of a geometry in which X* holds if and only if every positive element has a square root in the field.*

We note also that

(5.28)   *If X* holds, then two circles* $O_1(r_1)$ *and* $O_2(r_2)$ *intersect in two points if* $O_1O_2 - r_2 < r_1 < O_1O_2 + r_2;$ $r_2 \leqslant r_1.$

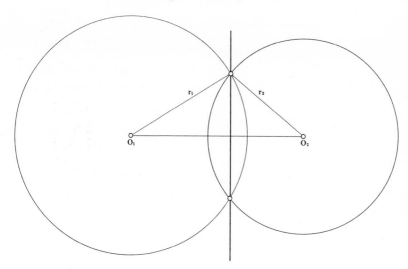

FIG. 5-24

In fact, the line joining the two points of intersection in this case is perpendicular to the *central* $l(O_1,O_2)$ and intersects it at the point $X \in [O_1,O_2]$ given by

$$(5.29) \qquad O_1X = \frac{r_1^2 - r_2^2 + O_1O_2^2}{2O_1O_2}.$$

This justifies the usual constructions for the perpendicular bisector (Fig. 5–25a), angle bisector (Fig. 5–25b), and regular triangle (Fig. 5–25c).

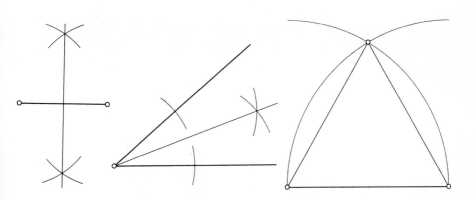

FIG. 5-25

The algebraic condition (5.27) can be given another turn. If $p = OO^g$ is the distance of the center O of $O(r)$ from a line g, then the points of intersection $g \cap O(r)$ are known as soon as we know the length $(r^2 - p^2)^{\frac{1}{2}} = r[1 - (p/r)^2]^{\frac{1}{2}}$.

(5.30)   *If an ordered field contains a square root for every element $1 - c^2$, $c^2 < 1$, then it contains a square root for every positive element.*

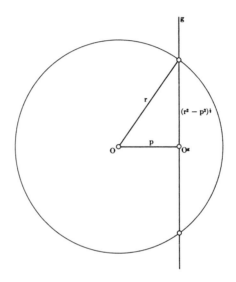

FIG. 5–26

The essential difference between the operations $(a^2 + b^2)^{\frac{1}{2}}$ and $(a^2 - b^2)^{\frac{1}{2}}$ $(a > b)$ can also be seen from the fact that the square of area $a^2 + b^2$ can be obtained from the squares of areas a^2 and b^2 simply by dividing the edge of the bigger square in the ratio $(a + b)/(a - b)$, cutting into pieces, and rearranging

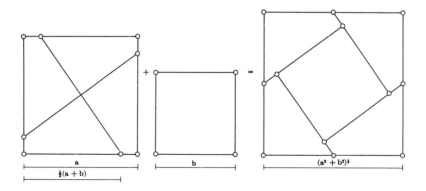

FIG. 5–27

(Fig. 5–27; see also Fig. 5–14), whereas the construction of $(a^2 - b^2)^{\frac{1}{2}}$ needs an application of (5.28) (Fig. 5–28).

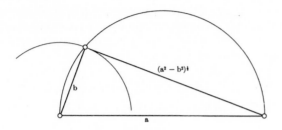

FIG. 5–28

We had proved that two triangles are congruent if their edges are pairwise congruent. This does *not* imply the existence of a triangle for given lengths a,b,c. For definiteness, let us assume $a \geqslant b \geqslant c$, $b + c > a$. For a fixed edge $a = [B,C]$ the triangle can be constructed from $A \in B(c) \cap C(b)$. The existence of the triangle depends on the validity of axiom X*.

From now on we assume axiom X*.

Except for the isoperimetric inequality (sec. 7–4), which properly belongs to calculus, most applications of axiom X* could be reduced to those of axiom X [propositions (4–3), (4–4)] at the expense of a great deal of work in abstract algebra. With axiom X* we need only simple geometric arguments.

Exercise 5–3

1. If R is the circumradius of a triangle $\triangle(A,B,C)$, prove that
    (a) $4R\alpha = abc$ (b) $2\alpha^2 = Rh_a h_b h_c$.

2. Compute t_A as a function of a, b, and c.

3. Find the set of all points of the plane at which two adjacent segments of one line subtend equal angles.

4. If $(A,B;X,Y)$ is a harmonic range, prove that $(X,Y;A,B)$ is, too.

5. Prove that $(A,t_A \cap a;I,I_a)$ form a harmonic range.

6. In a circle Γ draw a diameter $l(A,B)$ and a chord C,D perpendicular to the diameter. For any point $P \in \Gamma$, prove that the points $l(C,D) \cap l(P,A)$ and $l(C,D) \cap l(P,B)$ form a harmonic range with C and D.

7. Through the intersection of the diagonals of a trapezoid draw a parallel to the base. Prove that the point of intersection of the diagonals is the midpoint of the segment cut off by the two legs of the trapezoid.

8. In a trapezoid draw a parallel to the bases whose point of intersection with a leg divides that leg in the ratio $\lambda > 0$. If the bases of the trapezoid have lengths *a* and *b*, prove that the chord of the parallel cut off by the legs of the trapezoid has length

$$\lambda a + (1 - \lambda)b.$$

9. From the vertices of a triangle and its centroid draw the perpendiculars to a line in the exterior of the triangle. Of the four segments intercepted by the points and the line, prove that the last is the arithmetic mean of the first three. (Use problem 8.)

10. Through a vertex A of a parallelogram $ABCD$ draw a line l. Define $E = l \cap l(B,D)$, $F = l \cap l(C,D)$, $G = l \cap l(B,C)$. Prove that $AE^2 = EF \cdot EG$.

11. Find the set of all points at which two given circles $O_1(r_1)$ and $O_2(r_2)$ subtend equal angles.

12. Prove that from a point in the exterior of a circle there exist two tangents to the circle. Find a construction for these tangents.

13. In a right triangle draw semicircles of diameters q_1 and q_2. Compute the ratio of the segments cut off on the legs by these semicircles as a function of a/b.

14. Prove (5.29).

15. Show that the set of all elements $p + q\sqrt{2}$, p and q *rational*, is an ordered field with the usual addition and multiplication. Then show that (5.27) fails to hold for that field.

16. Starting from the rational numbers, let Ω be the set of all numbers obtained from rationals by a finite number of applications of the operation $(1 + c^2)^{\frac{1}{2}}$ and the field operations (addition, subtraction, multiplication, division). Ω is a set of real numbers, hence the arithmetical operations are defined for it.

    (a) Prove that Ω is the field of a geometry for which axiom X holds.
    (b) Show that $-1 + \sqrt{2} \in \Omega$. Does this element have a square root in Ω? What can you say about the validity of X* if coordinates are restricted to Ω in analytic geometry?

17. Sometimes a field may be ordered in different ways. Show that there exists only one possibility for order if the field belongs to a geometry for which X* holds.

18. On the set Ω we define an order by using the order of the number system for rationals only, and defining

$$(1 + c^2)^{\frac{1}{2}} < r$$

for $(1 + c^2)^{\frac{1}{2}}$ irrational, r positive rational.

    (a) Show that this defines a non-archimedean order on Ω.
    (b) Use (a) and problem 17 to show that the analytic geometry over Ω cannot satisfy axiom X*.

19. (a) A segment s is divided in the ratio of the *golden section* if the ratio of the length of the segment to the larger part is as the larger to the smaller part, $s \div d = d \div (s - d)$. Prove that the construction of the golden section is possible in a geometry based on axiom X.

    (b) A regular convex pentagon $ABCDE$ is inscribed in a circle $O(r)$. In addition, $F = l(A,D) \cap l(B,F)$, and G is the midpoint of the arc CD. The segment CG is the edge of the regular decagon in $O(r)$. Prove that the $\triangle(A,C,D)$, $\triangle(B,F,A)$, and $\triangle(O,C,G)$ are equiangular.

(c) Denote by s_5 the edge of the regular pentagon, by d_5 the diagonal of the regular pentagon, by s_{10} the edge of the regular decagon. From (b) prove that s_5 divides d_5 in the ratio of the golden section, as does s_{10} in r. Also, the radius and the edge of the regular decagon are the legs of a right triangle whose hypotenuse is s_5.

(d) Prove that a regular pentagon exists in any geometry based on axiom X.

20. Find an algebraic condition on the field of the geometry to guarantee that $\alpha/3$ exists for any angle α.

21. In a geometry with axiom X but without axiom X* we give (a) 2 edges, 1 angle; (b) 3 edges. Do the data always define a triangle [sas in case (a)]?

4. The Theorems of Menelaus and Ceva

(5.31)   *Three points E, F, G on the sides of a complete triangle △(A,B,C), distinct from the vertices, are collinear if and only if*

$$\frac{[\![BE]\!]}{[\![EC]\!]}\frac{[\![CF]\!]}{[\![FA]\!]}\frac{[\![AG]\!]}{[\![GB]\!]} = -1.$$

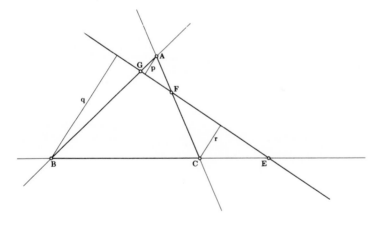

FIG. 5–29

This statement is known as the *theorem of Menelaus*. (Menelaus, an astronomer, also proved the corresponding theorem in spherical trigonometry.) First we assume that E, F, and G are the intersections of a line g with the sides of the triangle. Denote by p, q, and r the lengths ($\neq 0$) of the perpendiculars from the vertices to g. By the proportionality theorem (5.20)

$$\frac{BE}{CE} = \frac{q}{r} \qquad \frac{CF}{AF} = \frac{r}{p} \qquad \frac{AG}{BG} = \frac{p}{q},$$

hence

$$\frac{BE}{EC}\frac{CF}{FA}\frac{AG}{GB} = 1.$$

By Pasch's theorem (1.6), either none or two points of intersection are inner points of the edges of the triangle. Hence an odd number of the ratios of division appearing in the formula of the statement (5.31) are negative. This proves the statement if the three points E,F,G do exist. In accordance with the terminology introduced in the last chapter, we want to extend the validity of the formula to the case that g is parallel to one of the sides of the triangle. In this case one of the ratios is -1, the formula of (5.31) reduces to that of (5.20) and, therefore, is true.

   If three points E, F, G are given which satisfy the formula of Menelaus, they are seen to be collinear by an argument similar to that used in the proof of the converse proportionality theorem (5.21). Points E and F are distinct and define $l(E,F)$. If $G^* = l(E,F) \cap c$, then E, F, and G^* satisfy the formula of Menelaus. Therefore, G and G^* both divide $[A,B]$ in the same ratio. Since ratios uniquely determine points on a line, $G = G^*$, i.e., $G \in l(E,F)$.

   As an application we prove the *general theorems of Pappus and Desargues*.

(5.32)   *If the vertices of a hexagon are alternatingly on two straight lines (excluding their intersection), then the diagonal points are collinear.*

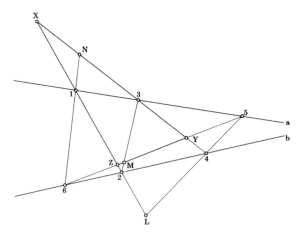

FIG. 5–30

In addition to the notation introduced in sec. 4–3, we also use $X = l(1,2) \cap l(3,4)$, $Y = l(3,4) \cap l(5,6)$, $Z = l(5,6) \cap l(1,2)$. First we assume that all three points do exist. We write down the formula of Menelaus for the $\triangle(X,Y,Z)$

and each one of the lines a, b, $l(2,3)$, $l(4,5)$, $l(6,1)$. If the points of the hexagon are distinct, none of these lines contains a vertex of the triangle. The formulas are:

$$\frac{[[Z1]]}{[[1X]]}\frac{[[X3]]}{[[3Y]]}\frac{[[Y5]]}{[[5Z]]} = -1 \qquad \frac{[[XL]]}{[[LZ]]}\frac{[[Z5]]}{[[5Y]]}\frac{[[Y4]]}{[[4X]]} = -1$$

$$\frac{[[Z2]]}{[[2X]]}\frac{[[X4]]}{[[4Y]]}\frac{[[Y6]]}{[[6Z]]} = -1 \qquad \frac{[[X1]]}{[[1Z]]}\frac{[[Z6]]}{[[6Y]]}\frac{[[YN]]}{[[NX]]} = -1,$$

$$\frac{[[X2]]}{[[2Z]]}\frac{[[ZM]]}{[[MY]]}\frac{[[Y3]]}{[[3X]]} = -1$$

and they yield by multiplication

$$\frac{[[Z1]]}{[[1X]]}\frac{[[X3]]}{[[3Y]]}\frac{[[Y5]]}{[[5Z]]}\frac{[[Z2]]}{[[2X]]}\frac{[[X4]]}{[[4Y]]}\frac{[[Y6]]}{[[6Z]]}\frac{[[X2]]}{[[2Z]]}\frac{[[ZM]]}{[[MY]]}\frac{[[Y3]]}{[[3X]]}\frac{[[XL]]}{[[LZ]]}\frac{[[Z5]]}{[[5Y]]} \cdot$$

$$\cdot\frac{[[Y4]]}{[[4X]]}\frac{[[X1]]}{[[1Z]]}\frac{[[Z6]]}{[[6Y]]}\frac{[[YN]]}{[[NX]]} = \frac{[[XL]]}{[[LZ]]}\frac{[[ZM]]}{[[MY]]}\frac{[[YN]]}{[[NX]]} = -1.$$

Theorem and proof are also valid if some (necessarily an odd number) diagonal points do not exist. The theorem (4.25) then appears as a special case of (5.32).

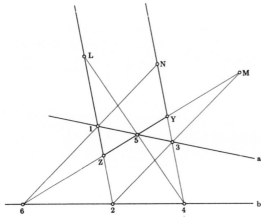

FIG. 5–31

If X does not exist but Y and Z do, the previous formulas remain valid (Fig. 5–31) if the terms containing X are deleted and -1 is everywhere changed into $+1$. The resulting formula

$$\frac{[[ZL]]}{[[YN]]} = \frac{[[ZM]]}{[[YM]]}$$

again implies that $N \in l(M,L)$.

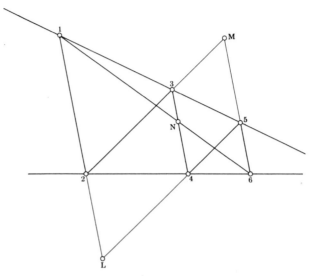

FIG. 5–32

The only remaining case is that in which neither X nor Y nor Z do exist (Fig. 5–32). Let $N^* = l(L,M) \cap l(3,4)$. As shown in Fig. 5–32, all three diagonal points must exist in this case. By the definitions,

$$\frac{[\![2L]\!]}{[\![3N^*]\!]} = \frac{[\![2M]\!]}{[\![3M]\!]} \qquad \frac{[\![3N]\!]}{[\![56]\!]} = \frac{[\![13]\!]}{[\![15]\!]} = \frac{[\![23]\!]}{[\![2M]\!]},$$

hence

$$\frac{[\![3N]\!]}{[\![3N^*]\!]} = \frac{[\![56]\!]}{[\![2L]\!]} \frac{[\![2M]\!]}{[\![3M]\!]} \frac{[\![23]\!]}{[\![23]\!]} = \frac{[\![56]\!]}{[\![34]\!]} \frac{[\![32]\!]}{[\![54]\!]} = \frac{[\![5(a \cap b)]\!]}{[\![3(a \cap b)]\!]} \frac{[\![3(a \cap b)]\!]}{[\![5(a \cap b)]\!]} = 1,$$

i.e., $N = N^*$.

The general form of the theorem of Desargues is:

(5.33)   *The points of intersection of corresponding sides of two perspective triangles are collinear. If in two triangles the points of intersection of corresponding sides are collinear, then the triangles are perspective.*

If the triangles are $\triangle(A,B,C)$ and $\triangle(A',B',C')$, perspective of center O, put $L = c \cap c'$, $M = a \cap a'$, $N = b \cap b'$. Taking into account our convention for ratios of division -1, the proof includes one of the affine Desargues theorem. We write down the Menelaus formula for

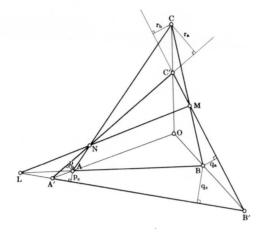

FIG. 5–33

$$\triangle(O,B,C) \text{ and } a' \quad \frac{[\![OB']\!]}{[\![B'B]\!]} \frac{[\![BM]\!]}{[\![MC]\!]} \frac{[\![CC']\!]}{[\![C'O]\!]} = -1$$

$$\triangle(O,C,A) \text{ and } b' \quad \frac{[\![OC']\!]}{[\![C'C]\!]} \frac{[\![CN]\!]}{[\![NA]\!]} \frac{[\![AA']\!]}{[\![A'O]\!]} = -1$$

$$\triangle(O,A,B) \text{ and } c' \quad \frac{[\![OA']\!]}{[\![A'A]\!]} \frac{[\![AL]\!]}{[\![LB]\!]} \frac{[\![BB']\!]}{[\![B'O]\!]} = -1$$

and multiply

$$\frac{[\![OB']\!]}{[\![B'B]\!]} \frac{[\![BM]\!]}{[\![MC]\!]} \frac{[\![CC']\!]}{[\![C'O]\!]} \frac{[\![OC']\!]}{[\![C'C]\!]} \frac{[\![CN]\!]}{[\![NA]\!]} \frac{[\![AA']\!]}{[\![A'O]\!]} \frac{[\![OA']\!]}{[\![A'A]\!]} \frac{[\![AL]\!]}{[\![LB]\!]} \frac{[\![BB']\!]}{[\![B'O]\!]}$$
$$= \frac{[\![BM]\!]}{[\![MC]\!]} \frac{[\![CN]\!]}{[\![NA]\!]} \frac{[\![AL]\!]}{[\![LB]\!]} = -1.$$

This proves the first statement of the theorem.

Conversely, if L, M, N are collinear, define $O = l(B,B') \cap l(C,C')$. The triangles $\triangle(N,C,C')$ and $\triangle(L,B,B')$ are perspective of center M, hence A, O, A' are collinear, Q.E.D. The proofs carry over to the case $l(A,A') \parallel l(B,B') \parallel l(C,C')$.

From the theorem we can obtain a metric characterization of the perspectivity of two triangles. Let p_b, p_c be the lengths of the perpendiculars from A to the sides b', c'. Length p_b is taken positive if the segment is in the half-plane of B' for b'; otherwise it is given the negative sign. Similarly we have vectors q_c, q_a from B and r_a, r_b from C. These quantities can be defined for any two triangles with distinct vertices. Then

$$\frac{[\![AL]\!]}{[\![LB]\!]} = -\frac{p_c}{q_c}, \quad \frac{[\![BM]\!]}{[\![MC]\!]} = -\frac{q_a}{r_a}, \quad \frac{[\![CN]\!]}{[\![NA]\!]} = -\frac{r_b}{p_b}.$$

(5.34)   *Two triangles of distinct vertices are perspective if and only if*

$$\frac{p_c q_a r_b}{q_c r_a p_b} = 1.$$

Closely connected with the theorem of Menelaus is that of *Ceva:*

(5.35)   *Three lines through the vertices of a triangle which meet the opposite sides at E, F, G are in a pencil if and only if*

$$\frac{[\![BE]\!]}{[\![EC]\!]} \frac{[\![CF]\!]}{[\![FA]\!]} \frac{[\![AG]\!]}{[\![GB]\!]} = 1.$$

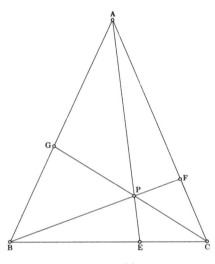

FIG. 5–34

We assume first that the three lines through the vertices are concurrent at P. We write down the formula of Menelaus for

$$\triangle(A,C,E) \text{ and } l(B,F) \qquad \frac{[\![AF]\!]}{[\![FC]\!]} \frac{[\![CB]\!]}{[\![BE]\!]} \frac{[\![EP]\!]}{[\![PA]\!]} = -1,$$

$$\triangle(A,E,B) \text{ and } l(C,G) \qquad \frac{[\![AP]\!]}{[\![PE]\!]} \frac{[\![EC]\!]}{[\![CB]\!]} \frac{[\![BG]\!]}{[\![GA]\!]} = -1,$$

and multiply to obtain the formula (5.35) after simplification. Conversely, if (5.35) holds, assume that the intersection P of the lines through A and B does exist. By the first result, the point $l(C,P) \cap c$ divides $[A,B]$ in the ratio prescribed for G; it must be identical to G. Since the theorem of Menelaus holds also if one of the ratios is -1, Ceva's theorem still subsists for lines in a pencil of parallels.

All our previous theorems about three concurrent lines through the vertices of a triangle are easy consequences of Ceva's theorem. For instance, the medians are concurrent since

$$\frac{[\![AM(A,B)]\!]}{[\![M(A,B)B]\!]} \frac{[\![BM(B,C)]\!]}{[\![M(B,C)C]\!]} \frac{[\![CM(C,A)]\!]}{[\![M(C,A)A]\!]} = 1 \cdot 1 \cdot 1 = 1.$$

For later use, we prove a result on isogonal lines. Two lines g and g' through a vertex of a triangle are isogonal conjugates if $g' = \sigma_{t_A} g$. (See sec. 4–2, and problem 4, exercise 2–1.)

(5.36)   *The product of the distances of two points on isogonal conjugates from one leg of the angle is equal to the corresponding product for the other leg.*

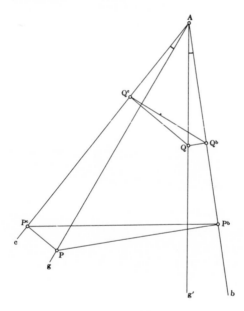

FIG. 5–35

If P and Q are the two points, and b,c the legs of the angle, then by definition $\triangle(A,Q^b,Q)$ and $\triangle(A,P^c,P)$ are equiangular, as are $\triangle(A,P^b,P)$ and $\triangle(A,Q^c,Q)$. By (5.22)

$$\frac{PP^c}{QQ^b} = \frac{AP^c}{AQ^b} = \frac{AP}{AQ} = \frac{AP^b}{AQ^c} = \frac{PP^b}{QQ^c}$$

or

$$PP^b \, QQ^b = PP^c \, QQ^c.$$

This result and Ceva's theorem can be used to prove the existence of isogonal conjugate points in a triangle. (See the definition in sec. 4–2.)

In $\triangle(A,B,C)$ take $E = g \cap a$, $E' = g' \cap a$. By (5.22),

$$\frac{BE}{EE^c} = \frac{c}{h_a},$$

hence by the previous result

$$\frac{BE \cdot BE'}{CE \cdot CE'} = \frac{BE \cdot BE' \cdot EE^b \cdot E'E'^b}{CE \cdot CE' \cdot EE^c \cdot E'E'^c} = \frac{c^2}{b^2}.$$

For three lines through the vertices and their respective isogonals this means

$$\frac{BE}{EC}\frac{CF}{FA}\frac{AG}{GB} = \frac{CE'}{E'B}\frac{AF'}{F'C}\frac{BG'}{G'A}.$$

The validity of Ceva's relation for E,F,G therefore implies that for E', F', and G', since E and E' are simultaneously either interior or exterior to $[B,C]$:

(5.37)   *The isogonals of three lines through the vertices of a triangle form a pencil if and only if the lines form a pencil.*

Exercise 5–4

1. If three lines through the vertices of a triangle are concurrent at P, show that

$$\frac{[\![PE]\!]}{[\![AE]\!]} + \frac{[\![PF]\!]}{[\![BF]\!]} + \frac{[\![PG]\!]}{[\![CG]\!]} = 1.$$

Use problem 15, exercise 5–1.

2. With the notation of the preceding problem, show that

$$\frac{[\![AP]\!]}{[\![AE]\!]} + \frac{[\![BP]\!]}{[\![BF]\!]} + \frac{[\![CP]\!]}{[\![CG]\!]} = 2,$$

$$\frac{[\![AP]\!]}{[\![PE]\!]} - \frac{[\![AF]\!]}{[\![FC]\!]} - \frac{[\![AG]\!]}{[\![GB]\!]} = 0.$$

3. Use Ceva's formula to show that the internal bisectors are concurrent, as well as one internal and two external bisectors, but that the three external bisectors of a triangle are not concurrent.

4. Use a metric theorem to prove the existence of the isotomic image of a point (exercise 2–3, problem 17).

5. Prove that in a right triangle, h, $l(B,\rho_{A,90^\circ}C)$, and $l(A,\rho_{B,-90^\circ}C)$ are concurrent.

6. If P is in the interior of the triangle and E, F, G are the intersections with the edges of the lines through P and the vertices, then prove that

$$\frac{[\![PA]\!][\![PB]\!][\![PC]\!]}{[\![PE]\!][\![PF]\!][\![PG]\!]} = 2 + \frac{[\![PA]\!]}{[\![PE]\!]} + \frac{[\![PB]\!]}{[\![PF]\!]} + \frac{[\![PC]\!]}{[\![PG]\!]}.$$

7. Prove that the tangents to the circumcircle at the vertices meet the opposite sides at collinear points.

8. If A, B, C, P, Q are distinct points in the plane, show that

$$l[A,l(P,B) \cap l(Q,C)] \quad l[B,l(P,C) \cap l(Q,A)] \quad l[C,l(P,A) \cap l(Q,B)]$$

form a pencil.

9. In the interior of a triangle are given three points P_a, P_b, P_c. It is assumed that $l(A,P_b)$ and $l(A,P_c)$ are isogonal and similarly for the other vertices. Prove that $l(A,P_a)$, $l(B,P_b)$, and $l(C,P_c)$ are concurrent.

10. Under the hypotheses of the preceding problem show that

$$l[P_a,l(B,P_c) \cap l(C,P_b)] \quad l[P_b,l(C,P_a) \cap l(A,P_c)] \quad l[P_c,l(A,P_b) \cap l(B,P_a)]$$

are concurrent.

11. Through three points A_1, A_2, A_3 draw parallels a_i ($A_i \in a_i$) and, in another direction, parallels b_i. Show that the three lines $l(a_i \cap b_j, a_j \cap b_i)$ ($i \neq j$) are concurrent.

12. A *complete quadrilateral* is the figure formed by four lines of which no three are concurrent. There are six vertices, the intersections of the lines. Two vertices are *opposite* if they are not on one of the sides of the quadrilateral. Prove that the three midpoints of the segments defined by opposite vertices are collinear.

13. On the sides of a triangle $\triangle(A_1, A_2, A_3)$ choose points X_i, Y_i ($\in a_i$) such that $[\![A_1 X_3]\!] = [\![Y_3 A_2]\!]$, and cyclic for the other sides. Show that the three lines

$$l[A_i, l(A_j, X_j) \cap l(A_k, Y_k)] \qquad\qquad i \neq j \neq k$$

are concurrent.

14. Prove the Pappus theorem if one or more vertices coincide.

15. Formulate and prove the converse of theorem (5.32).

16. Six points on a circle define sixty Pascal lines depending on the order of the numbers. The points (i) ($i = 1,2,3,4,5,6$) define fifteen lines $l(i,j)$. Prove that the Pascal lines belonging to the hexagons in which the order of the points is (1,2,3,4,5,6), (1,4,3,5,6,2), (1,6,3,2,5,4) are concurrent. Use Desargues's theorem on the triangles of sides $l(1,2)$, $l(3,4)$, $l(5,6)$; $l(4,5)$, $l(6,1)$, $l(2,3)$; $l(3,6)$, $l(2,5)$, $l(1,4)$.

17. Prove the generalization of (5.20): if the lines of a pencil are intersected by parallel transversals, the ratio of the segments cut off on a transversal by any two pairs of lines in the pencil is independent of the transversal.

18. Prove the generalization of the theorem of Menelaus to polygons: If a line intersects lines $l(A_i, A_{i+1})$, ($i = 1, \ldots, N$, $N + 1$ replaced by 1) at points P_i, then

$$\frac{[\![A_1 P_1]\!]}{[\![P_1 A_2]\!]} \frac{[\![A_2 P_2]\!]}{[\![P_2 A_3]\!]} \cdots \frac{[\![A_N P_N]\!]}{[\![P_N A_1]\!]} = (-1)^N.$$

19. Formulate and prove a generalization of Ceva's theorem to concurrent lines which pass through the vertices and intersect the *opposite* sides of a polygon of an *odd* number of edges.

20. Prove the statement of problem 27, exercise 4–2, by the theorem of Menelaus.

21. Through a point P draw parallels to the sides of a triangle. Compute the product of the ratios of division of P for the segments cut off on each parallel by the other two sides, the end points taken on the sides in cyclic order.

22. The lines which join opposite vertices of a complete quadrilateral (problem 12) are the *diagonals* of the quadrilateral. Prove that the two vertices and the two points of intersection with the other diagonals form a harmonic range on each diagonal.

5. Power

The main metric theorem about circles is an immediate consequence of the fundamental theorem (4.10) and the proportionality theorem (5.22).

(5.38)   *The product of the vectors of the two oriented segments defined by a point P and the two points of intersection of a line through P and a fixed circle Γ is constant for all lines through P which meet Γ. If P is in the exterior of Γ, the product is equal to the square of the length of a tangent drawn from P to Γ.*

Consider two chords of Γ through P which intersect Γ respectively at A,B and A',B' (Fig. 5–36). Then $\triangle(P,B,A')$ is equiangular with $\triangle(P,B',A)$ since

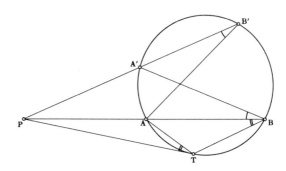

FIG. 5–36

$\hat{B} = \hat{B}'$ by (4.10) and the angle $\hat{P}$ is common to both triangles. Since the angle sum is 180°, equality of two angles implies equality of all angles. Hence, by (5.22),

$$\frac{[\![PA]\!]}{[\![PA']\!]} = \frac{[\![PB']\!]}{[\![PB]\!]}$$

or

$$[\![PA]\!] \cdot [\![PB]\!] = [\![PA']\!] \cdot [\![PB']\!].$$

Also, if T is the point of contact of a tangent from P to Γ, the triangles $\triangle(P,A,T)$ and $\triangle(P,T,B)$ are equiangular since $\hat{T} = \hat{B}$ by (4.15), and, again, $\hat{P}$ is common to both triangles. Theorem (5.22) implies, as before,

$$[\![PT]\!]^2 = [\![PA]\!][\![PB]\!].$$

[The existence of a tangent depends on axiom X*; see (5.39).] The value $\pi(P,\Gamma) = [\![PA]\!] \cdot [\![PB]\!]$ defined by (5.38) is the *power of P for the circle* Γ. The sign of π characterizes the interior and exterior of a circle:

$$\pi(P,\Gamma) \begin{cases} < 0 & P \text{ in the interior of } \Gamma \\ = 0 & P \in \Gamma \\ > 0 & P \text{ in the exterior of } \Gamma. \end{cases}$$

If $\Gamma = O(r)$ and $d = OP$ is the distance of P from the center of the circle, the power can be evaluated on the line $l(P,O)$:

(5.39) $\qquad \pi[P,O(r)] = (d - r)(d + r) = d^2 - r^2.$

We shall use the notion of power mainly to define and study pencils of circles.

(5.40) *The set of all points having equal power for two circles is a straight line perpendicular to the line joining the two centers. No point has equal power for two distinct concentric circles.*

The second statement follows immediately from (5.39) since $d^2 - r_1^2 \neq d^2 - r_2^2$ if $r_1 \neq r_2$. If the two circles are $O_1(r_1)$ and $O_2(r_2)$, $O_1 \neq O_2$, we compare the powers for two points P and Q on the same perpendicular p to the central line $l(O_1,O_2)$. If we put $X = p \cap l(O_1,O_2)$, then

$$\pi[Q,O_1(r_1)] = QO_1^2 - r_1^2 = ([\![QP]\!] + [\![PX]\!])^2 + XO_1^2 - r^2$$
$$= QP^2 + 2[\![QP]\!][\![PX]\!] + \pi[P,O_1(r_2)].$$

The additional terms in the last member are independent of the particular circles, hence

$$\pi[P,O_1(r_1)] - \pi[P,O_2(r_2)] = \pi[Q,O_1(r_1)] - \pi[Q,O_2(r_2)].$$

If P is a point of equal power for the two circles, all points on $p[l(O_1,O_2),P]$ have the same property. In particular, this is true for the intersection X of that perpendicular with the central. But X is uniquely defined by the equation

$$O_1X^2 - r_1^2 = ([\![O_1O_2]\!] - [\![O_1X]\!])^2 - r_2^2.$$

The formula obtained for X is identical with (5.29). This proves the theorem and shows that the line of equal power, the *radical axis*, of two intersecting circles is their common chord (the line through two points of common power zero). If two circles have a common tangent, this tangent is the radical axis since it is perpendicular to the central line at a point of common power zero. If the two circles do not intersect, the radical axis can be found by the following construction (Fig. 5–37). An arbitrary circle Γ is drawn which intersects

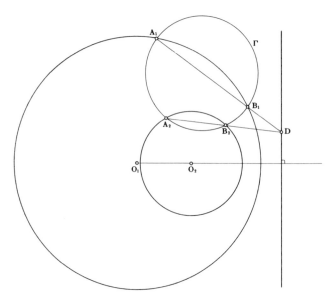

FIG. 5–37

$O_i(r_i)$ at A_i, B_i ($i = 1,2$). The point $D = l(A_1, B_1) \cap l(A_2, B_2)$ exists if the circles are not concentric. By (5.38),

$$\pi[D, O_1(r_1)] = [\![DA_1]\!][\![DB_1]\!] = [\![DA_2]\!][\![DB_2]\!] = \pi[D, O_2(r_2)],$$

hence the radical axis is $p[l(O_1, O_2), D]$.

The point of intersection of the radical axes of circles Γ_1 and Γ_2, and Γ_1 and Γ_3, is a point of equal power for Γ_2 and Γ_3; hence it is on the radical axis for these two circles.

(5.41)   *The radical axes defined by three circles are in a pencil.*

A set of circles is a *pencil of axis g* if g is the radical axis of any pair of circles chosen from the set. Pencils of circles will be studied in detail in chapter VIII. There we shall also fit sets (pencils) of concentric circles into the general definition.

By (5.40), all the centers of the circles of a pencil must be on one perpendicular to g. The preceding discussion of the construction of the radical axis shows that the axis may contain two, one, or no point of common power zero. A point of common power zero for two circles must be a point of power zero for all circles of the pencil. This gives us the possibility to classify the different kinds of pencils.

(5.42)   *There are three types of pencils of circles:*
        (a) circles through two fixed points
        (b) circles tangent to a fixed line at a fixed point
        (c) pencils of non-intersecting circles.

The *angle* of two intersecting circles $O_1(r_1)$ and $O_2(r_2)$ is defined as the angle of their tangents at one point of intersection. The elementary angle of intersection is well defined since the tangents at the two points of intersection (if there are two) are mapped into one another by $\sigma_{l(O_1,O_2)}$. All the circles perpendicular to a maximal pencil of type (b) must pass through the common point of contact of the pencil and be perpendicular to the common tangent; these circles also form a pencil of type (b).

In the case of a pencil of type (c), by (5.38) all the tangents drawn from a point P on the axis of the pencil to the circles of the pencil have equal length t. By the definition of the tangent, the circle $P(t)$ intersects the circles of the pencil at right angles. Since the common power is positive, $P(t)$ intersects the line of the centers of the pencil in two points. These points, then, are the centers of the circles of radius zero in the pencil. Therefore, all circles $P(t)$ for $P \in g$ must contain these two points (Fig. 5–38):

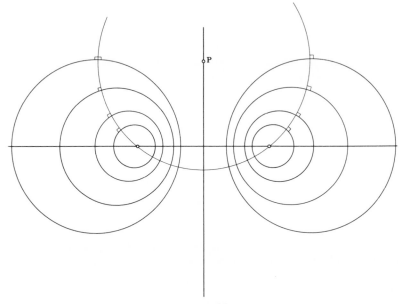

Fɪɢ. 5–38

(5.43)   *The circles perpendicular to the circles of a pencil of type* (c) *form a pencil of type* (a) *and vice versa. The circles perpendicular to the circles of a pencil of type* (b) *form a pencil of type* (b).

Exercise 5–5

1. Discuss theorem (5.43) in a geometry in which axiom X* is not valid.

2. (a) Let P_a be the point of contact of the incircle of a triangle with the edge a. Prove that $CP_a = p - a$.

(b) Prove that the lines joining the vertices to the points of contact of the incircle with the opposite edges are concurrent.

(c) If X is the point of intersection defined in (b), prove that

$$\frac{XP_a}{XA} \frac{XP_b}{XB} \frac{XP_c}{XC} = \frac{r}{4R} = \frac{\alpha[\triangle(A,B,C)]}{4pR}.$$

3. A circle whose center is on m_a intersects the sides b and c of a triangle at points B_1, B_2 and C_1, C_2. Define $A_1 = a \cap l(B_1, C_1)$, $A_2 = a \cap l(B_2, C_2)$. Prove that $A_2 = \sigma_{M_a} A_1$.

4. Prove that the internal and external angle bisectors of $\triangle(M_a, M_b, M_c)$ are the radical axes for the inscribed and exscribed circles of $\triangle(A,B,C)$.

5. Prove: the difference of the squares of the lengths of the tangents from a point to two circles is equal to twice the product of the distances of the centers and the distance of the point from the radical axis.

6. Prove that the common tangents to two circles subtend right angles at the points which are the circles of radius zero in their pencil. (Use problem 5.)

7. Prove: the orthocenter is the intersection of the radical axes of the circles described over the edges as diameters.

8. Show that the midpoints of the four common tangents to two circles are collinear.

9. Show that the product of the distances of the centers of the circles of radius zero in a pencil of type (c) from the center of any circle in the pencil is equal to the square of the radius of that circle.

10. Prove: the circles of a finite pencil of circles of type (a) divide all lines through one of the fixed points of the pencil in equal ratios.

11. Prove: if a variable chord of a circle Γ subtends a right angle at some point P, the sets (i) of the midpoints of the chords; (ii) of the feet of the perpendiculars from P on the chords; (iii) of the points of intersection of the tangents at the endpoints of the chord — all are circles in the pencil [of type (c)] defined by Γ and $P(0)$.

12. All circles which pass through a fixed point A and intersect a given circle Γ at points collinear with a fixed point B form a pencil. Prove this statement and find the type of the pencil.

13. Prove that the set of points for which the ratios of the powers for two given circles is a constant $\neq 1$ is a circle in the pencil of the two circles.

14. In $\triangle(A,B,C)$ one draws $g \parallel a$. Prove that h_a is the radical axis of the circles whose diameters are, respectively, $[B, g \cap b]$ and $[C, g \cap c]$.

15. On the sides of a complete triangle are given the points $E, E' \in a$, $F, F' \in b$, $G, G' \in c$. If the quadruples of points E, E', F, F'; F, F', G, G'; G, G', E, E' are concyclic, prove that all six points are concyclic.

16. Prove: if A, B, C, D are collinear, then the circles through A, B and those through C, D in pairs define radical axes which all pass through a fixed point.

17. Prove: if the intersection of the radical axes of three circles is in the interior of all three circles, then it is the center of a circle which intersects all three given circles at the end points of one of its diameters.

18. Prove: the set of points P such that

$$\pi[P, O_1(r_1)] - \pi[P, O_2(r_2)] = c$$

is a line parallel to the radical axis m such that $O_1 O_2 \cdot P \sigma_m P = c$.

19. If R is the circumradius of $\triangle(A, B, C)$, then

$$\frac{\pi[P, \Gamma(A, B, C)]}{R^2} = \frac{\alpha[\triangle(\sigma_a P, \sigma_b P, \sigma_c P)]}{\alpha[\triangle(A, B, C)]}.$$

Prove this formula and derive a condition on P for $\sigma_a P$, $\sigma_b P$, $\sigma_c P$ to be collinear.

20. Prove that $AH \cdot HF_a = BH \cdot HF_b = CH \cdot HF_c$.

21. Through a given point P draw a line intersected by a given circle Γ at points A, B for which PA/PB is a given ratio λ.

22. Through two given points draw a circle which on a given line intercepts a chord of given length.

Chapter VI

SIMILITUDE

1. Homothety

A *homothety $\eta_{O,\lambda}$ of center O and ratio λ ($\neq O$)* is a map of the plane onto itself such that for any point P:

(a) O,P, and $\eta_{O,\lambda}P$ are collinear

(b) $[\![O\eta_{O,\lambda}P]\!] = \lambda[\![OP]\!]$.

Since the ratio of division uniquely defines $\eta_{O,\lambda}P$ on the line $l(O,P)$, a homothety is a one-to-one map of the plane onto itself.

It is clear from the definition that

(6.1) $\eta_{O,\lambda}^{-1} = \eta_{O,1/\lambda}$

(6.2) $\eta_{O,-1} = \sigma_O.$

Also, $\eta_{O,1} = \iota$. However, we shall find it necessary to enlarge the definition of a homothety in the case of the ratio 1. The center O is a fixed point of $\eta_{O,\lambda}$.

By definition, every line through the center O of a homothety is mapped onto itself by $\eta_{O,\lambda}$. If $O \notin l$, we choose a point $A \in l$. Let l' be the parallel to l through $\eta_{O,\lambda}A$. By (5.20), any line through O which intersects l at B will intersect l' at a point B' for which $[\![OB']\!]/[\![OB]\!] = \lambda$. Hence $l' = \eta_{O,\lambda}l$.

(6.3)   *A homothety maps lines into parallel lines. The lines through the center of the homothety are mapped onto themselves.*

As a consequence,

(6.4)   *Oriented angles are conserved in any homothety.*

By the proportionality theorem (5.20), not only the segments OP but *all* segments are mapped so that their length is multiplied by $|\lambda|$. (As for real

152

numbers, $|\lambda| = \lambda$ if $\lambda > 0$, $|\lambda| = -\lambda$ if $\lambda < 0$.) By (5.9), the area of the image of a triangle is the product of the area of the triangle by λ^2. Since this factor is the same for all the triangles into which a polygon with interior can be divided, the result is true for all polygons that have an area.

(6.5)   *A homothety of ratio λ maps segments of length a into segments of length $|\lambda|\, a$, and polygons of area α into polygons of area $\lambda^2\alpha$.*

As a consequence,

$$\eta_{O,\lambda}A(r) = (\eta_{O,\lambda}A)(|\lambda|\,r).$$

The image of a circle in a homothety is a circle. We can say even more:

(6.6)   *Any two circles are images of one another in a homothety (in two ways if their radii are different).*

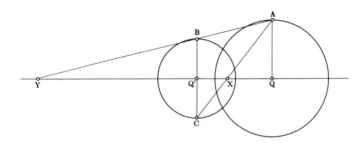

FIG. 6–1

Let the circles be $Q(r)$ and $Q'(r')$. On $Q(r)$ we choose a point $A \notin l(Q,Q')$. Through Q' we draw a parallel to $l(Q,A)$. It intersects $Q'(r')$ in two points. We denote by B the point of intersection in the halfplane of $l(Q,Q')$ defined by A. The other point of intersection is C. The point $X = l(A,C) \cap l(Q,Q')$ exists always and, by the proportionality theorem,

$$Q'(r') = \eta_{X,-r'/r}Q(r).$$

If the two circles are not congruent, then also $Y = l(A,B) \cap l(Q,Q')$ exists and

$$Q'(r') = \eta_{Y,r'/r}Q(r).$$

If $r = r'$, then

$$Q'(r') = \tau_{[QQ']}Q(r)$$

instead. This is an indication that a translation should also be called a homothety of ratio 1 and ideal center. If we adopt this language, we may remove the exceptional case from the statement (6.6). Also, the next proposition shows that the translations as homotheties of ratio 1 are needed to make a group out of the homotheties of the plane, just as the translations as rotations of angle zero are needed to complete the rotations to form a group. Therefore, it will be understood from now on that a homothety of ratio one is the identity if it has a center in the plane, and a translation if its center is an ideal point. The ideal point then is the pencil of lines parallel to the vector of the translation.

(6.7)   *The product of two homotheties of ratios λ_1 and λ_2 is a homothety of ratio $\lambda_1\lambda_2$ whose center is collinear with the centers of the two homotheties and divides the segment of their centers in the ratio $(\lambda_2 - 1)/\lambda_2(\lambda_1 - 1)$.*

The homotheties and translations form a group.

For any point P we put

$$P' = \eta_{O_2,\lambda_2}\eta_{O_1,\lambda_1}P.$$

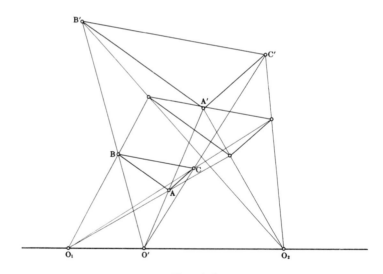

FIG. 6–2

For any segment $[A,B]$ the image $[A',B']$ is on a parallel line. If $\lambda_1\lambda_2 = 1$, then

$$[A',B'] = \tau_{[\![AA']\!]}[A,B].$$

Otherwise, $l(A,A')$ and $l(B,B')$ are concurrent at O'. By (5.20),

$$\frac{[\![O'A']\!]}{[\![O'A]\!]} = \frac{[\![O'B']\!]}{[\![O'B]\!]} = \frac{[\![A'B']\!]}{[\![AB]\!]} = \lambda_2\lambda_1.$$

If C is any point not collinear with A and B, then $\triangle(A,B,C)$ and $\triangle(A',B',C')$ have pairwise parallel sides. By the converse affine Desargues theorem (4.28) $l(C,C')$ is in a pencil with $l(A,A')$ and $l(B,B')$. Hence either $C' = \tau_{[\![AA']\!]}C$ or

$$C' = \eta_{O',\lambda_1\lambda_2}C,$$

as the case may be. The line $l(O_1,O_2)$ is mapped onto itself by the product of the two homotheties. This means that either the translation vector is parallel to that line, or $O' \in l(O_1,O_2)$.

O' is a fixed point of the product of the two homotheties:

$$\eta_{O_2,\lambda_2}\eta_{O,\lambda_1}O' = O',$$

i.e.,

$$\eta_{O_1,\lambda_1}O' = \eta_{O_2,1/\lambda_2}O'.$$

This means

$$\lambda_1[\![O_1O']\!] = [\![O_1O_2]\!] + \frac{1}{\lambda_2}[\![O_2O']\!]$$

or

$$\frac{[\![O_1O']\!]}{[\![O'O_2]\!]} = \frac{\lambda_2 - 1}{\lambda_2(\lambda_1 - 1)}.$$

If the product of the two homotheties is a translation, this ratio of division becomes equal to -1, in accordance with our conventions. We may also note the following useful criterion:

(6.8)   *If the product of the ratios is 1, the product of the homotheties is the identity if and only if it has a fixed point.*

Homotheties are often useful in construction problems. A few examples follow.

Example 1. Inscribe a square in a triangle so that its base is on the base of the triangle.

For an arbitrary point $X \in c$ we draw the square of edge XX^a. The desired square is the image of the first square in the homothety of center B and ratio $BY/B[b \cap l(B,Y)]$, where Y is the vertex of the square which is not on a side of the triangle (Fig. 6–3).

Example 2. Through a point of intersection P of two circles Γ and Γ' draw a common chord divided by P in a prescribed ratio λ.

Let the chord be $[A,A']$. From $[\![AP]\!]/[\![PA']\!] = \lambda$ it follows that

$$A' = \eta_{P,-1/\lambda}A,$$

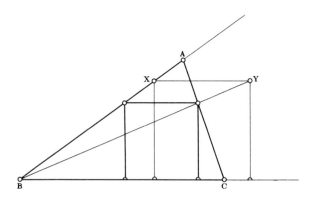

FIG. 6–3

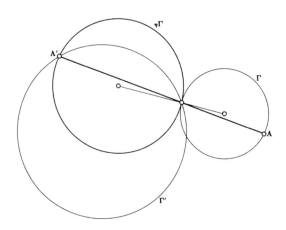

FIG. 6–4

hence

$$A' \in \eta_{P,-1/\lambda}\Gamma.$$

A' is the second point of intersection of Γ' and $\eta_{P,-1/\lambda}\Gamma$.

Example 3. Draw a triangle whose sides pass through three given points I,J,K and whose edges are divided by these points in prescribed ratios λ,μ,ν.

Since the conditions imply

$$A = \eta_{K,-1/\nu}\eta_{J,-1/\mu}\eta_{I,-1/\lambda}A,$$

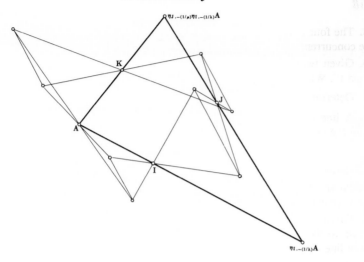

FIG. 6–5

A is the center of the homothety which is the product of the three homotheties indicated in the formula. As suggested by the proof of (6.7), it is found most easily by mapping an arbitrary segment through the composition of the three homotheties (Fig. 6–5). The problem is either impossible or indeterminate if $\lambda\mu\nu = -1$. In the latter case, it certainly is impossible if the three given points are not collinear.

Exercise 6–1

1. Prove that the results of sec. 6–1 are independent of axiom X*.

2. Prove that every translation is the product of two homotheties of ratios λ and $1/\lambda$.

3. Let $\mathfrak{IC}_P$ be the group of homotheties of center P, $\mathfrak{IC}$ the group generated by all homotheties.

    (a) Prove that the group $\mathfrak{I}$ of translations is a normal subgroup of $\mathfrak{IC}$.

    (b) Prove that $\mathfrak{IC}/\mathfrak{I}$ is isomorphic to the multiplicative group of the field of the geometry.

    (c) What is the homogeneous space $\mathfrak{IC}/\mathfrak{IC}_P$?

4. Prove that two homotheties commute if and only if their centers coincide.

5. Find the set of the feet of the perpendiculars from a fixed point A to the angle bisectors of a fixed line g and variable lines through A.

6. Let A,B be two fixed points, C variable on a circle. Find the set of the centroids of the triangles $\triangle(A,B,C)$.

7. Use the statement of problem 27, exercise 4–2, to prove that $P \in \Gamma(A,B,C)$ implies that $\sigma_a P$, $\sigma_b P$, $\sigma_c P$ are collinear and that this line contains the orthocenter H.

8. The four orthocenters of the triangles defined by four lines (no three of which are concurrent) are collinear. Use problem 7 to prove this theorem.

9. Given two distinct homotheties η_1 and η_2 which both map a circle Γ onto a circle Γ'. What is $\eta_2^{-1}\eta_1$?

10. Determine the data of $\eta_{O_1,\lambda_1}^{-1}\eta_{O_2,\lambda_2}\eta_{O_1,\lambda_1}$.

11. A line g intersects the sides of a complete triangle at points E,F,G distinct from the vertices. Prove directly that

$$\eta_{G,\llbracket GB \rrbracket / \llbracket GA \rrbracket}\eta_{F,\llbracket FA \rrbracket / \llbracket FC \rrbracket}\eta_{E,\llbracket EC \rrbracket / \llbracket EB \rrbracket} = \iota$$

and derive from this fact a new proof of the theorem of Menelaus.

12. Prove: the common tangents of two circles intersect the line of the two centers in the centers of the two homotheties which map the circles on one another.

13. Given two circles and a line, find a point on the line for which two tangents drawn to the circles make equal elementary and opposite oriented angles with the given line.

14. A is a fixed point; X is variable on a circle $O(r)$. What is the set of points $l(A,X) \cap t[l(A,O),l(O,X)]$?

15. On the leg a_1 of an angle of vertex P choose a point X. Let Γ_1 be the circle over the diameter $[P,X]$ and Γ_2 the circle tangent to the legs of the circle and to Γ_1 from the interior. Find the set (the locus) of the points of contact of the two circles.

16. Given two circles Γ_1, Γ_2 and a point P, find points $A_i \in \Gamma_i$ ($i = 1,2$) such that P divides $[A_1,A_2]$ in a prescribed ratio λ. State conditions for the existence of a solution.

17. Find a circle which passes through two given points and such that the intersection with a given line is a chord which subtends a given angle at the center of the circle.

18. Find the set of points whose distances from two given lines are in a given ratio.

19. Construct a triangle knowing the lengths b,c,t_A.

20. Construct a triangle knowing the lengths a,s_b and the ratio b/c.

21. In a convex quadrilateral inscribe a rhombus whose edges are parallel to the diagonals of the quadrilateral.

22. On a line g find a point equidistant from a given point P and a given line h. Assume $h \nparallel g$, $h \not\perp g$.

23. Prove: all lines through the point of contact of two mutually tangent circles intersect the circles at points which define parallel diameters.

24. Find a chord of a circle which by a given point is divided in a given ratio. When does the problem have a solution?

25. Prove that the four circles through a vertex of a cyclic quadrilateral and the midpoints of the adjacent edges are concurrent and their centers are concyclic.

2. Similitude

A *similitude* θ is any product of homotheties and reflections. Two sets in the plane are *similar* if one is the image of the other in a similitude. From the properties of isometries and homotheties it follows that

(6.9)   *A similitude is a one-to-one map which conserves elementary angles and in which all lengths are multiplied by the same factor.*

For any two segments $[A,B]$ and $[A',B']$ there exists a similitude which maps one onto the other. In fact, there exists a motion Σ such that $\Sigma A[B] = A'[B']$. Then

$$[A',B'] = \eta_{A',A'B/AB}\Sigma[A,B].$$

Let θ be this similitude. If θ' is any other similitude which maps $[A,B]$ onto $[A',B']$, then $\theta'\theta^{-1}$ by (6.9) is an isometry which maps $[A',B']$ onto itself, and hence, by axiom XII, it is either the identity map or $\sigma_{l(A',B')}$. In order to formulate this result, we define a similitude to be *direct* if it is the product of one homothety and a rotation or translation, and *indirect* if it is the product of one homothety and a line reflection or a glide reflection.

(6.10)   *A similitude is either direct or indirect. Two segments can be mapped one onto the other by exactly one direct and one indirect similitude.*

We note a few consequences.

(6.11)   *Two triangles are similar if and only if they are equiangular.*

By (6.9), similar figures have congruent elementary angles. If two triangles have congruent angles and one edge of the first is mapped onto the corresponding edge of the second triangle, then the images of the first and the second triangle are congruent by (asa), hence the triangles are similar. The corresponding result for polygons is more complicated.

(6.12)   *A similitude is determined by a triangle and its image.*

An edge and its image determine the similitude up to a reflection. The image of the third vertex then fixes the halfplane.

(6.13)   *The similitudes form a group* S.

The product of two similitudes is a similitude; the associative law holds for transformations; and similitudes have inverses. The identity map is a similitude.
    We also note an important case of commutativity:

(6.14)   *A homothety and a reflection at a line through the center of the homothety commute.*

For the proof, use (6.10) for a segment on the axis of reflection.
    In chapter II, we did classify the motions according to the minimal number of reflections needed in it. There exists a simpler theory for similitudes which are not motions.

(6.15)   *An indirect similitude which is not a motion is uniquely the product of a homothety and a reflection at a line through the center of the homothety.*

We deal first with the product of a homothety and one reflection.

$$\eta_{O,\lambda}\sigma_g = \eta_{O,\lambda}\sigma_{p(g,O)}\sigma_g\sigma_{p(g,O)}$$
$$= \eta_{O,\lambda}\eta_{O^g,-1}\sigma_{p(g,O)} = \eta_{O',-\lambda}\sigma_{p(g,O)}$$

and $O' \in p(g,O)$ by (6.7). Here O' is the unique fixed point of the map.

A glide reflection is the product of a line reflection and a point reflection, i.e., of a line reflection and a homothety. Therefore, the product of a glide reflection and a homothety is equal to the product of a line reflection and two homotheties, hence, by (6.7), to the product of a line reflection and one homothety.

(6.16)   *A direct similitude which is not a motion is uniquely the product of a homothety and a rotation about the center of the homothety.*

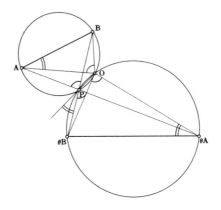

FIG. 6–6

Since the similitude θ is not a translation, there exists a segment $[A,B]$ such that $P = l(A,\theta A) \cap l(B,\theta B)$ does exist. Let O be the second point of intersection of $\Gamma(A,B,P)$ and $\Gamma(\theta A,\theta B,P)$. Also $O = P$ if the two circles are tangent to one another. We prove that O is the center of the homothety and the rotation and, therefore, the unique fixed point of the mapping. By the fundamental theorem on circles,

$$(l(O,A),l(O,B)) = (l(P,A),l(P,B)) = (l(P,\theta A),l(P,\theta B))$$
$$= (l(O,\theta A),l(O,\theta B)).$$

In the same way,

$$(l(A,O),l(A,B)) = (l(\theta A,O),l(\theta A,\theta B)).$$

This means that $\triangle(A,B,O)$ and $\triangle(\theta A,\theta B,O)$ are equiangular. By (6.10), θ is the unique direct similitude which maps $[A,B]$ onto $[\theta A,\theta B]$. Therefore,

$$\theta = \rho_{O,\frac{1}{2}(l(O,A),l(O,\theta A))}\eta_{O,O\theta A/OA}.$$

By (6.14), homothety and rotation commute.

A translation is the product of two homotheties. Therefore, the product of a homothety and a translation is a homothety.

(6.17)   *In a direct homothety θ of center O, all triangles $\triangle(A,O,\theta A)$ are similar.*

In fact, $\hat{O}$ is the angle of the rotation, and $AO/O\theta A$ is the ratio of the homothety. By the proportionality theorem, the triangles are equiangular.

We now turn to a study of products of similitudes. In order to obtain a more symmetric theory we introduce to two similitudes θ_1 and θ_2 the trans-

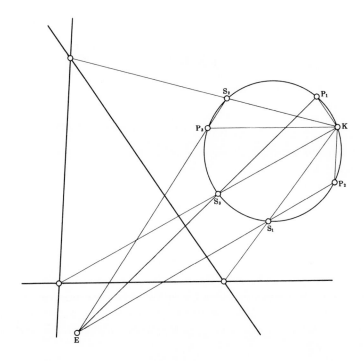

FIG. 6–7

formation $\theta_3 = (\theta_2\theta_1)^{-1}$. Then $\theta_3\theta_2\theta_1 = \iota$, and for the ratios of the respective homotheties we have $\lambda_3\lambda_2\lambda_1 = 1$. The *centers* (fixed points) of the homotheties are S_1, S_2, and S_3. For any line g we draw $g_1 = \theta_1 g$, $g_2 = \theta_2 g_1$, and $g_3 = \theta_3 g_2 = g$. The ratio of the distances of S_i from g_i and g_{i-1} is λ_i (indices mod 3). Since the product of the ratios is 1, the triangle formed by the lines g_i and the triangle $\triangle(S_1,S_2,S_3)$ are perspective by (5.34).

(6.18)   *If the images of a line in similitudes $\theta_2\theta_1$ and θ_1 form a triangle with the line, that triangle is perspective with the triangle formed by the centers of the similitudes θ_1, θ_2, and $\theta_2\theta_1$.*

From here on we assume that all similitudes are *direct*. In this case the angle between g_{i-1} and g_i is equal to the angle of the rotation of θ_i; it is independent of g. (For an indirect similitude that angle is twice the angle of g and the axis of reflection; it is a non-constant function of g.) This is not the only angle which is constant in the configuration.

(6.19)   *If θ is a direct similitude of center S, then the angle $\big(g,l(S,g \cap \theta g)\big)$ is the same for all g not through S.*

The proposition is still true for homotheties if the angle of parallels is defined to be zero. Given two lines g and h not through S, there exists a unique direct similitude θ_0 of center S which maps h into g. Angle and ratio of this similitude can be obtained from $\theta_0[S,S^h] = [S,S^g]$. The similitudes θ and θ_0 commute since they have the same center. Therefore,

$$\begin{aligned}
\big(g,l(S,g \cap \theta g)\big) &= \big(\theta_0 h,l(S,\theta_0 h \cap \theta\theta_0 h)\big) \\
&= \big(\theta_0 h,l(\theta_0 S,\theta_0 h \cap \theta_0\theta h)\big) \\
&= \theta_0\big(h,l(S,h \cap \theta h)\big) = \big(h,l(S,h \cap \theta h)\big).
\end{aligned}$$

Let K be the point of concurrence of the lines joining the vertices of the two triangles described in (6.18). The triangle $\triangle(K,g_{i-1} \cap g_i,g_i \cap g_{i+1})$ contains S_{i-1} and S_i on its sides. By (6.19) and the constancy of the angles (g_{i-1},g_i), the base angles of this triangle are independent of g. Therefore, also the angle $\hat{K}$ is the same for all lines g and their points K. This means that K is a point of a set characterized by the fact that the angle subtended at K by each one of the edges of $\triangle(S_1,S_2,S_3)$ is constant. This is possible only if $K \in \Gamma(S_1,S_2,S_3)$.

(6.20)   *The lines joining the vertices of the triangle formed by a line and its images in direct similitudes θ_1 and $\theta_2\theta_1$ to the centers of the similitudes θ_1,θ_2 and $\theta_2\theta_1$ are concurrent at the circumcircle of the centers.*

$\Gamma(S_1,S_2,S_3)$ is called the *circle of similitude* of θ_1 and θ_2.

The parallel $h = h_3$ to g through K can be obtained as the image of g in a homothety η of center S_1. Since η commutes with θ_1, we obtain for the parallel h_1 to g_1 through K:

$$h_1 = \eta g_1 = \eta \theta_1 g_3 = \theta_1 \eta g_3 = \theta_1 h_3.$$

It follows that $K = h_3 \cap \theta_1 h_3$, and, by (6.19), the angle $(h_3, l(K, S_1))$ is independent of h and K. But S_1 is a fixed point. Therefore, the second point of intersection P_3 of h_3 and the circle of similitude also must be fixed. The same argument can be used for h_1 and $h_2 = \theta_2 h_1$. The points P_1, P_2, P_3 obtained in this way are the *invariable points* of θ_1 and θ_2. We have proved:

(6.21)   *All concurrent triples of lines h, $\theta_1 h$, $\theta_2 \theta_1 h$ pass through the in-variable points and intersect on the circle of similitude.*

In particular, for $h = l(S_1, P_3)$ we obtain $h_1 = \theta_1 h = l(S_1, P_1)$. Since the lines are concurrent at S_1, also $S_1 \in \theta_2 h_1 = l(\theta_2 S_2, P_2)$. This gives another characterization of the invariable points:

(6.22) $\Gamma(S_1, S_2, S_3) \cap l(S_i, \theta_{i+1} S_i) = S_i \cup P_{i+1}.$

The angles of the rotations of the similitudes are equal to the angles subtended at the circle of similitude by the pairs of invariable points.

Exercise 6–2

1. Let S_P be the group of all similitudes of center P, S^+ the set of all direct similitudes.

   (a) Prove that S^+ is a group, but the set S^- of indirect similitudes is not a group.
   (b) Prove that $\mathcal{H}_P$ is a normal subgroup of S_P, but $\mathcal{H}$ is not a normal subgroup of S.
   (c) What is the group $S_P^+ / \mathcal{H}_P$?
   (d) What is S / S^+?
   (e) What are the elements of a coset of $\mathcal{H}$ in S^+?
   (f) Show that any two groups S_P, S_Q are conjugate in S.

2. Prove that $\sigma_{\theta g} = \theta \sigma_g \theta^{-1}$.

3. Let $[A, B]$, $[A', B']$ be two segments of different lengths. Let A_1 and A_2 divide $[A, A']$ in the ratios $\pm AB / A'B'$. Similarly, define B_1 and B_2 for $[B, B']$. Prove that the indirect similitude which maps $[A, B]$ onto $[A', B']$ is

$$\eta_{l(A_1, B_1) \cap l(A_2, B_2), AB/A'B'} \sigma_{l(A_1, B_1)}.$$

4. Find the center of $\eta_{P, \lambda} \rho_{O, \alpha}$ for $P \neq O$.

5. What is the statement corresponding to (6.11) for polygons?

6. What becomes of (6.18) if the three centers of similitude are collinear?

7. Prove that every point on the circle of similitude is the point of intersection of a concurrent triple h, $\theta_1 h$, $\theta_2\theta_1 h$ and that the six points S_1, S_2, S_3, P_1, P_2, P_3 completely determine the similitudes θ_1, θ_2, θ_3.

8. Prove that in the case $\theta_3\theta_2\theta_1 = \iota$, the triangle of the invariable points and that of the centers of similitude are perspective.

9. Prove: the lines $l(S_1,\theta_2 S_1)$, $l(S_2,\theta_3 S_2)$, $l(S_3,\theta_1 S_2)$ are concurrent.

10. Prove: let E be the point of concurrence of the lines joining the vertices in problem 8. If three points P, $\theta_1 P$, $\theta_2\theta_1 P$ are collinear, then the line also contains E, and $P \in \Gamma(E,S_2,S_3)$.

11. The triangle of the invariable points is inversely similar to the triangle of sides g, $\theta_1 g$, $\theta_2\theta_1 g$.

12. Prove: if $a \not\Vert b$ and a,b,c are not concurrent, then $\triangle(P,Q,R)$ and $\triangle(b \cap c, c \cap a, a \cap b)$ are directly similar if and only if

$$\sigma_R \sigma_Q \sigma_a \sigma_c \sigma_Q \sigma_P \sigma_c \sigma_b \sigma_P \sigma_R \sigma_b \sigma_a = \iota.$$

13. Through a point P draw a line which is concurrent with two lines whose intersection falls outside the sheet of paper available for your construction.

14. On the edges of a triangle construct three similar isosceles triangles. The triangles over b and c are in the exterior of the triangle; the one over a is in the half-plane of A. Prove that A and the three vertices form a parallelogram.

15. Draw a square of which one vertex is given and two consecutive vertices are on two given lines.

16. Draw a triangle of given angles $\hat{A}$ and $\hat{C}$ for which the vertex A is given and the other two vertices are on given lines.

17. Let g be a line through a point A and $\mathcal{G}$, the group of direct similitudes θ for which $\theta A \in g$. Show that the images for the transformations of $\mathcal{G}$ of any other fixed point B also are on a line. How is that line situated in the plane?

18. Through a point in the plane draw vectors perpendicular to the sides of a triangle and whose length is a constant multiple of the length of the corresponding edge of the triangle. Show that the sum of the three vectors is zero.

19. Construct a quadrilateral similar to a given one and whose sides pass through four given points. State conditions for the existence of a solution.

20. Given a point P and a line g, on g find two points X and Y such that $\angle XPY$ be a given angle and PX/PY a given ratio.

21. If, for a fixed point O and the points X of a set S, we construct triangles which are directly similar to a given triangle $\triangle$ and for which $[O,X]$ is one edge, prove that the third vertices of the triangles are the points of a set directly similar to S.

22. For a given direct similitude θ and a set S, let T be the set of points which divide $[X,\theta X]$ in a fixed ratio, $X \in S$. Prove that T is directly similar to S.

23. For a given direct similitude θ and a set S, construct the triangles $\triangle(X,\theta X,Y)$ directly similar to a given triangle. Show that the set of the third vertices Y is directly similar to S if $X \in S$.

24. Prove that $\eta_{\theta O,\lambda} = \theta\eta_{O,\lambda}\theta^{-1}$.

3. The Triangle

In the next two sections we use homotheties and similitudes to derive some theorems about triangles and circles.

The sides of the triangle $\triangle(M_a, M_b, M_c)$ are parallel to those of $\triangle(A,B,C)$. The triangles, therefore, are equiangular, hence similar. Since the sides are parallel, the similarity cannot contain any rotation other than a point reflection. For the same reason, the oriented angles of the triangles are equal; the similarity must be direct. Hence it is a homothety. Corresponding points are joined by the medians. They must be concurrent at the center G of the homothety. This is a new proof for the existence of the centroid (2.39). The homothety is

$$\triangle(M_a, M_b, M_c) = \eta_{G,-1/2}\triangle(A,B,C).$$

The orthocenter of the triangle of the midpoints is the circumcenter of the original triangle. This means that

$$O = \eta_{G,-1/2}H.$$

The formula contains a new proof of the theorem (2.41) about the Euler line.

Next we refer to Fig. 4–10 and the notations introduced in sec. 4–2. The results obtained there can be reformulated as

$$\eta_{H,1/2}S_a = F_a \qquad \text{by (4.20)}$$

$$\eta_{H,1/2}T_a = M_a \qquad \text{by (4.22).}$$

The points $O_a = M(A,H)$, etc., are the images of the vertices in the same homothety:

$$\eta_{H,1/2}A = O_a.$$

All these points are on the circle $\eta_{H,1/2}\Gamma(A,B,C)$.

(6.23) *The feet of the altitudes, the midpoints of the edges, and the midpoints of the segments from the orthocenter to the vertices are concyclic.*

For obvious reasons, the circle is called the *nine-point circle* of the triangle. Its center $N = M(H,O)$ is on the Euler line.

The triangle $\triangle(F_a, F_b, F_c)$ of the feet of the altitudes is the *orthic triangle* of $\triangle(A,B,C)$. The triangles $\triangle(A,F_b,F_c)$, $\triangle(B,F_c,F_a)$, and $\triangle(C,F_a,F_b)$ are the *associated triangles*. By (4.20),

$$\triangle(F_a, F_b, F_c) = \eta_{H,1/2}\triangle(S_a, S_b, S_c).$$

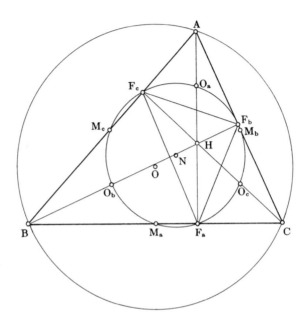

FIG. 6–8

We first prove

(6.24)   *The altitudes are the angle bisectors of the orthic triangle.*

The altitudes are mapped into themselves in the homothety of center *H*. Therefore, it is sufficient to prove that

$$\text{angle } S_c A = \text{angle } AS_b \qquad \text{on } \Gamma(A,B,C).$$

This follows immediately from the fact that both angles are equal to angle $F_c F_b$ on the circle of diameter $[B,C]$.

The *tangential triangle* of $\triangle(A,B,C)$ is formed by the tangents to the circumcircle at the vertices. Since *A* is the midpoint of the arc $S_c S_b$, the tangent to the circumcircle at *A* is parallel to the chord $l(S_c, S_b)$. By the argument which proved the existence of the centroid, this shows

(6.25)   *Orthic and tangential triangles are homothetic.*

The circumcircle of $\triangle(A,B,C)$ is the incircle of the tangential triangle. (6.24) shows that the orthocenter is the incenter of the orthic triangle. The homothety of (6.25) maps *O* into *H*; its center must be on the Euler line.

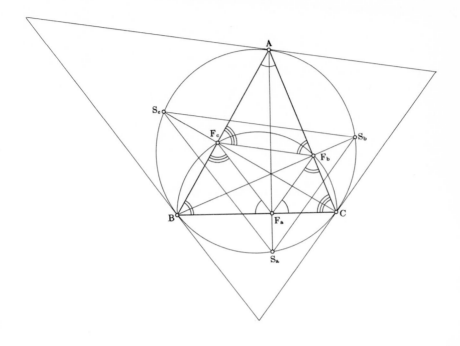

F<small>IG</small>. 6–9

(6.24) can be used to solve a problem belonging to the theory of chapter II: What is the glide reflection $\sigma_c\sigma_b\sigma_a$? The axis of this glide reflection can be found as the *unique* line mapped into itself by the product of symmetries. The axis is the side $l(F_c,F_a)$ of the orthic triangle since

$$\sigma_c\sigma_b\sigma_a l(F_c,F_a) = \sigma_c\sigma_b l(F_b,F_a) = \sigma_c l(F_b,F_c) = l(F_a,F_c).$$

The translation vector of the glide reflection is obtained by finding the image of F_a. The argument indicated in Fig. 6–10 shows that its length is equal to the perimeter of the orthic triangle.

(6.26)   *The product of the three reflections at the sides of a triangle is a glide reflection whose axis is a side of the orthic triangle and whose vector is equal in length to the perimeter of the orthic triangle.*

Next we turn to a study of the associated triangles. The oriented angle $\hat{F}_b$ in $\triangle(A,F_b,F_c)$ is the angle CF_c in the circle $M_a(a/2)$ of diameter $[B,C]$.

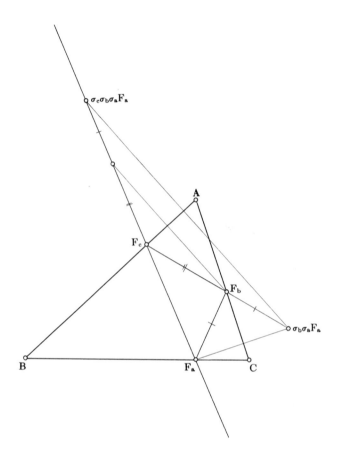

FIG. 6–10

Hence it is equal to the oriented angle $-\hat{B}$ of $\triangle(A,B,C)$. Similarly, $\hat{F}_c = -\hat{C}$. Hence $\triangle(A,F_b,F_c)$ is indirectly similar to $\triangle(A,B,C)$ by a reflection at t_A and a homothety of center A. As a consequence, all associated triangles are directly similar to one another. An inspection of the angles (see Fig. 6–9) shows that a similitude θ_1 of center F_c maps $\triangle(A,F_b,F_c)$ onto $\triangle(F_a,B,F_c)$. The rotation is that which brings $l(F_b,F_c)$ onto c. In the same manner, a similitude θ_2 of center F_a maps $\triangle(F_a,B,F_c)$ onto $\triangle(F_a,F_b,C)$, and a similitude θ_3 of center F_b maps $\triangle(F_a,F_b,C)$ back onto $\triangle(A,F_b,F_c)$. By construction,

$$\theta_3\theta_2\theta_1 = \iota.$$

Therefore, we can apply the theory of sec. 2. *The nine-point circle is the circle of similitude* of the maps θ_i. Since $\theta_1F_b = B$, and cyclically for the other vertices, the vertices are the points $\theta_{i+1}S_i$: by (6.22), *the points O_a,O_b,O_c are the invariable points*. The diameter $[A,H]$ of $O_a(AO_a)$ subtends right angles at the feet F_b and F_c. Therefore, these points are on the circle:

(6.27)   *The points O_a,O_b,O_c are the circumcenters of the associated triangles.*

By (6.21), corresponding lines through the invariable points intersect at the circle of similitude. Incenters and circumcenters are mapped on corresponding points in a similitude:

(6.28)   *The three lines joining the incenter and the circumcenter of the associated triangles are concurrent at the nine-point circle.*

The point of concurrence is called the Feuerbach point of the triangle. With somewhat greater effort, we may prove that it is also the point of contact of incircle and nine-point circle.

Metric relations obtained from considerations of homothety and similitude reduce to applications of the proportionality theorem.

Exercise 6–3

1. Prove that the Euler lines of the associated triangles are concurrent at the nine-point circle.

2. Show that the circumcenter of the tangential triangle is on the Euler line of the original triangle.

3. Show that the Euler line of the triangle of the points of contact of the inscribed circle passes through the circumcenter.

4. Prove that the Euler lines of the triangles $\triangle(A,B,C)$, $\triangle(H,B,C)$, $\triangle(A,H,C)$, $\triangle(A,B,H)$ are concurrent.

5. Show that for any point $X \in \Gamma(A,B,C)$, the segment $[X,H]$ is bisected (at the nine-point circle) by the Simson line of X (exercise 4–2, problem 27; see also exercise 6–1, problem 7).

6. The edges of a triangle $\triangle(A,B,C)$ are, cyclically, images of one another in three direct similitudes whose product is the identity. The centers of similitude are the vertices of *Brocard's second triangle*, the circle of similitude is the *Brocard circle*, and the triangle of the invariable points is *Brocard's first triangle*. A *symmedian* is the isogonal image of a median, e.g., $y_a = \sigma_{t_A}s_a$. Prove:

   (a) The centers of similitude are the midpoints of the chords cut off from the symmedians by the circumcircle.

   (b) The point of concurrence of the lines joining the vertices A,B,C and the corresponding vertices of Brocard's second triangle is the isogonal image of the centroid, the *symmedian* point of $\triangle(A,B,C)$.

   (c) The vertices of Brocard's first triangle are, respectively, on $l(O,M_a)$, $l(O,M_b)$, $l(O,M_c)$.

   (d) The lines joining the corresponding vertices of the first and second Brocard triangles are concurrent at the centroid of the original triangle.

7. Prove: the first Brocard triangle is inversely similar to $\triangle(A,B,C)$.

8. If in the statement of theorem (4.23) the hypothesis is added that $\triangle(P,Q,R)$ be similar to $\triangle(A,B,C)$ for some order of the vertices, three cases can arise.

(a) If $\triangle(P,Q,R) = \theta\triangle(A,B,C)$, show that the point of concurrence of the three circles is the circumcenter of $\triangle(A,B,C)$.

(b) If $\triangle(P,Q,R) = \theta\triangle(B,C,A)$, the point of concurrence is the *positive Brocard point;* for $\triangle(P,Q,R) = \theta\triangle(C,A,B)$ it is the *negative Brocard point.* Show that these points are uniquely defined.

9. Prove: the lines joining the positive Brocard point to the vertices make equal angles with the edges. The lines joining the negative Brocard point to the vertices make equal angles with the edges taken in inverse order. (The common angle is the *Brocard angle* of the triangle.)

10. The *pedal triangle* of a point P is the triangle $\triangle(P^a,P^b,P^c)$. Show that the Brocard points of a triangle are also Brocard points of their own pedal triangles.

11. Show that the two Brocard points are isogonal conjugates of one another.

12. On the edges of a triangle $\triangle(A,B,C)$ one draws triangles $\triangle(A_1,B,C)$, $\triangle(A,B_1,C)$, $\triangle(A,B,C_1)$ directly similar to $\triangle(P,Q,R)$, a fixed triangle. Also, let the triangles $\triangle(A_2,B_1,C_1)$, $\triangle(A_1,B_2,C_1)$, $\triangle(A_1,B_1,C_2)$ be directly similar to $\triangle(P,Q,R)$. Prove that

(a) $l(A,A_1)$, $l(B,B_1)$, $l(C,C_1)$ are concurrent

(b) $[\![A_2A]\!] = [\![AA_1]\!]$, $[\![B_2B]\!] = [\![BB_1]\!]$, $[\![C_2C]\!] = [\![CC_1]\!]$.

13. What is the set of the points

$$X(g) = l(B^g,M_c) \cap l(C^g,M_b)$$

for all lines g through the vertex A of $\triangle(A,B,C)$?

14. In the notation of Fig. 4–10, add $Y_a = t_A \cap a$. Prove that $AX_a \cdot AY_a = bc$.

For the remaining problems we use the standard notations: R the circumradius, r the inradius, r_a the radius of the excircle of center I_a. In previous exercises we have derived the formulae $\alpha = pr$ (exercise 5–1, problem 10) and $4R\alpha = abc$ (exercise 5–3, problem 1).

15. Prove that $r_a/r = p/(p-a)$.

16. Prove:

(a) $r_a + r_b + r_c = r + 4R$

(b) $r_a r_b + r_b r_c + r_c r_a = p^2$

(c) $r_a^{-1} + r_b^{-1} + r_c^{-1} = r^{-1}$.

17. In $\triangle(A,B,C)$ we draw a line through C which intersects c in an interior point. The two partial triangles obtained in this way are indicated by references (1) and (2). Prove:

$$\frac{r}{r_c} = \frac{r^{(1)}}{r_c^{(1)}} \frac{r^{(2)}}{r_c^{(2)}}$$

$$\frac{r + r_c}{R} = \frac{r^{(1)} + r_c^{(1)}}{R^{(1)}} + \frac{r^{(2)} + r_c^{(2)}}{R^{2)}}.$$

18. Prove $\alpha^2 = rr_ar_br_c$.

19. Prove $h_a^{-1} + h_b^{-1} + h_c^{-1} = r_a^{-1} + r_b^{-1} + r_c^{-1}$.

20. Prove that $M_a(R/2)$, $M_b(R/2)$, $M_c(R/2)$ are concurrent at the center of the nine-point circle.

4. Three Circles

First we prove a proposition that will be needed in the theory of circular transformations.

(6.29)   *The product of the two segments determined on any line through the center of homothety of two circles by two points of intersection with the circles which are not images of one another in the homothety is constant.*

Naturally, it is supposed here that the line intersects the two circles. If the two points are $A \in \Gamma_1(r_1)$ and $B \in \Gamma_2(r_2)$, let A' be the image of B in the homothety of center X. Then

$$XA \cdot XB = XA \cdot XA' \cdot \frac{XB}{XA'} = \mid \pi(X,\Gamma_1) \mid \frac{r_2}{r_1}$$

is independent of the line through X.

For the remainder of this section we study the configuration generated by three circles $M_i(r_i)$ $(i = 1,2,3)$. We assume that the three centers are not

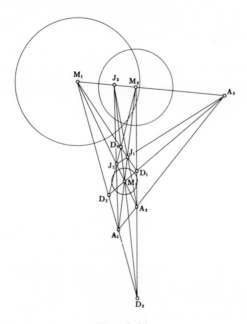

Fɪɢ. 6–11

collinear and that the radii are not equal. To obtain a symmetric notation, we denote the centers of homothety which are internal points of the segments $[M_i, M_j]$ by J_k ($i \neq j \neq k$), the centers which are external points by A_k.

(6.30) A_1, A_2, A_3 are collinear, as are the three groups of points A_i, J_j, J_k $(i \neq j \neq k)$.

This is an immediate corollary of (6.7), which implies that the product of three homotheties can be the identity only if the centers are collinear. In our case,

$$\eta_{A_2, r_3/r_1} \eta_{A_3, r_1/r_2} \eta_{A_1, r_2/r_3} M_3 = M_3.$$

The product of the homotheties is the identity by (6.8). In the same way, the collinearity of J_1, J_2, A_3 follows from

$$\eta_{A_3, r_2/r_1} \eta_{J_2, -r_1/r_3} \eta_{J_1, -r_3/r_2} M_2 = M_2,$$

and similarly for the other triples.

Next we study the lines $j_k = l(M_k, J_k)$ and $a_k = l(M_k, A_k)$.

(6.31) j_1, j_2, j_3 are in a pencil, as are the three groups a_i, a_j, j_k $(i \neq j \neq k)$.

The proof is by the general Desargues theorem. For j_1, j_2, j_3 we use $\triangle(M_1, M_2, M_3)$ and $\triangle(J_1, J_2, J_3)$. By (6.30), corresponding sides meet at collinear points (the A's). Therefore, the two triangles are perspective. For the other groups of lines we use the same argument for $\triangle(M_1, M_2, M_3)$ and $\triangle(A_i, A_j, J_k)$.

The points of intersection are $D_0 = j_1 \cap j_2 \cap j_3$, $D_k = a_i \cap a_j \cap j_k$. The following proposition is easily checked:

(6.32) D_0 is collinear with M_i, J_i, D_i for $i = 1, 2, 3$. Also the three sets of points A_i, M_i, D_j, D_k are collinear.

If one of the points D_i does not exist, this statement shall mean that the line of the other three points is in the pencil of the ideal point D_i.

If $M_3(r_3)$ touches the other two circles, then the points of contact are J_1 and J_2 if the other circles both are in the exterior of $M_3(r_3)$. They are A_1 and A_2 if the other two circles are in the interior of $M_3(r_3)$. In both cases, the line joining the two points of contact is one that appears in theorem (6.30):

(6.33)   *If a circle touches two other circles, either both interior or both exterior, then the line through the two points of contact contains the exterior center of homothety of the two circles.*

Exercise 6–4

1. The cross ratio of four lines and four collinear points has been defined in exercise 5–1, problems 29, 30. Prove:

(a) The centers of two circles and the two centers of homothety form a harmonic range.

(b) If four concurrent lines pass through the points of a harmonic range, their cross ratio is -1.

(c) The cross ratio of the four lines passing through M_i, J_i, or A_i (Fig. 6–11) is -1.

(d) The four groups of points mentioned in theorem (6.32) all are harmonic ranges.

2. Study the degeneracy of the theorems of sec. 4 if: (a) the M_i are collinear, (b) $r_1 = r_2$.

3. If a circle touches two other circles, one from the interior and the other one from the exterior, show that then the line through the two points of contact passes through the interior center of homothety of the two circles.

4. If circles are drawn about the intersection of the tangents to a circle at opposite vertices of a cyclic quadrilateral whose radii are the respective lengths of the tangents, show that then the intersections of opposite sides of the quadrilateral are the centers of homothety of the two circles constructed for the tangents.

5. Prove: if a circle Γ is perpendicular to both Γ_1 and Γ_2, then all the lines which connect a point of $\Gamma \cap \Gamma_1$ with one of $\Gamma \cap \Gamma_2$ pass through a center of homothety of Γ_1 and Γ_2.

6. Prove that, under the hypotheses of problem 5, the product of the segment from the center of homothety to the points of intersection is independent of Γ.

7. Prove that the circle whose center is the interior center of homothety of two circles and whose radius is the square root of the product defined in (6.29) intersects all circles perpendicular to the given ones at endpoints of a diameter.

8. If $O_i(r_i)$ are circles of a pencil, prove that

$$[\![O_1O_2]\!]r_3^2 + [\![O_2O_3]\!]r_1^2 + [\![O_3O_1]\!]r_2^2 + [\![O_1O_2]\!][\![O_2O_3]\!][\![O_3O_1]\!] = 0.$$

9. Given any four points none of which is on the sides of the triangle formed by the other three, prove that there exist three circles such that the four given points are the points D_0, D_1, D_2, D_3.

Chapter VII

GEOMETRIC INEQUALITIES

1. The Triangle Inequality

The straight line is the shortest connection between two points. Since we restrict our attention to the measure of straight segments, we formulate the minimal property for polygonal lines:

(7.1)   *For any finite number of points $P_1, \ldots, P_n$*

$$\sum_{i=1}^{n-1} P_i P_{i+1} \geqslant P_1 P_n.$$

Equality holds only if the points are collinear and

$$P_i \in [P_{i+1}, P_{i-1}].$$

For three points, this is the *triangle inequality*

(7.2) $P_1 P_2 + P_2 P_3 \geqslant P_1 P_3$

which says that, in a triangle, the sum of two edges is larger than the third edge. If $P_2 \in [P_1, P_3]$, the equality is the definition of the addition of lengths. If the three points are not collinear, the inequality follows from the minimum

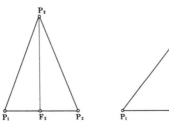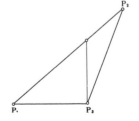

Fig. 7-1

174

property (4.5) of the perpendicular. We denote by $F_2 = P_2^{l(P_1,P_3)}$ the foot of the altitude through P_2 in $\triangle(P_1,P_2,P_3)$.

If $F_2 \in (P_1,P_3)$, then, by (4.5),

$$P_1P_2 + P_2P_3 > P_1F_2 + F_2P_3 = P_1P_3.$$

If, say, $F_2 = P_3$, then, by the same result,

$$P_1P_2 + P_2P_3 > P_1P_3 + P_2P_3 > P_1P_3.$$

If one of the base angles, say $\hat{P}_3$, is obtuse, then

$$P_1P_2 + P_2P_3 > P_1P_2 > P_1\{l(P_1,P_2) \cap p[l(P_1,P_3),P_3]\} > P_1P_3.$$

If the three points are collinear but $P_2 \notin [P_1,P_3]$, then either $P_1P_2 > P_1P_3$ or $P_2P_3 > P_1P_3$. This completes the proof of (7.2).

The general statement (7.1) can now be proved by complete induction. The statement is true for $n = 3$. We assume it to be true for n. For any $n + 1$ points $P_1, \ldots, P_{n+1}$, we have by induction hypothesis and (7.2)

$$\sum_{i=1}^{n} P_iP_{i+1} = \sum_{i=1}^{n-1} P_iP_{i+1} + P_nP_{n+1} \geqslant P_1P_n + P_nP_{n+1} \geqslant P_1P_{n+1}.$$

Hence the statement (7.1) is true in general. The case of equality also follows by induction from the case of equality in the triangle inequality.

The triangle inequality is the basic tool in many investigations connected with problems about maxima and minima. We give a few examples.

Example 1. Given two points A, B, in one halfplane of a line l, find $X \in l$ such that

$$AX + XB = \text{minimum.}$$

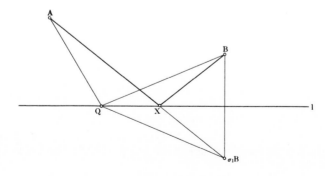

FIG. 7–2

For any $Q \in l$,

$$AQ + QB = AQ + Q\sigma_l B \geqslant A\sigma_l B.$$

Therefore, the minimum for $AX + XB$ is $A\sigma_l B$. It is attained for

$$X = [A, \sigma_l B] \cap l.$$

Example 2. In the interior of a triangle $\triangle(A,B,C)$ find a point P such that

$$AP + BP + CP = \text{minimum}.$$

We assume first that no angle in $\triangle(A,B,C)$ is $\geqslant 120°$. For any point P in the interior of the triangle we construct

$$\triangle(B,Q,C') = \rho_{B,60°}\triangle(B,P,A).$$

$\triangle(B,P,Q)$ and $\triangle(A,B,C')$ are equilateral since they are isosceles, and the angle at the vertex is $60°$ in both triangles. In particular, the point C' is the

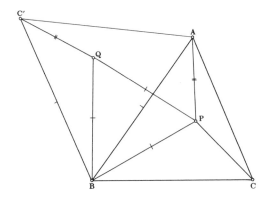

FIG. 7–3

vertex of the equilateral triangle over the edge c in the exterior of the triangle; it is independent of the choice of P. Also,

$$AP + BP + CP = C'Q + QP + PC \geqslant CC'.$$

A minimum is obtained if P and Q are on $l(C,C')$, i.e., if $\angle BPC = 120°$. Since the names can be chosen arbitrarily, the minimum is obtained at the point at which all three edges subtend an angle of $120°$. This point is identical to the intersection

$$l(A, \rho_{C,60°}B) \cap l(B, \rho_{A,60°}C) \cap l(C, \rho_{B,60°}A)$$

of the lines which join each vertex to the third vertex of the equilateral triangle over the opposite edge in the exterior of the triangle. This point exists as the

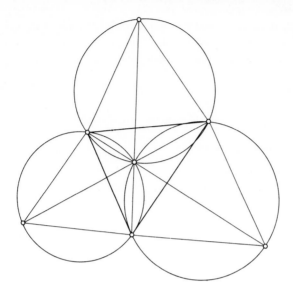

FIG. 7–4

intersection of the circumcircles of the equilateral triangles. In fact, from $P \in \Gamma(C,A,\rho_{A,60°}C) \cap \Gamma(A,B,\rho_{B,60°}A)$, it follows that

$$\left(l(P,A),l(P,C)\right) = 120°$$
$$\left(l(P,B),l(P,A)\right) = 120°\,;$$

hence

$$\left(l(P,C),l(P,B)\right) = \left(l(P,C),l(P,A)\right) + \left(l(P,A),l(P,B)\right)$$
$$= -240° = 120°$$

and $P \in (B,C,\rho_{C,60°}B)$.

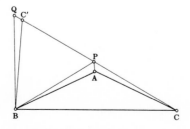

FIG. 7–5

If one angle of the triangle is $\geqslant 120°$, the intersection P of the circumcircles will either be a vertex or a point in the exterior of the triangle. In this case, Q is no longer a point of $[C,C']$, and our reasoning is no longer valid. The vertex of the greatest angle becomes the solution of our problem if points on the triangle are accepted. In its original formulation, the problem admits no solution if one of the angles is $\geqslant 120°$.

Exercise 7–1

1. Draw the common chord of maximal length through a point of intersection of two circles.

Prove the following formulae:

2. $b + c - 2a < 2s_a < b + c$.

3. $t_A \leqslant 2\,bc/(b + c) \leqslant (bc)^{\frac{1}{2}} \leqslant [p(p - a)]^{\frac{1}{2}}$.

4. $p - a \leqslant t_A \leqslant p$.

5. Prove: if P is in the interior of $\triangle(A,B,C)$, then

$$BP + PC < b + c.$$

6. Prove: if P is in the interior of $\triangle(A,B,C)$, then

$$p < AP + BP + CP < 2p.$$

7. Let four distinct points A_1, A_2, A_3, A_4 be given.

(a) If A_4 is in the interior or on an edge of $\triangle(A_1, A_2, A_3)$, for all points P in the plane, prove

$$PA_1 + PA_2 + PA_3 + PA_4 \geqslant A_4A_1 + A_4A_2 + A_4A_3.$$

Equality holds only for $P = A_4$.

(b) If no A_i is on or in the triangle formed by the other three points, prove that $PA_1 + PA_2 + PA_3 + PA_4$ is minimal for the point of intersection of the diagonals of the convex quadrilateral defined by the four points.

8. Prove that the sum of the lengths of the diagonals of a convex quadrilateral is bigger than the semi-perimeter and less than the perimeter.

9. Show that the sum of the distances of a point in the interior of a convex polygon to the vertices is greater than the semi-perimeter and smaller than the perimeter.

10. Show that the sum of the lengths of the medians of a triangle is contained between the semi-perimeter and the perimeter.

11. Given two parallel lines and two points in the two halfplanes in opposite direction, find the shortest connection between the two points if the portion between the two parallels must be a segment of given direction.

12. On a given line find a point such that the sum of its distances from two given points is minimal.

13. On a given line find a point such that the difference of its distances from two given points is maximal.

14. For positive λ, μ, ν, find P such that

$$\lambda PA + \mu PB + \nu PC = \text{minimum}.$$

15. Prove: $s_a \geqslant t_A$. Equality is only for the isosceles triangle.

2. The Billiard Ball Problem

A reflection argument may also be used for *Problem 3:* In a given triangle inscribe another triangle of minimal perimeter.

We reflect the given triangle in a and in the images of b and c in the successive reflections. The perimeter of an inscribed triangle $\triangle(P,Q,R)$ re-appears as a polygonal line which connects P and

$$P^* = \sigma_{\sigma_{\sigma_a b}\sigma_a c \sigma_{\sigma_a b}\sigma_a} P$$
$$= \sigma_{\sigma_a b}\sigma_a c \sigma_a \sigma_{\sigma_a b}\sigma_{\sigma_a b}\sigma_a P$$
$$= \sigma_a \sigma_b \sigma_a \sigma_a \sigma_c P = \sigma_a \sigma_b \sigma_c P.$$

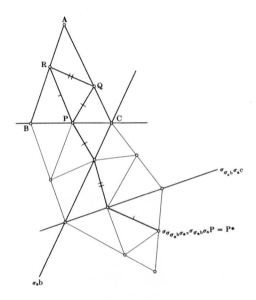

FIG. 7–6

By (6.26), $\sigma_a \sigma_b \sigma_c$ is a glide reflection whose axis is on one side of the orthic triangle. In a glide reflection γ, $(P, \gamma P)$ is the hypotenuse of a right triangle, one of whose legs is the vector of translation, the other one being equal in length to twice the distance of P from the axis of γ. Hence $P \gamma P$ is smallest if P is on the axis, and this also is the only case in which the perimeter of $\triangle(P,Q,R)$ is mapped into collinear segments. Therefore, the orthic triangle is the only possible solution of our problem. However, this gives a solution only if the orthic triangle really is inscribed, i.e., if the feet of the altitudes are interior points of the edges. This happens if and only if all angles of the triangle are acute.

If $\hat{C} = 90°$, the orthic triangle degenerates into the altitude of the triangle, counted twice. It is possible to find triangles inscribed in $\triangle(A,B,C)$ whose perimeter differs from $2h$ by less than an arbitrary amount. There is no smallest inscribed triangle; $2h$ is a lower bound for the perimeters of all inscribed triangles.

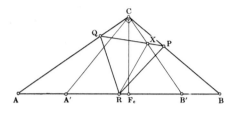

FIG. 7–7

The situation is similar if $\hat{C}$ is obtuse. The orthic triangle is not in-scribed, hence the problem has no solution. It is still true that the perimeter of any triangle is $> 2h_c$. For an obtuse triangle, the points $A' = c \cap p(a,C)$ and $B' = c \cap p(b,C)$ are points of (A,B). For any inscribed triangle $\triangle(P,Q,R)$, two of the vertices are on the edges of either $\triangle(A,B',C)$ or $\triangle(A',B,C)$. For the argument, we assume that Q and R are points of $\triangle(A,B',C)$. Let $X = (B',C) \cap (P,Q)$. By the triangle inequality

$$RP + PX > RX,$$

hence the perimeter of $\triangle(P,Q,R)$ is greater than that of $\triangle(X,Q,R)$. The latter triangle is inscribed in the right triangle $\triangle(A,B',C)$, of which h_c is the height. By our previous result, the perimeter of $\triangle(P,Q,R)$ is greater than $2h_c$. It is possible to find inscribed triangles whose perimeter is arbitrarily close to $2h_c$. Simply choose $R = F_c$ and P, Q near the vertex C.

(7.3)   *In a triangle with three acute angles, the inscribed triangle of minimal perimeter is the orthic triangle. In all other cases no inscribed tri-angle of minimal perimeter exists, but the perimeters of the inscribed triangles are all greater than twice the shortest height.*

Before we treat the analogous problem for polygons, we want to give it another interpretation. If the perimeter of the inscribed triangle is minimal, then, for fixed P and Q, the point R must solve the problem of example 1 for the line c. Hence any two edges of the orthic triangle make congruent angles with the side of the original triangle on which they meet. [This is a new proof of (6.24).] Hence our construction gives a particular solution of the *Billiard Ball Problem:*

Example 4. Given a table in the shape of a convex polygon, find all possible paths for which a material point, moving in straight segments and reflected in the edges under equal angles, will return to its starting point. In order to make the problem definite, we assume that the ball may start from one of the vertices, but if it meets a vertex on its way, it comes to rest there.

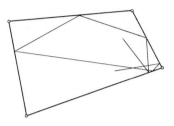

FIG. 7-8

For the triangle, obvious solutions are the orthic triangle and the altitudes run through twice. Any other polygonal line starting from some point P will after three reflections end up at a point Q distinct from P. But $(\sigma_a\sigma_b\sigma_c)^2$ is a translation τ whose vector is parallel to a side of the orthic triangle and whose length is twice the perimeter of the orthic triangle. The segment $[P,\tau P]$ is the image in six reflections at successive images of a, b, and c of a closed polygon whose sides are parallel to those of the orthic triangle. Starting from any point on a suitable interval of a (viz., so that the parallels to the sides of the orthic triangle will hit b,c,a,b,c,a, in this order, see Fig. 7-9), the polygon whose vertices are on the edges of the triangle and whose sides are parallel to those of the orthic triangle solves the billiard ball problem. It closes after two *turns*. A turn may be defined as a union of segments having

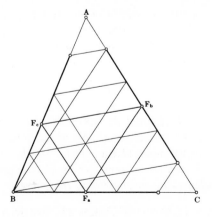

FIG. 7-9

exactly one point on each of the edges of the triangle. This solution is valid only for acute triangles. For obtuse triangles, the parallels to the sides of the orthic triangle will not meet the edges in the right order, and, therefore, they will not remain parallel to the prescribed directions.

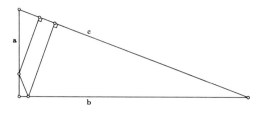

FIG. 7–10

For a right triangle, we may obtain other solutions. For example, there exists a polygonal path which has two edges parallel to the altitude and which is reflected into itself by the hypotenuse (Fig. 7–10). The sequence of the lines at which the path is reflected is b,a,c,a,b,c. Hence this path corresponds to

$$\sigma_c\sigma_b\sigma_a\sigma_c\sigma_a\sigma_b = \sigma_c\sigma_\sigma\sigma_C,$$

which is a translation as a product of reflections at two parallels. We call a path of the billiard ball *regular* if the ball always touches all the edges in their cyclic order. The solution we have obtained for the acute triangle is regular, that for the right triangle is not. The enumeration of all possible irregular paths is very messy. We shall restrict our attention to regular paths. Some problems about irregular paths are given in the exercises.

As pointed out before, there also cannot exist a regular path in an obtuse triangle.

For the acute triangle, we still have to discuss the operations $(\sigma_a\sigma_b\sigma_c)^n$. If n is odd, this is a glide reflection whose axis is that of $\sigma_a\sigma_b\sigma_c$. If n is even, it is a multiple of the translation $(\sigma_a\sigma_b\sigma_c)^2$. If the edges of any polygon are mapped into collinear segments by successive reflections at the sides in cyclic order, the polygon is identical to one obtained either for $\sigma_a\sigma_b\sigma_c$ or for $(\sigma_a\sigma_b\sigma_c)^2$, covered several times.

(7.4)   *If a regular path of a billiard ball in a triangle is closed, it is closed after at most two turns. Its length is equal to either the perimeter or twice the perimeter of the orthic triangle. Regular paths exist only in acute triangles. The edges of all polygons corresponding to closed regular paths are parallel to those of the orthic triangle.*

Next we look for regular closed paths and inscribed *n*-gons of minimal perimeter in a convex *n*-gon. Let the edges of the polygon be $a_1, \ldots, a_n$.

Then any inscribed regular polygonal turn is mapped into a sequence of segments by successive reflections at a_1, $\sigma_{a_1}a_2$, $\sigma_{\sigma_{a_1}a_2}\sigma_{a_1}a_3$, ... As for the triangle, the product of these reflections is

$$\Sigma = \sigma_{a_1}\sigma_{a_2}\cdots\sigma_{a_n}.$$

The formula is best proved by induction. It is true for $n = 3$. We assume that it is true for the product Σ^* of reflections generated by $n - 1$ lines $a_2, \ldots,$ a_n. Then Σ is obtained from Σ^* by reflecting all lines at a_1 and multiplying from the right by σ_{a_1}:

$$\Sigma = \sigma_{a_1}\Sigma^*\sigma_{a_1}\sigma_{a_1} = \sigma_{a_1}\Sigma^*.$$

If n is odd, Σ is a glide reflection, and an inscribed polygon is mapped into a straight line if and only if it is mapped into the axis of the glide reflection. As for the triangle we obtain

(7.5)   *An inscribed $(2k + 1)$-gon of minimal length and regular closed paths in a convex $(2k + 1)$-gon of sides $a_1, \ldots, a_{2k+1}$ exist if and only if the axis of the glide reflection $\sigma_{a_1}\cdots\sigma_{a_{2k+1}}$ intersects the images of the sides in successive reflections in their cyclic order. In this case, there is only one polygon of minimal length. All other regular closed paths close after two turns; their edges are parallel to those of the minimal polygon.*

We do not go into a discussion of the degenerate minimal sets which appear if no inscribed $(2k + 1)$-gon of minimal perimeter does exist.

If $n = 2k$ is even, let α_i be the angle (a_{2i-1}, a_{2i}). Then

$$\Sigma = (\sigma_{a_1}\sigma_{a_2})(\sigma_{a_3}\sigma_{a_4})\cdots(\sigma_{a_{2k-1}}\sigma_{a_{2k}})$$
$$= \rho_{a_1\cap a_2,\alpha_1}\rho_{a_3\cap a_4,\alpha_2}\cdots\rho_{a_{2k-1}\cap a_{2k},\alpha_k}$$

is a rotation of angle $\alpha = \sum_{i=1}^{k}\alpha_i$. If $\alpha/360°$ is not rational, no power of Σ will map a straight line onto itself. If $\alpha/360°$ is an integer, Σ either is a translation or the identity. In the first case, all paths in one direction close after one turn; in the second case, all paths close after one turn. Since the product of two rotations about distinct centers never is the identity, the second case is possible only for $2k \geqslant 6$. If $\alpha/360° = p/q$, with p and q being relatively prime integers, then Σ^q is either a translation or the identity, but no Σ^r $(1 \leqslant r < q)$ maps a line onto itself. This gives the following statement:

(7.6)   *The existence of inscribed minimal polygons and closed regular paths in a convex polygon of an even number of edges depends on the double sum α of the angles at alternating vertices. If $\alpha/360°$ is not* *rational, there are no closed regular paths and no minimal inscribed 2k-gon. If α/360° is integer, there exist an infinity of closed regular paths, and every closed regular path is a polygon of minimal perimeter. In this case, either the edges have a fixed direction or every regular path is closed. If α/360° is the ratio of two relatively prime integers p/q, there is no inscribed polygon of minimal perimeter. All regular closed paths close after exactly q turns. Either all regular closed paths have parallel edges, or all regular paths are closed. A polygon in which all regular paths are closed has at least six edges.*

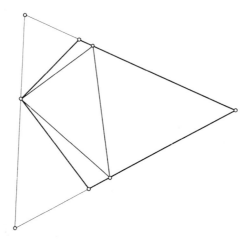

FIG. 7–11

It should be noted that even if α/360° is not rational, there may exist an inscribed polygon of minimal perimeter such that one of its vertices coincides with a vertex of the given polygon and the other vertices are on the remaining 2k − 2 edges of the given polygon. This, then, really is a problem about a minimal 2k − 1-gon in a 2k − 1-gon and, therefore, a case of degeneracy.

In this connection we may mention another problem which is of great importance in modern mathematics and which is just the opposite of our problem here. A curve is *ergodic* in a domain if it comes arbitrarily close to any point in the domain. The ergodic problem for the convex polygon seems to be difficult.

Exercise 7–2

1. Prove that the ratio of an edge of a triangle to the corresponding edge of the orthic triangle is equal to the ratio of the circumradius to the distance of the edge from the circumcenter.

2. Prove that the perimeter of the orthic triangle of an acute triangle is $2\alpha/R$.

3. Prove: if all points (except the vertices) of the edges of a triangle are vertices of a closed regular path, then the triangle is equilateral.

4. Prove: if a, b, and c are not in a pencil, then

$$\sigma_b\sigma_c\sigma_a\sigma_b\sigma_a\sigma_c\sigma_b\sigma_f = \iota$$

if and only if f is the side $l(P,Q)$ of the pedal triangle in the triangle defined by the three lines.

5. Prove: in a convex polygon of an odd number of edges, every billiard ball will, after two turns, come back to every edge under the same angle, as long as it turns regularly.

6. Prove that all parallel paths corresponding to two regular turns of a billiard ball in a convex polygon have equal length.

7. Find a triangle inscribed in a right triangle whose perimeter exceeds twice the height by less than a given ϵ.

8. Prove that a quadrilateral is cyclic if it has a regular path which closes after one turn. The path is given by the pedal quadrilateral, defined by the projections of the intersection of the diagonals onto the edges.

9. Give a complete discussion of the possibilities for a quadrilateral of minimal perimeter inscribed in a cyclic quadrilateral.

10. If a cyclic quadrilateral has a non-acute angle, show that there exists a closed path of a billiard ball which begins and ends at the corresponding vertex and meets both opposite edges.

11. Prove: if a non-cyclic quadrilateral has two non-acute opposite angles, the perimeter of any inscribed quadrilateral is greater than twice the length of the diagonal joining the vertices of these angles.

12. If a non-cyclic quadrilateral does not have two non-acute opposite angles, choose the names so that $\hat{A}$ is non-acute, $\hat{C}$ and $\hat{D}$ non-obtuse. If $\angle AC\rho_{C,-90°}D > \hat{B}$, prove that the lower bound for the perimeters of the inscribed quadrilaterals is the perimeter of the closed path of vertex A. Otherwise, prove that it is the perimeter of $\triangle(A,B,G)$, where G solves the problem of example 1 for $A,B,l(C,D)$.

13. Prove: a triangle admits a closed path of four edges only if it is isosceles.

14. Prove: an acute triangle may admit a closed path of five vertices. This is possible if and only if one of the triangles formed by the lines a, $\sigma_b c$, b (for some choice of the names) is acute.

15. Prove that the condition for the existence of a closed path of seven edges is: triangle from a, $\sigma_b c$, $\sigma_c b$ is acute.

16. Prove: an irregular closed path of six edges is possible only in a right triangle.

17. Prove: (a) The triangle of minimal perimeter cut off from the legs of an angle by lines passing through a fixed point in the interior of the angle is the triangle for which the given point becomes the point of contact of the excircle.

(b) The same minimal triangle can be characterized by: the exterior bisectors of the base angles and the perpendicular to the base at the point are concurrent.

(c) For a given $\triangle(A,B,C)$, let $\triangle(A',B',C')$ be any triangle circumscribed to it.

The only triangle which simultaneously solves problem (a) for A in $\hat{A}$, B in $\hat{B}$, C in $\hat{C}$ is $\triangle(I_a, I_b, I_c)$.

(d) If a circumscribed triangle is distinct from the triangle of the excenters, there exists a circumscribed triangle of smaller perimeter.

(e) Nevertheless, the triangle of the excenters is not the circumscribed triangle of minimal perimeter.

18. Prove: if the angles β_i of a convex $2k$-gon satisfy

$$\beta_1 + \beta_3 + \cdots + \beta_{2k-1} - (\beta_2 + \beta_4 + \cdots + \beta_{2k}) = \frac{p}{q} \cdot 180°,$$

then a regular path will return to a given edge after q turns under the same angle.

19. Given a rectangle of sides a,b,c,d, center M, and perimeter p, find the hexagon MA_1BCDA_2 ($A_i \in a$, $B \in b$, $C \in c$, $D \in d$) of minimal perimeter, and compute that perimeter.

3. The Erdös-Mordell Inequality

In this section we discuss a set of inequalities which have their origin in a problem proposed by Paul Erdös in the *American Mathematical Monthly* in 1935. Erdös's problem was solved by L. J. Mordell and D. F. Barrow in 1937. The treatment given here follows a paper by Sir A. Oppenheim in the same *Monthly*, 1961.

For any point P in the interior of a triangle $\triangle(A_1, A_2, A_3)$, we denote by $p_i(P) = PP^{a_i}$ the distance of P from the edge a_i, and by $x_i(P) = PA_i$ the

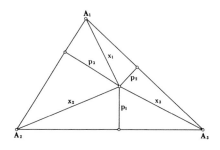

FIG. 7–12

distance from the vertex A_i. In the course of the following discussion, the point P will be kept fixed; therefore, we shall write p_i, x_i for $p_i(P), x_i(P)$. Then

$$a_1(x_1 + p_1) \geqslant a_1 h_1 = 2\alpha[\triangle(A_1, A_2, A_3)] = a_1 p_1 + a_2 p_2 + a_3 p_3$$

or

$$(7.7) \qquad a_1 x_1 \geqslant a_2 p_2 + a_3 p_3.$$

Equality holds only if $P \in h_1$. We multiply the inequality by p_1/a_1:

$$p_1 x_1 \geq \frac{a_2}{a_1} p_1 p_2 + \frac{a_3}{a_1} p_1 p_3.$$

Two similar inequalities are obtained by cyclic permutation of the indices. We sum all three inequalities and obtain

$$p_1 x_1 + p_2 x_2 + p_3 x_3 \geq \left(\frac{a_2}{a_1} + \frac{a_1}{a_2}\right) p_1 p_2 + \left(\frac{a_3}{a_2} + \frac{a_2}{a_3}\right) p_2 p_3 + \left(\frac{a_1}{a_3} + \frac{a_3}{a_1}\right) p_3 p_1.$$

Equality holds only for $P = H$.

One of the most important inequalities in mathematics is the relation between the arithmetic and geometric means:

$$(7.8) \qquad \frac{a+b}{2} \geq (ab)^{\frac{1}{2}} \qquad a \geq 0, b \geq 0.$$

The inequality is a direct consequence of the fact that squares are non-negative (this is true in all ordered fields). In fact, $(a - b)^2 \geq 0$ implies $(a + b)^2 \geq 4ab$, and this is equivalent to (7.8) with the additional information that equality holds only for $a = b$. For $a = x^2$, $b = y^2$, it follows that

$$\frac{x}{v} + \frac{y}{x} = \frac{x^2 + y^2}{(x^2 y^2)^{\frac{1}{2}}} \geq 2$$

with equality only for $x = y$. If we use this in our previous inequality, we obtain

$$(7.9) \qquad p_1 x_1 + p_2 x_2 + p_3 x_3 \geq 2(p_1 p_2 + p_2 p_3 + p_3 p_1)$$

with equality only for the center of the equilateral triangle.

If we apply (7.8) to the right-hand side of (7.7), we get

$$a_1 x_1 \geq 2(a_2 a_3 p_2 p_3)^{\frac{1}{2}}$$

and two similar inequalities obtained by permutation of the indices. We multiply the three inequalities and obtain after simplification

$$(7.10) \qquad x_1 x_2 x_3 \geq 8 p_1 p_2 p_3.$$

Let P' be the isogonal conjugate of P. From the equiangular right triangles,

$$\frac{x_1}{p_2} = \frac{x_1(P')}{p_3(P')} \qquad \frac{x_2}{p_1} = \frac{x_2(P')}{p_3(P')};$$

hence

$$\frac{x_1(P')}{x_2(P')} = \frac{x_1 p_1}{x_2 p_2}$$

and similarly for the other indices. This means that

$$x_i(P') = \lambda x_i p_i,$$

where λ is independent of the index i. Also, by (5.36),

$$\frac{p_i(P')}{p_j(P')} = \frac{p_j}{p_i} = \frac{p_j p_k}{p_i p_k} \qquad\qquad k \neq i, j$$

or

$$p_i(P') = \mu p_j p_k \qquad\qquad i \neq j \neq k,$$

where μ is independent of the index i. From

$$\frac{x_1}{p_2} = \frac{\lambda x_1 p_1}{\mu p_2 p_1}$$

it follows that $\lambda = \mu$.

If P is an interior point of the triangle, so is P'. Therefore, (7.9) is valid for P'. This means that

$$p_2 p_3 x_1 p_1 + p_3 p_1 x_2 p_2 + p_1 p_2 x_3 p_3 \geqslant 2(p_2 p_3 p_3 p_1 + p_3 p_1 p_1 p_2 + p_1 p_2 p_2 p_3)$$

or

$$(7.11) \qquad x_1 + x_2 + x_3 \geqslant 2(p_1 + p_2 + p_3)$$

with equality only for the center of the equilateral triangle. (7.11) is the Erdös-Mordell inequality.

Exercise 7-3

1. Prove: any relation between homogeneous polynomials of the same degree in the variables x_i, p_i is transformed into another valid relation by the substitution $x_i \rightarrow x_i p_i$, $p_i \rightarrow p_j p_k$.

2. Define $u_i(P) = P[l(A_i, P) \cap a_i]$. The expression $x_i + u_i$ is the length of the intersection of $l(A_i, P)$ and the interior of the triangle. Prove:

(a) $\Sigma(x_i + u_i) \leqslant 3p$.
(b) $x_i + u_i$ is less than the greatest edge of the triangle.
(c) The sum of the u_i is less than the length of the greatest edge.
(d) The sum of the x_i is at least equal to p, which is greater than the length of the greatest edge.
(e) $\dfrac{x_1}{u_1} + \dfrac{x_2}{u_2} + \dfrac{x_3}{u_3} \geqslant 6$.
(f) $x_1 x_2 x_3 \geqslant 8 u_1 u_2 u_3$.

3. In this problem the triangle is supposed to be *acute*. Prove:

(a) $2\Sigma p_i(H) \leqslant 6r \leqslant 2\Sigma p_i(G) \leqslant 2\Sigma p_i(O) = \Sigma x_i(H) \leqslant 3R$
(b) $6r \leqslant 2\Sigma x_i(I) \leqslant \Sigma x_i(H)$.

4. Prove that in any triangle:

(a) $s_a + s_b + s_c \leqslant 4R + r$

(b) $t_A + t_B + t_C \leqslant 3(R + r)$

(c) $h_a + h_b + h_c \leqslant 2R + 5r$.

5. Prove: $t_A + t_B + t_C \leqslant 3\Sigma p_i(O)$. Equality is only for the equilateral triangle.

6. Prove the following:

(a) $t_A^2 + t_B^2 + t_C^2 \leqslant p^2$

(b) $t_A t_B + t_B t_C + t_C t_A \leqslant r_a r_b + r_b r_c + r_c r_a$

(c) $t_A^2 t_B^2 + t_B^2 t_C^2 + t_C^2 t_A^2 \leqslant rp(4R + r)$

(d) $t_A t_B t_C \leqslant rp^2$.

7. Given two triangles $\triangle$ and $\triangle'$, prove that

$$a^2(-a'^2 + b'^2 + c'^2) + b^2(a'^2 - b'^2 + c'^2) + c^2(a'^2 + b'^2 - c'^2) \geqslant 16\alpha(\triangle)\alpha(\triangle').$$

Prove the following inequalities:

8. $0 < 1 + \cos \hat{A} \cos \hat{B} \cos \hat{C} \leqslant \frac{9}{8}$.

9. $0 < \cos \hat{A} \cos \hat{B} \cos \hat{C} \leqslant \frac{1}{8}$.

10. $\sqrt{3} \leqslant (1 + \cos \hat{A} \cos \hat{B} \cos \hat{C})/\sin \hat{A} \sin \hat{B} \sin \hat{C}$.

11. $0 < \sin \hat{A} + \sin \hat{B} + \sin \hat{C} \leqslant 3\sqrt{3}/2$.

12. $1 < \cos \hat{A} + \cos \hat{B} + \cos \hat{C} \leqslant 3/2$.

13. $1 < \sin \hat{A}/2 + \sin \hat{B}/2 + \sin \hat{C}/2 \leqslant 3/2$.

14. $2 < \cos \hat{A}/2 + \cos \hat{B}/2 + \cos \hat{C}/2 \leqslant 3\sqrt{3}/2$.

15. $\cos \hat{A}/2 \cos \hat{B}/2 \cos \hat{C}/2 \leqslant 3\sqrt{3}/8$.

16. $\sin \hat{A}/2 \sin \hat{B}/2 \sin \hat{C}/2 \leqslant 1/8$.

17. $4\Sigma h_i h_j \leqslant 12\sqrt{3}\alpha \leqslant 54Rr \leqslant 3\Sigma a_i a_j \leqslant 4\Sigma r_i r_j$.

18. Define $M_k(x) = (\frac{1}{3}\Sigma x_i^k)^{\frac{1}{k}}$, and $M_0(x) = (x_1 x_2 x_3)^{\frac{1}{3}}$. If at least two angles of a triangle are $\leqslant 60°$, then

$$M_k(h) \leqslant \frac{\sqrt{3}}{2} M_k(a), \qquad k \geqslant 0.$$

4. The Isoperimetric Inequality

Finally, we investigate the relations between the perimeter L and the area $A = \alpha(P_n)$ of a convex n-gon P_n. First we prove that for given L and n the regular n-gon has maximal area. Next we translate this result into the language of inequalities. *In the whole section we shall assume that our geometry is over the field of real numbers.* While this is indispensable only for the second part, the hypothesis assures the existence of a regular n-gon for all perimeters and all $n \geqslant 3$ as required in the first part.

Two polygons are said to be *isoperimetric* if they have the same perimeter.

(7.12)   *On any set of isoperimetric rectangles, the area is a strictly mono-tone decreasing function of the difference of the lengths of the edges, taken in absolute value.*

Let one rectangle have edges of length a,b, $a > b$ and consider an isoperimetric rectangle of edges a',b'. We assume that

$$a > a' \geqslant L/2 \geqslant b' > b.$$

The hypothesis of isoperimetry, $a + b = a' + b'$, implies

$$a - a' = b' - b > 0.$$

The desired result follows from

$$ab = a'b + (a - a')b$$
$$a'b' = a'b + (b' - b)a' > ab.$$

This reasoning has a simple geometric meaning which can be read from Fig. 7–13.

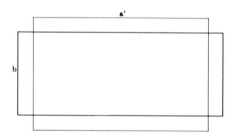

$$\text{FIG. } 7\text{–}13$$

As a first corollary we note that the square has strictly the greatest area in the set of isoperimetric rectangles of given perimeter L. Another corollary is

(7.13)   *On the set of triangles of given perimeter and given length of base, the area is a strictly monotone decreasing function of the absolute value of the difference of the lengths of the legs.*

Let us assume that the edges of a first triangle are a,b,c and those of a second triangle are a',b',c. For definiteness, we may assume that

$$a - b > a' - b' \geqslant 0.$$

By hypothesis, the semi-perimeter p is the same for both triangles. By (5.19a), we have to compare the values of the area function

$$\alpha^2 = p(p - a)(p - b)(p - c) = p(p - c)[p^2 - (a + b)p + ab],$$
$$\alpha'^2 = p(p - a')(p - b')(p - c) = p(p - c)[p^2 - (a' + b')p + a'b'].$$

The hypothesis of isoperimetry implies

$$a + b = a' + b'.$$

Hence, by (7.12), $a'b' > ab$, and $\alpha'^2 > \alpha^2$. Since $\alpha \geqslant 0$, it follows that $\alpha' > \alpha$, as stated in the theorem.

A corollary is

(7.14)   *The isosceles triangle has strictly the greatest area among all triangles of given perimeter and base.*

The statement of the next proposition is known as *Lhuilier's inequality.* It is typical for a great number of similar relations.

(7.15)   *Let L be the perimeter, A the area of a convex polygon P_n, and A^* the area of the polygon circumscribing the unit circle whose edges are parallel to the edges of P_n. Then $L^2 - 4A^*A \geqslant 0$. Equality holds only if P_n is circumscribed to a circle.*

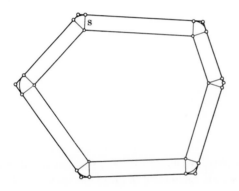

FIG. 7–14

For a given P_n we construct a new polygon P_n^s, the *inner parallel polygon* at distance s. To each edge we draw the parallel at distance s in the interior of P_n. We choose s small enough so that parallels of consecutive edges intersect at the vertices of a convex polygon, P_n^s. The projections of a vertex of P_n^s onto the corresponding edges of P_n are the points of contact of the edges and the circle of radius s whose center is the vertex. Area and perimeter of P_n^s are denoted by A^s, L^s. The strip between P_n and P_n^s is composed of rectangles over the edges of P_n^s and quadrilaterals at the edges. The total area of the rectangles is $L^s s$. By translations the quadrilaterals can be brought together to form a polygon whose sides are parallel to those of P_n and which is circumscribing a circle of radius s. The area of the union of the quadri-

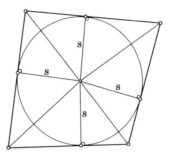

FIG. 7–15

laterals, therefore, is A^*s^2. A polygon circumscribed to a circle can be split into triangles whose altitudes all are equal to the radius of the circle. Therefore,

(7.16)   *The area of a polygon circumscribing a circle is equal to the product of the radius of the circle and the semi-perimeter of the polygon.*

Together we obtain for the inner parallel polygons

$$L = L^s + 2A^*s,$$
$$A = A^s + L^s s + A^* s^2,$$

which gives

$$A^* s^2 - Ls + A = A^s.$$

For s increasing from zero, there certainly exists a first value $s = s_0$ for which the inner parallel polygon shrinks to a segment or a point, i.e., for which $A^{s_0} = 0$. This means for the discriminant of the quadratic equation for s that

$$L^2 - 4A^*A \geqslant 0.$$

If the discriminant vanishes, s_0 is a double root and $2s_0 = L/A^*$. But the relation $L = 2A^*s_0$ can hold only if the polygon is circumscribing the circle of radius s_0.

Now we can prove our main result.

(7.17)   *The regular n-gon has strictly the greatest area among all n-gons of equal perimeter.*

The proof is in two steps. If the given *n*-gon is equilateral, we skip step one. If the *n*-gon is not equilateral, we construct a new *n*-gon which is equilateral, isoperimetric with the given one, and of greater area. As a preparation to the construction, we draw a diagonal to cut off a triangle from the polygon.

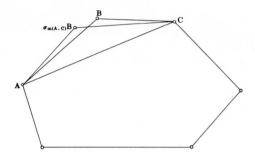

FIG. 7–16

Then we replace the triangle by its image in the reflection in the perpendicular bisector of the diagonal. The new polygon has the same perimeter and area as the given one. By a finite number of applications of this process, we may obtain a polygon in which the shortest and the longest edges are adjacent, i.e., on which there exist three consecutive vertices A,B,C such that

$$AB > L/n > BC.$$

We replace $\triangle(A,B,C)$ by a $\triangle(A,B',C)$ in the same halfplane of $l(A,C)$. The edges of the new triangle are

$$AB' = L/n \qquad B'C = AB + BC - (L/n).$$

The point B' is well defined as the intersection of two circles in a halfplane of the central line. By construction

$$|AB' - B'C| < AB - BC.$$

Hence, by (7.13), $\alpha[\triangle(A,B,C)] < \alpha[\triangle(A,B',C)]$. After at most n repetitions of this process, we obtain an equilateral polygon (all edges of length L/n) whose area is strictly greater than $\alpha(P_n)$.

If the equilateral polygon is not circumscribing a circle, then by Lhuilier's inequality its area is strictly smaller than that of the n-gon circumscribing a circle and of the same A^*. Therefore, we have to consider only equilateral polygons circumscribing a circle $O(r)$. By (7.16), $A = 1/2Lr$, hence A is a maximum when r is a maximum. Let the vertices of the n-gon be $P_1, \ldots, P_n$ in cyclic order. Then

$$\triangle(P_{i-1},P_i,O) = \sigma_{l(O,P_i)}\triangle(P_{i+1},P_i,O).$$

All triangles defined by the center O and two consecutive vertices are congruent. For the angles at the vertices this means

$$\hat{P}_1 = \hat{P}_3 = \cdots = \hat{P}_{2i+1} = \cdots$$
$$\hat{P}_2 = \hat{P}_4 = \cdots = \hat{P}_{2i} = \cdots.$$

Hence, for n odd, all angles are equal.

(7.18)   *An equilateral polygon of an odd number of vertices, which is cir-*
          cumscribing a circle, is a regular polygon.

If $n = 2k$ is even, the angle $\hat{O}$ in each triangle is $180/k°$. For a given segment
$[P_1, P_2]$ the set of possible choices for O is given by (4.18), Fig. 4–9. Obviously,

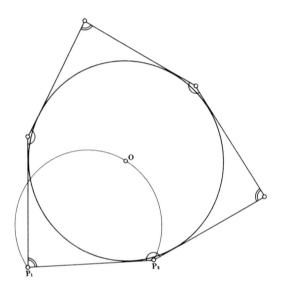

FIG. 7–17

the altitude of O over $l(P_1, P_2)$ is maximal if O is on $m(P_1, P_2)$. This means
that the polygon of maximal area is the regular polygon. Theorem (7.17) is
now completely proved.

The perimeter L_n and the area A_n of the regular n-gon circumscribing
the unit circle are

$$L_n = 2n \sin(\pi/n)   A_n = n \sin(\pi/n) \cos(\pi/n);$$

hence

$$L_n^2/A_n = 4n \tan(\pi/n).$$

For any polygon, the ratio L^2/A is invariant in a homothety. Therefore, the
ratio L_n^2/A_n is valid for all regular n-gons and (7.17) becomes

(7.19)   *For all convex n-gons, $L^2/A \geq 4n \tan(\pi/n)$. Equality holds only*
          for the regular n-gon.

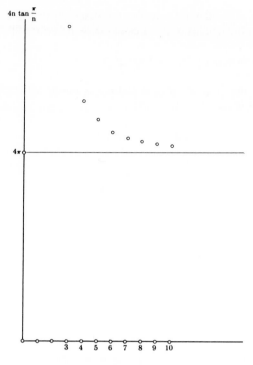

FIG. 7–18

The function $4n \tan (\pi/n)$ is strictly decreasing since a regular n-gon can be considered as an irregular $(n + k)$-gon by putting additional k vertices on the edges. Hence, for equal perimeter the area of the regular $(n + k)$-gon is greater than that of the n-gon. Also it follows from the known inequality

$$\tan x > x \text{ for } \pi/2 > x > 0$$

that

$$4n \tan (\pi/n) > 4n(\pi/n) = 4\pi.$$

Therefore,

(7.20) $\quad L^2 - 4\pi A > 0$

is an *isoperimetric inequality* independent of n.

Calculus may be used to derive another form of the isoperimetric inequality. We assume known, from calculus, the definition of the arc length and the fact that an arc of circle is smaller than the length of any circumscribed polygonal arc. Therefore, in the construction of P_n^s, L is bigger than the sum of L^s and the lengths of the arcs of circles described about the vertices:

(*) $L^s + 2\pi s < L$.

This inequality holds for s between 0 and a maximum s_0 characterized as the smallest value for which $A^{s_0} = 0$. Since

$$A = A^s + \int_0^s L^s \, ds \qquad\qquad s \leqslant s_0$$

and, by (*)

$$\int_0^{s_0} L^s \, ds + 2\pi \int_0^{s_0} s \, ds < L \int_0^{s_0} ds,$$

it follows that

$$A + \pi s_0^2 < Ls_0$$

or

(7.21) $L^2 - 4\pi A > (L - 2\pi s_0)^2 \geqslant 0.$

This not only is a new proof of (7.20), but, since every closed convex curve in the plane of analytic geometry can be approximated arbitrarily close by polygons, it is valid, with an $\geqslant$ sign, for all closed convex curves. In particular, the parenthesis is zero only for the circle:

(7.22)   *Among all closed convex curves of perimeter L, the circle of radius $L/2\pi$ has the greatest area.*

Exercise 7–4

1. Prove: a non-convex polygon with interior is contained in a convex polygon of greater area and smaller perimeter.

2. Prove: if a trapezoid does not admit the perpendicular bisector of its base as an axis of symmetry, then its area is smaller than that of the trapezoid of equal bases, equal perimeter, and having a common perpendicular bisector for its bases.

3. Prove: among all the triangles with two given legs the area is maximal for the right triangle.

4. In the set of n-gons for which one edge and the perimeter are given, and the two angles adjacent to the given edge are required to be supplementary, what is the polygon of maximal area?

5. If the angles of an n-gon are given, if one angle adjacent to the base is 90°, the other one $< 90°$, and the sum of the lengths of the remaining $n - 1$ edges is given, what is the polygon of maximal area?

6. In the set of n-gons for which the sum of $n - 1$ lengths of edges and one acute angle adjacent to the nth edge are given, find the polygon of maximal area. In particular, discuss this problem for triangles and quadrilaterals.

7. Find the maximal n-gon of given perimeter for which in addition one angle is given.

8. Prove that the isosceles triangle has maximal area in the set of triangles with one given angle and a given sum of the edges adjacent to this angle.

9. Prove that the isosceles triangle has maximal area in the set of triangles of given perimeter and one given angle.

10. Among all the transversals which divide the area of a triangle into two equal parts, find the shortest and the longest.

11. Given two polygons P_i ($i = 1,2$) of area A_i and perimeter L_i, find homothetic images of the polygons such that $L(\eta_1 P_1) + L(\eta_2 P_2)$ is a given length and $\alpha(\eta_1 P_1) + \alpha(\eta_2 P_2)$ a maximum.

12. Given the bases and the perimeters of two disjoint triangles, find those for which the sum of the areas is maximal (Problem of Pappus).

13. Prove the following:

    (a) The triangle of minimal area cut off from the legs of an angle by lines passing through a fixed point in the interior of the angle is the one for which the given point is the midpoint of the base.

    (b) On the legs of an elementary angle are given two points which are joined by an arc which makes the sector cut off from the angle a convex set. Of all the lines of support of the arc that one whose intercept is bisected at the point of support cuts off the triangle of minimal area from the legs of the angle.

    (c) If a closed convex curve has a circumscribed triangle of minimal area, the points of contact are the midpoints of the edges of the triangle. (In the plane of analytic geometry, the existence of a minimal triangle can be established by a topological argument.)

    (d) Of all polygons of a given number of edges circumscribed to a circle, the regular polygon has the least area.

14. Prove that $\alpha[\triangle(A,B,C)] \leqslant (3^{\frac{3}{2}}/2)Rr$.

15. Prove that $abc \geqslant 8 \cdot 3^{-\frac{3}{4}}\alpha^{\frac{3}{2}}$.

16. Let A_n be the area of the regular n-gon circumscribing the unit circle, and let α_n be the area of the regular n-gon inscribed in the unit circle. Prove that

$$A_{2n} = \frac{2A_n\alpha_{2n}}{A_n + \alpha_{2n}}$$
$$\alpha_{2n} = \sqrt{A_n\alpha_n}.$$

From $A_4 = 4$, $\alpha_4 = 2$, compute A_{512}, α_{512}. Explain why these formulae can be used to compute π (method of Archimedes).

Chapter VIII

CIRCULAR TRANSFORMATIONS

1. Circle Preserving Maps

Similitudes are not the most general transformations of a plane onto itself which map lines onto lines. That would be the so-called semi-linear transformations which will not be studied in this book. However, in an important special case, similitudes can be characterized by their action on lines and circles.

(8.1)   *A one-to-one map of an archimedean plane onto itself which maps circles onto circles and lines onto lines is a similitude.*

A map ϕ which satisfies the hypotheses of the theorem must map halfplanes onto halfplanes by axioms III and IV. Also, since it is one-to-one, it must map parallel lines onto parallel lines. Hence ϕ preserves the property of a quadrilateral to be a parallelogram and, in particular, that of being a cyclic parallelogram, i.e., a rectangle. This means that ϕ conserves right angles. Right angles are subtended by diameters of circles, hence ϕ maps diameters onto diameters, centers of circles onto centers of circles, and midpoints of segments onto midpoints of segments.

Line reflections can be defined by circles, since

$$A(AX) \cap B(BX) = X \cup \sigma_{l(A,B)}X.$$

By our hypotheses,

$$\phi[A(AX)] = \phi A(\phi A\phi X),$$

hence

$$\phi\sigma_{l(A,B)}X = \sigma_{l(\phi A,\phi B)}\phi X = \sigma_{\phi l(A,B)}\phi X$$

or

(*) $\sigma_{\phi g} = \phi\sigma_g\phi^{-1}$

for all lines *g*. A similar transformation formula then holds also for products of line reflections.

Now we introduce two mutually perpendicular lines through a point *O* and use them as a coordinate system (see sec. 5–1). All points in the plane are represented by couples of oriented lengths (x,y). There exists a unique similitude θ which maps $\triangle[\phi O,\phi(1,0),\phi(0,1)]$ onto $\triangle[O,(1,0),(0,1)]$ since both triangles are isosceles right triangles, hence equiangular. The map $\Psi = \theta\phi$ is one-to-one, maps circles onto circles, lines onto lines, the positive *x*-axis onto itself, and, in particular, the unit segment of that axis onto itself. Since Ψ maps circles of center *O* into circles of center *O*, we can define a map ψ of the field of oriented segments onto itself by

$$\Psi(x,y) = [\psi(x),\psi(y)].$$

The segment $a + b$ on the *x*-axis is $[\![O\tau_a\tau_b O]\!]$. By $(*)$

$$\Psi\tau_a\tau_b O = \tau_{\Psi_a}\tau_{\Psi_b}\Psi O = \tau_{\Psi_a}\tau_{\Psi_b}O,$$

hence

$$\psi(a + b) = \psi(a) + \psi(b).$$

Since Ψ maps rectangles onto rectangles, also

$$\psi(ab) = \psi(1)\psi(ab) = \psi(a)\psi(b).$$

Finally,

$$a > 0 \text{ implies } \psi(a) > 0$$

since Ψ maps the positive ray onto itself. These relations say that ψ is an isomorphism (a one-to-one homomorphism, sec. 3–1) both of the additive and the multiplicative groups of the field of lengths, and that it preserves the ordering of the field. We call ψ an *order-preserving automorphism* of the field. The result of this geometric investigation is, for $\phi = \theta^{-1}\Psi$,

(8.2)   *A one-to-one map of the plane onto itself which maps circles onto circles and lines onto lines is the product of a similitude and a map whose action on the coordinate axes is an order-preserving automorphism of the field of the geometry.*

Theorem (8.1) now follows from the algebraic result:

(8.3)   *An order-preserving automorphism of an archimedean field is the identity map.*

It is sufficient to show that $\psi(x) = x$ for $x > 0$. In the statement of the axiom of Archimedes, we put $a = x - y$, $b = 1$. Then $x > y > 0$ implies that there exists an integer n_0 such that

$$x - y < 1/n_0.$$

There exists a k such that $2^k > n_0$. The previous inequality tells us that there exists at least one positive integer m such that

$$y \leqslant m \cdot 2^{-k} \leqslant x.$$

This shows that a positive element x of an archimedean field is uniquely determined by the set $T(x)$ of elements $m \cdot 2^{-k}$ such that $m \cdot 2^{-k} \leqslant x$.

Now $\psi(1) = 1$, also $\psi(2) = \psi(1) + \psi(1) = 2$, and, in general, $\psi(m) = m$ for integer m. Since ψ is also a multiplicative isomorphism, $\psi(m^{-1}) = \psi(m)^{-1} = m^{-1}$ for integer m. Hence $\psi(m \cdot 2^{-k}) = \psi(m)\psi[(2^k)^{-1}] = m \cdot 2^{-k}$, and $\psi[T(x)] = T(x)$. Then since $T(x)$ uniquely defines x,

$$\psi(x) = x. \qquad \text{Q.E.D.}$$

Exercise 8–1

1. Prove that a one-to-one map of the plane onto itself which maps circles onto circles also maps lines onto lines if and only if it maps centers of circles onto centers of circles.

2. Given a circle $A(AB)$ and two points C,D, find the points of $A(AB) \cap l(C,D)$ using a compass only.

3. Given two points A,B, find additional points of $l(A,B)$ using a compass only.

4. Given three points A,B,C, find a second point of the parallel to $l(A,B)$ through C.

2. Inversion

For a deeper study of circles we introduce *inversion*, or *reflection in a circle*. For a given circle $O(r)$, the image $X^* = \sigma_{O(r)}X$ of a point $X \neq O$ is defined by

$$(8.4) \qquad [\![OX]\!] \cdot [\![OX^*]\!] = r^2.$$

The map of O is not defined, and no point has O as its image. Since the definition is symmetric in X and X^*, $\sigma_{O(r)}$ is an involution of the plane from which the point O has been deleted. Since it is not a map of the whole plane onto itself, $\sigma_{O(r)}$ is not a transformation of the plane. We shall later extend the definition of $\sigma_{O(r)}$ to that of a transformation of some plane.

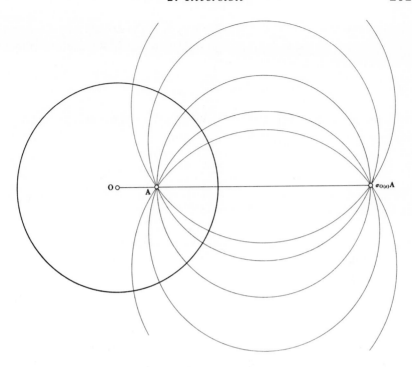

FIG. 8–1

For the geometric interpretation of the definition, we recall that the angle of two circles was defined as the angle of their tangents at a point of intersection. For any circle Γ through X and X^*, $\pi(O,\Gamma) = r^2$. This means that the radius from O to a point of intersection of $O(r)$ and Γ is tangent to Γ:

(8.5)   *Two points are images of one another in an inversion at a circle if and only if that circle is perpendicular to all the circles of the pencils defined by the two points.*

Since O, X, and X^* are collinear, the pencil through X and X^* has to be replaced by the pencil tangent to $l(O,X)$ in the case $X = X^*$. By definition, this happens if the distance of X from O is r:

(8.6)   *X is a fixed point of an inversion if and only if it is on the circle of inversion.*

From the axiomatic point of view, it is interesting to note that not only the definition (8.4), but also the characterization (8.5), make sense in all our geometries.

(8.7)   *The intersection of two perpendicular circles exists in a geometry based on axiom X.*

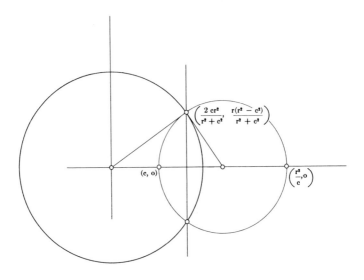

$$\left(\frac{2\,cr^2}{r^2+c^2},\ \frac{r(r^2-c^2)}{r^2+c^2}\right)$$

(c, o)

$\left(\frac{r^2}{c},o\right)$

FIG. 8–2

If $\Gamma \perp O(r)$, we choose as x-axis the line defined by the two centers and as y-axis the perpendicular through O. The x-axis intersects Γ [by (4.3)] in two points of coordinates $(c,0)$ and $(r^2/c,0)$. A simple computation on equi-angular triangles, shown in Fig. 8–2, gives the coordinates of the two points of intersection by rational functions:

$$\left[\frac{2cr^2}{r^2+c^2},\ \pm\frac{r(r^2-c^2)}{r^2+c^2}\right],$$

and these elements exist in every field.

In a geometry which satisfies axiom X*, a simple construction of the image under inversion is shown in Fig. 8–3. The proof follows from $OX/OT = OT/OX^*$ since $\triangle(O,X,T)$ and $\triangle(O,T,X^*)$ are equiangular.

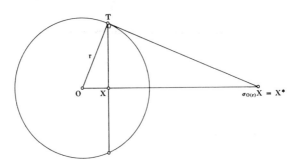

T

r

O   X

$\sigma_{O(r)}X = X^*$

FIG. 8–3

We study now the action of an inversion on lines and circles. By definition,

(8.8)   *Lines through the center of the circle of inversion are mapped onto themselves by the inversion.*

For any other line g, define

$$X^* = (\sigma_{O(r)}O^g)^{l(O,X)}.$$

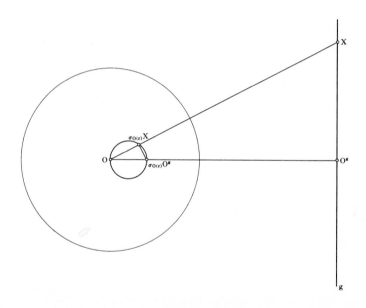

F<small>IG</small>. 8–4

From the equiangular triangles $\triangle(O,O^g,X)$ and $\triangle(O,X^*, \sigma_{O(r)}O^g)$ it follows that $OX^*/O\sigma_{O(r)}O^g = OO^g/OX$ or

$$OX \cdot OX^* = OO^g \cdot O\sigma_{O(r)}O^g = r^2,$$

i.e., $\qquad\qquad X^* = \sigma_{O(r)}X.$

The segment $[O,\sigma_{O(r)}O^g]$ subtends right angles at all points $\sigma_{O(r)}X$, $X \in g$.

(8.9)   *The image of a line not through the center of the circle of inversion is on the circle whose diameter is the segment defined by the center and the image of the projection of the center onto the line.*

The only point which is not in the image is the center O itself.

The image of a circle which does not pass through the center is given by (6.29).

(8.10)   *The image of a circle* Γ *which does not pass through the center of the circle of inversion* $O(r)$ *is the circle* $\eta_{O,r^2/\pi(O,\Gamma)}\Gamma$. *The inversion pairs those points of the circles which are not images of one another in the homothety.*

The situation may become clearer in the language of analytic geometry. The formula for the inversion of the point (x,y) in the unit circle of center $O = (0,0)$ is

$$\sigma_{O(1)}(x,y) = \left(\frac{x}{x^2 + y^2}, \frac{y}{x^2 + y^2} \right),$$

since the two points are on one ray through O, and the product of their distances from O is 1. The equation of a circle is

(*) $Ax^2 + Ay^2 + Bx + Cy + D = 0.$

If the coordinates of $\sigma_{O(1)}(x,y)$ are substituted for (x,y), we obtain

$$A\,\frac{1}{x^2 + y^2} + B\,\frac{x}{x^2 + y^2} + C\,\frac{y}{x^2 + y^2} + D = 0.$$

Since $x^2 + y^2 \neq 0$, this is equivalent to

(**) $A + Bx + Cy + D(x^2 + y^2) = 0.$

This says, in general, that the inverse image of a circle is a circle. But the equation of the circles also represents *lines* for $A = 0$, and circles through the origin for $D = 0$. The passage from (*) to (**), therefore, contains both (8.10) and (8.9). This suggests that, for the study of inversions, lines should be treated as a special kind of circles. This leads us to the following definition:

A Möbius circle, or M-circle, is a circle or a line.

Then we can sum up the essential contents of (8.8), (8.9), and (8.10) by

(8.11)   *Inversions map M-circles onto M-circles.*

In this connection we also want to remedy the fact that $\sigma_{O(r)}$ is not defined for O. By definition, a point at distance d from O is mapped into a point at distance r^2/d. If d is very small, r^2/d is very large. Therefore, it is reasonable to add to the plane a single new point ∞ which is connected with the points of the plane by

$$\sigma_{O(r)}\, O = \infty \qquad \sigma_{O(r)}\, \infty = O.$$

∞ is the *point at infinity.* A *circle of center* ∞ is any circle in the plane; the *interior of* a circle of center ∞ is the exterior of the circle in the elementary definition. In the plane, a line g contains a point P if and only if g has points in the interior of every circle of center P. Since a line has points outside every circle in the plane, it has points in the interior of every circle of center ∞. Therefore, the following definition is natural:

For all lines g, ∞ ∈ g *and* $\sigma_g \infty = \infty$.

Alternatively, we say that *the lines are the M-circles which contain* ∞. This definition makes lines correspond to circles through O without exception. The plane extended by a point ∞ is called the *Gauss* plane. Inversions are transformations of the Gauss plane.

It should be noted that the "closure" of the plane by one point at infinity is a device for the easy formulation of properties invariant under the group generated by inversions. If other groups are considered, another language might be appropriate. For instance, if we consider maps of the plane which map lines into lines but not circles into circles, the appropriate language is that of ideal points, i.e., pencils of lines as introduced in chapter II. The maximal pencils of parallel lines then are considered as "points" on one "line at infinity." All these elements added to the plane just express our freedom to fit the definitions to our needs; they do not carry any metaphysical meaning. (But they show that mathematics, far from being an example of mechanical determinism, illustrates the human freedom of choice.)

We come back to the general theory. By (6.33) there exists a circle which touches a given circle Γ at a fixed point X and $\sigma_{O(r)}\Gamma$ at $\sigma_{O(r)}X$. Therefore, the tangents t to Γ at X and t^* to $\sigma_{O(r)}\Gamma$ at $\sigma_{O(r)}X$ are tangents to one circle and, as such, symmetric with respect to the perpendicular bisector of the points of contact:

$$t^* = \sigma_{m[X,\sigma_{O(r)}X]}t.$$

If two circles intersect at X, let t_i $(i = 1,2)$ be the tangents at X, and t_i^* the tangents to the images at $\sigma_{O(r)}X$. The mapping of t onto t^* does not depend on the particular circle, hence

$$(t_1^*,t_2^*) = \sigma_{m[X,\sigma_{O(r)}X]}(t_1,t_2).$$

The same relation still holds if t is identified to itself as an M-circle, and t^* is the tangent to the circle which is its image in the inversion. The proof can be read from Fig. 8–5. Then we have proved in all cases:

(8.12)   *Inversion maps oriented angles of M-circles into their negatives.*

We may also note that (8.5) holds for all M-circles since all circles through X and $\sigma_g X$ must have their center on g, and hence are ⊥ g. In addition, $l(X,\sigma_g X) \perp g$.

If an M-circle Γ is inverted in an M-circle Γ_1, then, by (8.12), the pencils of M-circles perpendicular to Γ are transformed into pencils perpendicular to $\sigma_{\Gamma_1} \Gamma$. By (8.5) this implies

$$\sigma_{\sigma_{\Gamma_1}\Gamma}\sigma_{\Gamma_1}X = \sigma_{\Gamma_1}\sigma_{\Gamma}X$$

for all X, or

(8.13)   *The relation* $\sigma_{\sigma_{\Gamma_1}\Gamma} = \sigma_{\Gamma_1}\sigma_{\Gamma}\sigma_{\Gamma_1}^{-1}$ *is valid for Möbius-circles.*

Since the formal properties are retained, we may consider line reflections as inversions at a special class of M-circles.

Exercise 8–2

1. In the space of analytic geometry, the space of ordered triples (X, Y, Z) of real numbers, we project the plane $Z = 0$ into the unit sphere $X^2 + Y^2 + Z^2 = 1$ from the point $(0, 0, -1) = S$. To each point $P = (x, y)$ in the plane we associate the intersection of $l(P, S)$ with the sphere distinct from S.

     (a) Prove that the image of (x, y) has coordinates

$$X = \frac{2x}{1 + x^2 + y^2} \qquad Y = \frac{2y}{1 + x^2 + y^2} \qquad Z = \frac{1 - x^2 - y^2}{1 + x^2 + y^2}.$$

     (b) Prove that the image of the M-circle

$$A(x^2 + y^2) + Bx + Cy + D = 0$$

is the intersection of the unit sphere with the plane

$$BX + CY + (D - A)Z + (D + A) = 0$$

and hence is a circle.

     (c) Prove that the image of an M-circle contains the point S if and only if the M-circle is a straight line.

     (d) Prove that the unit sphere is a one-to-one image of the Gauss plane.

     (e) Let $T:(x, y) \rightarrow (X, Y, Z)$ be the map of the plane onto the sphere. (T^{-1} is known as the stereographic projection.) Also let $U:(X, Y, Z) \rightarrow (X, Y, -Z)$ be the *reflection* of the sphere in the plane $Z = 0$. The transformation $T^{-1}UT$ is a map of the Gauss plane onto itself. What is it?

2. Find an explicit formula for an inversion which maps a given line g onto a given circle $\Gamma = A(a)$.

3. If $\sigma_{O(r)}g_1 \cong \sigma_{O(r)}g_2$, then g_1 and g_2 are equidistant from O.

4. A figure S is *anallagmatic* if $\sigma_\Gamma S = S$ for some M-circle Γ. Prove: An anallagmatic set is the image in an inversion of a set which has an axis of symmetry.

5. The *polar* of a point X relative to a circle $O(r)$ is $p[l(O, X), \sigma_{O(r)}X]$.

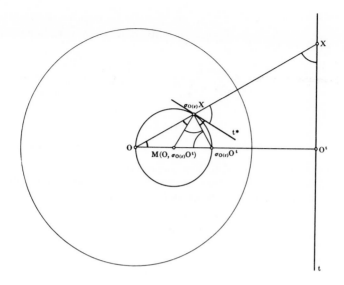

Fig. 8–5

(a) If X is in the exterior of the circle, show that the polar is the line joining the points of contact of the two tangents from X to the circle.

(b) Denote the polar of X for a fixed circle by $p(X)$. Prove that $p[p(X_1) \cap p(X_2)] = l(X_1, X_2)$.

(c) Prove that the polars of all the points on a line form a pencil whose vertex is the point of which the given line is the polar.

(d) Prove that the Gauss plane is not an appropriate set for the study of polars.

6. *Peaucellier's cell* is the following mechanism: Two rods of equal length a are attached to a point O. At each of the end points two other rods of length b are attached. The two pairs of rods coming from different joints are linked at points X and Y to form a rhombus of edge b.

(a) Prove that $Y = \sigma_{O[(a^2-b^2)^{1/2}]} X$.

(b) If in any deformation of the linkage X is constrained to move on an arc of a circle through O (e.g., by a rod attached to X and a suitable fixed point P), then Y moves on a straight segment.

7. *Hart's linkage* is the mechanism described in Fig. 8–6: $CD = AB$, $AD = BC$. The points M, N, O are subject to

$$MB/MC = ND/NA = OD/OC.$$

The whole assembly can be moved freely about its joints, but the point O is kept fixed at all times.

(a) Prove that M, N, O are collinear.

(b) Prove that N is the image of M in some inversion $\sigma_{O(r)}$, r depending on the position of C.

(c) If the point C is kept fixed, N will move on a straight segment.

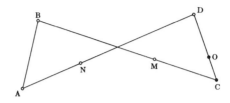

FIG. 8–6

3. The Group of Circular Transformations

(8.14)   *A one-to-one map of an archimedean Gauss plane onto itself which maps M-circles onto M-circles is either a similitude or the product of an inversion and a motion.*

Let ϕ be the map of the Gauss plane. If $\phi\infty = \infty$, then ϕ is also a one-to-one map of the plane (without the point ∞) which conserves circles and lines; hence it is a similitude by (8.1). In particular, the product of two inversions of a common center O is a similitude for which O is a fixed point; it is a homothety of center O. The definition (8.4) shows that

(8.15) $\sigma_{O(r_2)}\sigma_{O(r_1)} = \eta_{O,(r_2/r_1)^2}.$

Hence, we may give a preassigned value to the image of a given circle of the plane by an appropriate choice of the radius of the circle of inversion.

If $\phi\infty = P$, then $\sigma_{P(r)}\phi\infty = \infty$; hence $\sigma_{P(r)}\phi$ is a similitude for all positive r. By the preceding remark, r can be chosen in order to make $\sigma_{P(r)}\phi$ an isometry since a given circle can be mapped onto a congruent one. Then the map ϕ is represented as

$$\phi = \sigma_{P(r)}\Sigma.$$

The following developments are again independent of the archimedean axiom. However, we shall denote by the *group* $\mathcal{C}$ *of circular transformations* the group generated by all similitudes and all inversions. Only in an archimedean plane is that group identical to the group of all M-circle preserving transformations.

The theory of the products of reflections was based on the three-reflections theorem (2.3). This theorem has a natural generalization to the group $\mathcal{C}$.

We define a set of M-circles to be a *pencil* if it is: (a) either a pencil of lines as defined in sec. 2–1, (b) or a pencil of circles as defined in sec. 5–5, (c) or a set of concentric circles. There are two types of pencils (a), three types of pencils (b), and one of type (c). These six types reduce to three under the action of the group of circular transformations.

(8.16)   *By an appropriate inversion:*

A pencil of circles through two fixed points can be mapped onto a pencil of concurrent lines;
A pencil of lines tangent to a fixed line at a fixed point can be mapped onto a pencil of parallel lines;
A pencil of non-intersecting circles can be mapped onto a pencil of concentric circles.

In the first case, we invert in any circle whose center is one of the points of intersection of the circles. The pencil of concurrent lines appears as the pencil of M-circles concurrent at a point of the plane and at ∞. In this theory, it is natural to enlarge the definition of a pencil of circles to that of a pencil of M-circles and to admit also the line which joins the two points of intersection of the circles of the pencil. By (5.43), the inversion chosen maps the circles of the perpendicular pencil of non-intersecting circles onto the pencil of circles perpendicular to the pencil of concurrent lines, i.e., onto the pencil of concentric circles whose common center is the vertex of the pencil of lines.

The pencil of circles tangent to a fixed line at a given point (or better, the pencil of M-circles tangent to an M-circle at a fixed point) is inverted at a circle whose center is the point of contact. The circles of the pencil are mapped into straight lines that are perpendicular to the perpendiculars to the common tangent at the point of contact. This is a pencil of parallel lines.

The three-reflections theorem of the group $\mathfrak{C}$ now reads:

(8.17)   *A product of three inversions is equal to one inversion if and only if the three M-circles of inversion are in a pencil.*

For pencils of lines, this is (2.3) (Remember that now we consider line reflections as inversions at a special class of M-circles.) For pencils of concentric circles it follows from (8.15) that

(8.18) $\sigma_{O(r_3)}\sigma_{O(r_2)}\sigma_{O(r_1)} = \sigma_{O(r_1 r_3 / r_2)}$.

Any other pencil of three circles Γ_i ($i = 1,2,3$) can be inverted by some σ_Γ into a pencil of circles Γ_i^* for which the theorem is true. By (8.13) there exists a Γ^* in the maximal pencil defined by the Γ_i^* such that

$$\sigma_{\Gamma_3}\sigma_{\Gamma_2}\sigma_{\Gamma_1} = \sigma_\Gamma\sigma_{\Gamma_3^*}\sigma_{\Gamma_2^*}\sigma_{\Gamma_1^*}\sigma_\Gamma = \sigma_\Gamma\sigma_{\Gamma^*}\sigma_\Gamma = \sigma_{\sigma_\Gamma\Gamma^*}.$$

Just as for reflections, the "only if" part of the theorem follows from a discussion of the possible types of products of inversions.

Two M-circles always define a pencil. Therefore, by (8.16) we have to distinguish *three* types of products of two inversions. If two circles intersect in two distinct points,

$$\Gamma_1 \cap \Gamma_2 = A_1 \cup A_2,$$

let α be the oriented angle of the tangents to Γ_1 and Γ_2 at A_1. The product of the inversions is called the *rotation* about the pair of points A_1, A_2 of angle α:

$$\sigma_{\Gamma_1}\sigma_{\Gamma_2} = \rho_{A_1, A_2; 2\alpha} = \rho_{A_2, A_1; -2\alpha}.$$

(8.17) implies that this rotation is the image of a rotation defined by the product of line reflections. Therefore, it depends only on α and the ordered pair of points A_1, A_2. Any two circles in the pencil of lines through A_1 and A_2 and which intersect under angle α at A_1 will define the same rotation.

For $\alpha = 90°$, the rotation becomes the *reflection* in the pair of points A_1, A_2. This case is characterized by

(8.19) $\sigma_{\Gamma_1}\sigma_{\Gamma_2} = \sigma_{\Gamma_2}\sigma_{\Gamma_1}$ *for* $\Gamma_1 \neq \Gamma_2$ *if and only if* $\Gamma_1 \perp \Gamma_2$.

A line is perpendicular to a circle if and only if it is a diameter. This gives a characterization of diameters by a property of reflections:

(8.20) $\sigma_g \sigma_{O(r)} = \sigma_{O(r)}\sigma_g$ *if and only if* $O \in g$.

The product of two inversions at circles which touch one another is called a *horocyclic* transformation. The reason for this name will be given in the next chapter. By (8.17), every horocyclic transformation is the transform of a translation in euclidean geometry. Such a translation depends only on the distance of the two lines which generate the translation and their direction. If we invert in a circle of radius 1 about a point of contact of the circles, we see that (Fig. 8–7):

(8.21)   *The horocyclic transformation defined by two mutually tangent circles depends only on the direction of their common tangent and the function $(r_2 - r_1)/r_1 r_2$ of their radii.*

The product of two inversions at disjoint circles is called a *translatory* transformation. Here again we shall justify the name in the next chapter. By (8.16), two pairs of circles in the same pencil define the same translatory transformation if and only if they are mapped onto two pairs of circles which define the same homothety by (8.15).

The detailed behavior of products of the transformations introduced in this section is, in general, quite distinct from that of the corresponding products of line reflections. For example, the product of two reflections at pairs of points is, in general, a rotation. It will be a horocyclic transformation if the pairs have one common point and the three centers are collinear. It will be translatory if the four points are concyclic and the two pairs define disjoint arcs on the circle.

The theory of products of three inversions is parallel to that of products of three reflections. We may assume that the three M-circles Γ_1, Γ_2, and Γ_3 are not in one pencil.

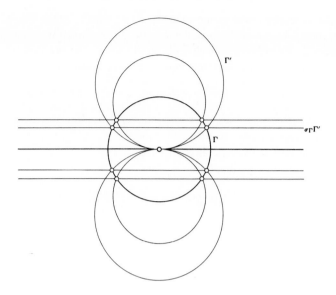

FIG. 8–7

The discussion of the products of two inversions shows that a product of two inversions can be written as the product of inversions at two other M-circles of the same pencil of which one may be prescribed arbitrarily. If the pencil is not one of concentric circles, one of the M-circles can be taken as a line, the radical axis of the pencil. If we use this argument for the pencils defined by Γ_1, Γ_2 and then for the replacement of Γ_2 and Γ_3, we see that the product of three inversions at M-circles is equal to either the product of two line reflections and an inversion, or the product of one line reflection and inversions in two concentric circles. In the second case we obtain an indirect similitude, the product of a line reflection and a homothety.

The same argument can be used for products of any number of inversions.

(8.22)   *An element of the group of circular transformations is either a similitude or the product of an inversion and a motion.*

We prove the theorem by complete induction. The preceding argument establishes the theorem for all products of $\leqslant 3$ inversions. We assume that the theorem is true for all products of $\leqslant n$ inversions. Take now any product of $n + 1$ inversions,

$$\mu = \sigma_{\Gamma_{n+1}}\sigma_{\Gamma_n} \cdots \sigma_{\Gamma_2}\sigma_{\Gamma_1}.$$

If the pencil defined by Γ_2 and Γ_1 is not one of concentric circles, μ is the product of a line reflection and a product of n inversions. Hence it is a transformation of the type described by the theorem. If Γ_2 and Γ_1 are concentric, $\sigma_{\Gamma_2}\sigma_{\Gamma_1}$ is a homothety and μ is the product of $n-1$ reflections at M-circles and a homothety. By hypothesis, μ is either a similitude or the product of an inversion and a similitude. In the latter case, μ can be written

$$\mu = \sigma_\Gamma \eta \Sigma \qquad\qquad \eta \in \mathfrak{IC} \quad \Sigma \in \mathfrak{M}.$$

But every homothety is the product of two inversions. Hence $\sigma_\Gamma \eta$ is the product of three inversions and hence either the product of an inversion and a motion or a similitude. This proves the theorem in all cases.

An immediate consequence is

(8.23)   *An element of the group of circular transformations is the product of at most four inversions.*

Exercise 8–3

1. What is the statement corresponding to (8.14) in a non-archimedean geometry?

2. Prove that the second kind of map characterized by (8.14) can also be obtained by using first an inversion and then a motion.

3. Prove that $\sigma_{\eta\Gamma} = \eta\sigma_\Gamma\eta^{-1}$, and, more generally, $\sigma_{\theta\Gamma} = \theta\sigma_\Gamma\theta^{-1}$.

4. The reflection at the pair of points P,Q will be denoted by $\sigma_{P,Q}$.
   (a) The perpendicular bisector of two points P,Q is the only line a for which

   (*) $\sigma_a\sigma_{P,Q}\sigma_a\sigma_{P,Q} = \iota.$

   (b) Find all the M-circles a which satisfy (*).

5. A direct similitude is always equal to the product of two inversions.

6. Any two rotations of the same angle but about different pairs of points are images of one another in a product of two inversions.

7. Find an inversion that transforms three given circles into circles with collinear centers.

8. Prove the formula $\rho_{A_1,A_2;\alpha}\rho_{A_1,A_3;\beta} = \rho_{A_1,B;\alpha+\beta}$.

9. If for two circles A and B the circle T is defined by $\sigma_T A = B$, then
   (a) T belongs to the pencil of A and B.
   (b) $\sigma_B\sigma_T\sigma_A\sigma_T = \iota.$
   (c) There exist two circles T if and only if A and B intersect in two distinct points.

10. $\mathfrak{IC}$ is not a normal subgroup of $\mathfrak{C}$.

11. $\mathcal{S}$ is not a normal subgroup of $\mathfrak{C}$.

12. The translatory transformations and the identity form a normal subgroup of $\mathfrak{C}$.

13. What is the group which is the factor group of $\mathfrak{C}$ modulo the group described in problem 12?

14. Describe a homogeneous space of the group $\mathfrak{C}$ which is in one-to-one correspondence with the ordered pairs of points of the plane.

15. Formulate the theorem corresponding to (8.14) in an archimedean plane for which the validity of axiom X* is not assumed.

16. All elements of $\mathcal{C}$ are the product of at most three involutions.

4. Geometry of the Circle

The proof of (8.17) is characteristic for most applications of inversions in euclidean geometry: By the use of an appropriate inversion [usually suggested by (8.16)], a statement about circles can be translated into one about lines and vice versa.

A number of theorems can be transformed into other interesting statements simply by operating an inversion on the configuration described by the theorem. For example, let us translate the fundamental theorem about angles subtended by an arc of circle (4.10): All angles subtended at the circle by an arc of the circle are equal. If the center of the circle of inversion is not on the given circle, the result is:

(8.24)   *If A and B are points of a circle Γ and O is any point not on Γ, then for all $X \in \Gamma$ the circles $\Gamma(A,O,X)$ and $\Gamma(B,O,X)$ meet under the same oriented angle computed at X.*

If the center of inversion is a point of Γ, we obtain instead:

(8.25)   *If A,B,O are three non-collinear points, then the angles of the circles $\Gamma(A,O,X)$ and $\Gamma(B,O,X)$ are the same for all $X \in l(A,B)$.*

If the point A itself is the center of the circle of inversion, Γ becomes a line and $l(A,X)$ is mapped into itself:

(8.26)   *If A is a point not on a line g and $B \in g$, then for all $X \in g$ the angle of $l(A,X)$ and $\Gamma(A,B,X)$ is constant as an oriented angle.*

Inversions are also useful tools in the solution of problems about circles. We give some examples.

Example 1. Two distinct points A_1,A_2 are given on a circle Γ. Find the set of the points of contact of all circles which touch one another and which touch Γ, respectively, at A_1 and A_2.

For the solution, we use an inversion σ whose center is a point of Γ distinct from the A_i. Then the problem is to find the set of points of contact σX of two circles $\sigma\Gamma_i$ $(i = 1,2)$ which touch one another and touch $l(\sigma A_1,\sigma A_2)$, respectively, at σA_i. Let t be the common tangent to the circles at σX. Then

$$[\sigma A_1, t \cap l(\sigma A_1,\sigma A_2)] \cong [t \cap l(\sigma A_1,\sigma A_2),\sigma X] \cong [t \cap l(\sigma A_1,\sigma A_2),\sigma A_2];$$

hence $t \cap l(\sigma A_1,\sigma A_2) = M(\sigma A_1,\sigma A_2)$ and

$$\sigma X \in M(\sigma A_1,\sigma A_2)(\tfrac{1}{2}\sigma A_1 \sigma A_2) \perp \sigma\Gamma.$$

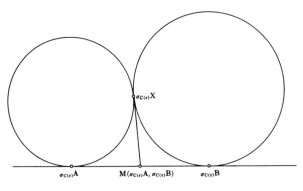

FIG. 8–8

The points X are on the circle through A_1 and A_2 and perpendicular to Γ.

Example 2. Given are three halfcircles which are mutually tangent (Fig. 8–9). If $A_3 \in [A_1,A_2]$, then Γ_i is the halfcircle of diameter $[A_i,A_{i+1}]$ (put

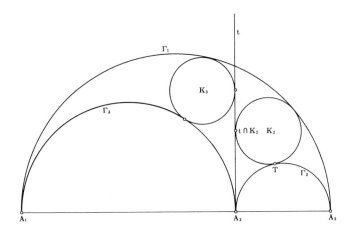

FIG. 8–9

$A_4 = A_1$). Let t be the tangent common to Γ_2 and Γ_3 at A_3, and K_i $(i = 2,3)$ the circle tangent to t, Γ_1, and Γ_i. Prove that

(8.27) $K_2 \cong K_3$.

The proof shows the advantages that can be obtained from a good choice of the radius of the circle of inversion. On the configuration of Fig. 8–9 we let act the inversion $\sigma_{A_3(k)}$ where $k^2 = -\pi(A_3,\Gamma_1) = 4r_2r_3$. (We take the liberty of replacing the halfcircles by full circles without a change in notation.)

$\sigma_{A_3(k)}\Gamma_i$ ($i = 2,3$) are lines parallel to $\sigma_{A_3(k)}t = t$. The diameter of $\sigma_{A_3(k)}K_2$ is equal to the distance of $\sigma_{A_3(k)}\Gamma_2$ from t, and this is equal to the distance $4r_2r_3/2r_2 = 2r_3$ of $\sigma_{A_3(k)}A_2$ from A_3. By (8.10), the radius of $\sigma_{A_3(k)}\Gamma_1$ is $(k^2/k^2)r_1 = r_1$. By the same theorem,

$$K_2 = \eta_{A_3,k^2/\pi[A_3,\sigma_{A_3(k)}K_2]}\sigma_{A_3(k)}K_2.$$

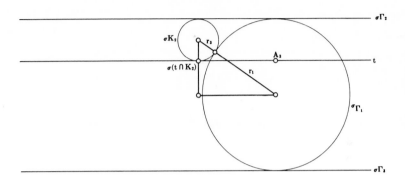

FIG. 8-10

From Fig. 8-10 it may be seen that

$$\pi(A_3,\sigma_{A_3(k)}K_2) = A_3(\sigma_{A_3(k)}t \cap K_2)^2$$
$$= (r_1 + r_3)^2 - (r_1 - r_3)^2 = 4r_1r_3.$$

For the radius ρ_2 of K_2 this implies

$$\rho_2 = \frac{4r_2r_3}{4r_1r_3}r_3 = \frac{r_2r_3}{r_1} = \frac{r_2r_3}{r_2 + r_3}.$$

The formula is symmetric in the indices 2 and 3. Therefore, the analogous computation for ρ_3 will give the same result, $\rho_2 = \rho_3$. This proves (8.27).

Example 3. In the same basic figure formed by the halfcircles Γ_1, Γ_2, and Γ_3 of the preceding example, we inscribe an infinite sequence of circles Ω_i. Circle $\Omega_0 = \Gamma_2$, and Ω_i is tangent to Γ_1, Γ_3, Ω_{i-1} (hence also to Ω_{i+1}). We denote by r_i the radius of Ω_i, by h_i the distance of the center of Ω_i from the base line $l(A_1,A_2)$, and by t_i the length of the tangent from A_1 to Ω_i. For some fixed n, we transform the configuration by $\sigma_{A_1(t_n)}$. The circle Ω_n is perpendicular to the circle of inversion. Its points of intersection with the circle of inversion are fixed in the transformation, hence

$$\sigma_{A_1(t_n)}\Omega_n = \Omega_n.$$

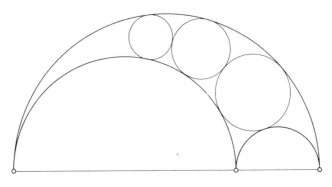

FIG. 8–11

$\sigma_{A_1(t_n)}\Gamma_1$ and $\sigma_{A_1(t_n)}\Gamma_3$ become parallel lines tangent to Ω_n. The same lines are tangent to the images of all other circles Ω_i. All these circles, therefore, are mapped into circles of radius r_n and, since h_n is not changed in the mapping, Fig. 8–12 shows that

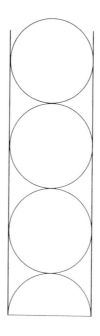

FIG. 8–12

(8.28) $h_n = 2nr_n.$

Example 4. Another problem of tangent circles is the following. Given are two circles Γ_1 and Γ_2, one in the interior of the other. We draw a circle Ω_1

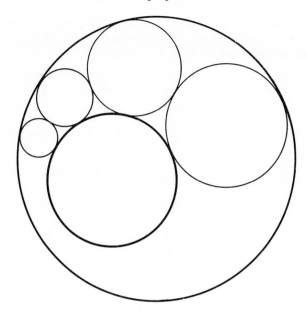

FIG. 8–13

tangent to Γ_1 and Γ_2, and then Ω_i tangent to Γ_1, Γ_2, and Ω_{i-1}. In general, this process (if at all possible) will continue indefinitely. Is it possible to draw Ω_1 such that, for some k, $\Omega_k = \Omega_1$?

It is possible to invert Γ_1 and Γ_2 into two concentric circles. Then all circles Ω_i are mapped into congruent circles, and our problem has a solution if and only if the angle subtended by any $\sigma\Omega_i$ at the common center of $\sigma\Gamma_1$ and $\sigma\Gamma_2$ is a rational part of 360° (provided, naturally, that such an angle exists in our geometry). The whole configuration admits the rotations about the center of the concentric circles: if the construction is possible for one initial position of $\sigma\Omega_1$, it is so for all positions.

(8.29)   *If a sequence of circles Ω_i is inscribed in a ring domain bounded by circles in such a way that consecutive circles touch each other, then the circles perpendicular to the boundaries of the domain and tangent to the circles of the sequence intersect at a constant angle. The sequence of circles closes after a finite number of steps if and only if that angle is a rational part of 360°, independent of the position of Ω_1.*

Exercise 8–4

1. For any two circles A and B let T(A,B) be a circle of the pencil defined by A and B for which $\sigma_{T(A,B)}A = B$, see exercise 8–3, problem 9. Given three circles Γ_1,

Γ_2, Γ_3, concurrent at a point O but which do not form a pencil, and also circles A_i in the pencil of Γ_j and Γ_k ($i \neq j \neq k$). We write T_i for $T(\Gamma_j, \Gamma_k)$. Prove: If A_1, A_2, A_3 are in a pencil, so are $\sigma_{T_1}A_1$, $\sigma_{T_2}A_2$, $\sigma_{T_3}A_3$.

2. Given three circles Γ_1, Γ_2, Γ_3, concurrent at a point O but which do not form a pencil. Let M_i be the circle through O, perpendicular to Γ_i, and such that

$$\sigma_{M_i}\Gamma_i \cap \Gamma_k = \Gamma_i \cap \Gamma_j \qquad\qquad i \neq j \neq k.$$

Let B_i be any circle through O and perpendicular to Γ_i. Prove that the $\sigma_{M_i}B_i$ ($i = 1,2,3$) form a pencil if and only if the B_i do.

3. Given are three circles A, B, Γ which do not form a pencil but which all pass through a point O. Prove that the relation

$$\sigma_A\sigma_H\sigma_A\sigma_B\sigma_\Gamma\sigma_H\sigma_B\sigma_\Gamma = \iota$$

is true only for the circle H through O, $B \cap \Gamma$, and perpendicular to A.

4. Given six points A_i, B_i ($i = 1,2,3$). If

$$\Gamma(A_1, A_2, B_3) \cap \Gamma(A_1, B_2, A_3) \cap \Gamma(B_1, A_2, A_3)$$

is a point P, prove that

$$\Gamma(B_1, B_2, A_3) \cap \Gamma(B_1, A_2, B_3) \cap \Gamma(A_1, B_2, B_3)$$

is also a point Q.

5. Given four circles which, in cyclic order, intersect in four pairs of points: $\Gamma_i \cap \Gamma_{i+1} = A_i \cup B_i$. If the four points A_i are concyclic, prove that the points B_i are, too.

6. Prove: if, for any six points,

$$\Gamma(A_1, B_1, C_1), \ \Gamma(A_1, B_2, C_2), \ \Gamma(A_2, B_1, C_2), \ \Gamma(A_2, B_2, C_1)$$

are concurrent at a point O, then

$$\Gamma(A_2, B_2, C_2), \ \Gamma(A_2, B_1, C_1), \ \Gamma(A_1, B_2, C_1), \ \Gamma(A_1, B_1, C_2)$$

are also concurrent.

7. Prove that the four points of contact of four circles which are mutually tangent in cyclic order lie on a circle.

8. Prove: three circles A, B, Γ are concurrent or concentric if and only if

$$\sigma_A\sigma_B\sigma_\Gamma\sigma_A\sigma_B\sigma_\Gamma\sigma_B\sigma_\Gamma\sigma_A\sigma_B\sigma_\Gamma\sigma_A\sigma_\Gamma\sigma_B\sigma_A\sigma_\Gamma\sigma_B\sigma_\Gamma\sigma_B\sigma_A\sigma_\Gamma\sigma_B = \iota.$$

9. Prove: if A, B, Γ are concurrent at O and if for some point P,

$$\sigma_A\sigma_B\sigma_\Gamma\sigma_{P,O}\sigma_\Gamma\sigma_B\sigma_A\sigma_{P,O} = \iota,$$

then the three circles are in a pencil.

10. Prove: if A, B, C, O are concyclic, then the three points of intersection, in pairs, of the circles over the diameters $[A,O]$, $[B,O]$, $[C,O]$ are collinear.

11. Prove: (a) The three circles $\Gamma(O, \sigma_O A_i, \sigma_{m_i} A_i)$ of a triangle $\triangle(A_1, A_2, A_3)$ of circumcenter O are concurrent.

(b) If O, B, and C are fixed and A varies on a circle, prove that the point of intersection of the circles described in problem (a) also varies on a circle.

12. Let $\triangle(A_1,B_1,C_1)$ be the tangential triangle of $\triangle(A,B,C)$, and define A_2 by $l(A,A_1) \cap \Gamma(A,B,C) = A \cup A_2$. Prove that the circles $\Gamma(A,A_2,M_a)$, $\Gamma(B,B_2,M_b)$, $\Gamma(C,C_2,M_c)$ belong to a pencil of intersecting circles.

13. A transversal meets the sides of $\triangle(A,B,C)$ at points E,F,G. For a fixed point O in the plane define X by

$$O \cup X = l(O,E) \cap \Gamma(O,B,C).$$

Y and Z are obtained by cyclic permutation. Prove that O,X,Y,Z are concyclic.

14. For three circles Γ_i $(i = 1,2,3)$, concurrent at a point O, define A_k as the second point of intersection of Γ_i and Γ_j $(i \neq j \neq k)$, and put $p[l(O,A_k),O] \cap \Gamma(O,A_i,A_j) = O \cup B_k$. Prove that O and the B_i are concyclic.

15. Prove: for any two circles, all lines $l(\sigma_{\Gamma_2}X, \sigma_{\Gamma_2}\sigma_{\Gamma_1}X)$, $X \in g$ pass through a fixed point.

16. Solve the problem of example 1 if it is asked that the two circles Γ_1 and Γ_2 be perpendicular to one another.

17. In example 2, show that the tangent common to Γ_i and K_i passes through A_{i-1}.

18. Γ is a fixed circle; Γ_1 and Γ_2 are two circles tangent to Γ and which intersect at two points. Let A be the point of intersection whose distance from the center of Γ is greatest. For any circle X which touches both Γ_1 and Γ_2, define M and N as its points of intersection with Γ. Find the set of centers of $\Gamma(A,M,N)$.

19. Γ and Γ' are two mutually perpendicular circles. For any pair of mutually perpendicular diameters, $[A,B]$ of Γ, $[A',B']$ of Γ', prove that the four lines defined by the end points of the diameters pass in pairs through the points of intersection of the two circles.

20. Two perpendicular circles intersect at A and B. For any point C on the first, and any D on the second circles, prove that $\Gamma(A,C,D) \perp \Gamma(B,C,D)$.

21. If A,B,C,D are not concyclic or collinear, prove that the circles $\Gamma(A,B,C)$, $\Gamma(A,B,D)$ intersect under the same angle as $\Gamma(A,C,D)$, $\Gamma(B,C,D)$.

22. The nine-point circle is the inverse of the common external tangent, other than the side of the triangle, to two excircles of the triangle, in an inversion in the circle perpendicular to both excircles and whose center is the midpoint of the common edge. Prove this statement and deduce from it Feuerbach's theorem: The nine-point circle touches the excircles and the incircle.

23. Prove: if two circles Γ_1 and Γ_2 are situated such that there exists a triangle $\triangle$ inscribed to Γ_1 and circumscribed to Γ_2, then $\sigma_{\Gamma_2}\Gamma_1$ is the nine-point circle of the triangle of the points of contact of $\triangle$ and Γ_2. All admissible triangles $\triangle$ have the same nine-point circle.

24. Construct a circle tangent to a given Γ and passing through two given points A,B.

25. Construct a circle perpendicular to a given Γ and passing through two given points A,B.

26. Construct a circle tangent to two given circles and passing through a given point.

27. Find a circle tangent to three given circles.

5. Applications to Metric Geometry

The definition of an inversion implies that for any pair A,B of points

$$\frac{OB}{OA} = \frac{O\sigma_{O(r)}A}{O\sigma_{O(r)}B}.$$

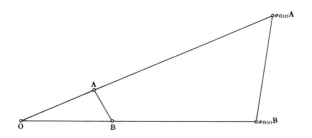

FIG. 8–14

Also, the angle $\hat{O}$ is common to $\triangle(O,A,B)$ and $\triangle(O,\sigma_{O(r)}A,\sigma_{O(r)}B)$. Hence the two triangles are equiangular and

$$\frac{AB}{OB} = \frac{\sigma_{O(r)}A\sigma_{O(r)}B}{O\sigma_{O(r)}A}.$$

The two equations together yield

$$(8.30) \qquad \sigma_{O(r)}A\sigma_{O(r)}B = \frac{O\sigma_{O(r)}B}{OA}AB = \frac{r^2}{OA \cdot OB}AB.$$

For a first application of this formula we take four points A,B,C,D and invert in a circle $A(r)$. The triangle inequality

$$\sigma_{A(r)}B\sigma_{A(r)}C + \sigma_{A(r)}C\sigma_{A(r)}D \geqslant \sigma_{A(r)}B\sigma_{A(r)}D$$

becomes

$$\frac{r^2}{AB \cdot AC}BC + \frac{r^2}{AC \cdot AD}CD \geqslant \frac{r^2}{AB \cdot AD}BD.$$

Equality holds only if $\sigma_{A(r)}C \in [\sigma_{A(r)}B,\sigma_{A(r)}D]$, i.e., if C is a point of that arc BD of $\Gamma(A,B,D)$ which does not contain A. Multiplication by $AB \cdot AC \cdot AD/r^2$ gives the formula of *Ptolemy's theorem:*

(8.31)   *For any four points in the plane,*

$$AD \cdot BC + AB \cdot CD \geqslant AC \cdot BD.$$

Equality holds if and only if A,B,C,D in their order are the vertices of a convex cyclic quadrilateral.

Next we apply inversion to the Erdös-Mordell and related inequalities discussed in sec. 7–3. There we have defined the lengths x_i, p_i as distances of a point P in the interior of a triangle $\triangle(A_1, A_2, A_3)$ from the vertices and the angles. Let x'_i, p'_i be the corresponding quantities for P in the interior of the triangle $\triangle[\sigma_{P(1)}A_1, \sigma_{P(1)}A_2, \sigma_{P(1)}A_3]$. By definition,

$$(*) \qquad\qquad x'_i = \frac{1}{x_i} = \frac{1}{x_1 x_2 x_3} x_j x_k \qquad\qquad i \neq j \neq k.$$

The segment whose length is p'_i is perpendicular to the line $l[\sigma_{P(1)}A_j, \sigma_{P(1)}A_k]$. This line is the image in $\sigma_{P(1)}$ of $\Gamma(P, A_j, A_k)$. Therefore, the segment is mapped into a diameter of length $2R(P, A_j, A_k)$ of the circle $\Gamma(P, A_j, A_k)$. With the notations introduced in Fig. 4–10, we see that $\triangle(A, F_a, C)$ is equiangular with $\triangle(A, T_a, B)$ and, hence, $h_a/b = c/2R$. In our case this means

$$2R(P, A_j, A_k) = \frac{x_j x_k}{p_i}$$

and

$$(**) \qquad\qquad p'_i = \frac{p_i}{x_j x_k} = \frac{1}{x_1 x_2 x_3} p_i x_i.$$

All the inequalities derived in sec. 7–3 are homogeneous in the variables x_i, p_i. Since they are true for all triangles, they also hold for the x'_i, p'_i. The common factor appearing in the formulae $(*)$ and $(**)$ will cancel if we substitute the primed quantities. This proves

(8.32) *Any relation between homogeneous polynomials of the same degree in the variables x_i, p_i is transformed into another valid relation by the substitution*

$$\text{S: } x_i \to x_j x_k \qquad p_i \to p_i x_i.$$

In particular, (7.11) becomes

$$x_2 x_3 + x_3 x_1 + x_1 x_2 \geqslant 2(p_1 x_1 + p_2 x_2 + p_3 x_3),$$

which together with (7.9) yields

(8.33) $\qquad x_1 x_2 + x_2 x_3 + x_3 x_1 \geqslant 4(p_1 p_2 + p_2 p_3 + p_3 p_1).$

The substitution used in sec. 7–3 was

$$\text{T: } x_i \to x_i p_i \qquad p_i \to p_j p_k.$$

The substitution **STS** is, after division by a common factor $x_1^2 x_2^2 x_3^2 p_1 p_2 p_3$,

$$x_i \rightarrow 1/p_i \qquad p_i \rightarrow 1/x_i,$$

which gives for (7.11), (8.33), and (7.10),

(8.34) $\quad \dfrac{1}{p_1} + \dfrac{1}{p_2} + \dfrac{1}{p_3} \geqslant 2\left(\dfrac{1}{x_1} + \dfrac{1}{x_2} + \dfrac{1}{x_3}\right)$

(8.35) $\quad \dfrac{1}{p_1 p_2} + \dfrac{1}{p_2 p_3} + \dfrac{1}{p_3 p_1} \geqslant 4\left(\dfrac{1}{x_1 x_2} + \dfrac{1}{x_2 x_3} + \dfrac{1}{x_3 x_1}\right)$

(8.36) $\quad \dfrac{1}{p_1 p_2 p_3} \geqslant 8\,\dfrac{1}{x_1 x_2 x_3}.$

Exercise 8–5

1. Prove Euler's formula $OI^2 = R^2 - 2Rr$ (O circumcenter, I incenter, R circumradius, r inradius).

2. On the altitudes of a triangle define points A',B',C' by $HA \cdot HA' = HB \cdot HB' = HC \cdot HC'$. Prove that H is the incenter or one of the excenters of $\triangle(A',B',C')$.

3. If from a point of a circle the three vertices are drawn to the vertices of an equilateral triangle inscribed in the circle, prove that one of the segments is equal to the sum of the other two.

4. Prove the second theorem of Ptolemy: A,B,C,D form a convex cyclic quadrilateral if and only if

$$\frac{AC}{BD} = \frac{AB \cdot AD + BC \cdot CD}{BA \cdot BC + DA \cdot DC}.$$

5. Prove: $p_1 + p_2 + p_3 \geqslant 2\left(\dfrac{p_1 p_2}{x_1} + \dfrac{p_2 p_3}{x_2} + \dfrac{p_3 p_1}{x_3}\right).$

6. Prove: $x_1^k + x_2^k + x_3^k \geqslant 2^k(p_1^k + p_2^k + p_3^k) \quad k = 1,2,3.$

7. How many elements has the group of substitutions generated by **S** and **T** if two substitutions are considered identical if they differ only by a constant factor?

8. Prove: if $X \in O(r)$, then for any point P,

$$XP^2 / X\sigma_{O(r)}P^2 = OP / O\sigma_{O(r)}P.$$

9. Prove: if $\sigma_{O(r)}\Gamma = \Gamma$, then for any point P

$$\pi(P,\Gamma)/\pi(\sigma_{O(r)}P,\Gamma) = OP/O\sigma_{O(r)}P.$$

10. Prove: $\triangle[\sigma_{O(r)}A, \sigma_{O(r)}B, \sigma_{O(r)}C]$ is equiangular with $\triangle(\sigma_a O, \sigma_b O, \sigma_c O).$

Chapter IX

HYPERBOLIC GEOMETRY

1. The Hyperbolic Group

There can be no doubt that geometry has an experimental and intuitive background. The basic notions of geometry correspond in a very efficient way to important features of the physical world. For instance, axiom I can

FIG. 9–1

be used as an efficient tool to check the quality of a ruler: A line is drawn between two points. Then the ruler is turned by 180°, and a new line is drawn between the points. The ruler is acceptable if and only if there is only one line connecting the two points! In the same way, all our axioms have a very practical background.

On the other hand, the formulation of our system of axioms makes geometry an autonomous deductive science. We prove our theorems without appeal to experience or intuition outside the framework given by the axioms. As a consequence, our theorems will be true for *any* realization of the axioms whatsoever. The theory of the preceding chapter shows that all theorems of euclidean geometry remain true if we translate them by the following dictionary:

for	plane	*read*	Gauss plane minus one point O
	line		M-circle through O
	circle		M-circle not through O
	angle		angle
	perpendicular		perpendicular
	length AB		$AB/OA \cdot OB$
	reflection σ_g		inversion $\sigma_{\sigma_{O(1)}g}$.

We say that the M-circles through a fixed point of the Gauss plane form a *model* of the lines of euclidean geometry. Together with the points of the Gauss plane other than O, we obtain a *model* of euclidean geometry. This means that we have a set of elements called Points, and a set of subsets called Lines, such that the Points and Lines satisfy all the axioms which we have imposed on the points and lines of euclidean geometry. In our example, the model is a result of the inversion of standard geometry at $O(1)$. This map is one-to-one, and preserves M-circles and perpendicularity. Then it is easy to check that the axioms hold.

The example of the circle geometry shows that the axiomatic approach gives geometry a life independent of the experimental and intuitive substratum of which it is an abstraction. We can even go one step further and give the name of geometry to any theory that studies the action of a group of transformations on a set. The general usage today restricts the name of geometry to theories that satisfy a number of regularity conditions. This properly is the subject of investigations into the foundations of geometry. We shall be interested in this chapter only in one special type of geometry distinct from the euclidean. That *hyperbolic geometry* presents itself naturally within the theory of circular transformations; it is important for its relations to euclidean geometry.

We have seen in secs. 8–4 and 8–5 that the inversion which defines our new model of euclidean geometry can also be used to give new theorems of euclidean geometry. This is its main importance since, as an abstract system, the new model is *isomorphic* to plane euclidean geometry. In a generalization of the language introduced in chapter 3, two structures are called *isomorphic* if there exists between them a one-to-one map which carries elements into elements and relations into relations. In our case, this means that geometries are isomorphic if between their planes there exists a one-to-one map which conserves the validity of the axioms. We have discussed before that our axioms are weak enough to allow for different non-isomorphic euclidean planes (e.g., those with or without trisectors for all angles). The relations between the different non-isomorphic euclidean geometries are properly studied in the foundations of geometry. In this chapter we are interested in finding a new system which is not isomorphic to any euclidean geometry.

From the group theoretical point of view, euclidean geometry is the study of those properties of sets in the plane which are invariant under the action of the group $\mathcal{S}$ of similitudes (or the group $\mathfrak{M}$ of motions). $\mathcal{S}$ as subgroup of the group of circular transformation is characterized as the biggest group, all of whose transformations leave the point ∞ fixed. The role of $\mathcal{S}$ in our circular model of euclidean geometry is played by the largest subgroup of $\mathcal{C}$, which leaves the point O fixed. This subgroup is $\sigma_{O(1)}\mathcal{S}\sigma_{O(1)}^{-1}$, and hence it is isomorphic to $\mathcal{S}$ by (3.8). The isomorphy of the circular model with euclidean geometry follows immediately from (3.19). We can hope to get an essentially different plane if we replace $\mathcal{S}$ by the group of all circular transformations which map a fixed M-circle A onto itself. If $G(A)$ is the group of all circular transformations which map A onto itself and B is any other circle, then there exists an inversion σ for which $B = \sigma A$ and, by (8.13), $G(B) = \sigma G(A)\sigma^{-1}$. The groups $G(A)$ and $G(B)$ are conjugate in $\mathcal{C}$; they are isomorphic. Therefore, the structure of the geometry will not depend on the choice of the M-circle A. We prefer to work with a fixed unit circle A. An isomorphic geometry would be obtained if A were chosen as a straight line, or as a circle of radius $\neq 1$. A will be called *the absolute* of the new geometry.

In the circular model of euclidean geometry, the point O had to be excluded from the "plane." In the same way, the fixed circle A must be excluded from the new geometry since its points cannot be transformed into points not on A by transformations of $G(A)$. If we want to obtain a theory resembling euclidean geometry, it is therefore reasonable that we restrict our attention to one of the two domains into which A divides the Gauss plane. We study the interior of A which we shall call the *hyperbolic plane*. The group that we are interested in is the group $\mathcal{Y}$ of all circular transformations which map A onto itself and the interior of A onto itself. $\mathcal{Y}$ is the *hyperbolic group*. The geometry obtained by the action of $\mathcal{Y}$ on the hyperbolic plane is *hyperbolic geometry*.

The lines in the euclidean plane are the sets of fixed points of reflections. Accordingly, it is reasonable to define as *hyperbolic lines* the intersection with the interior of A of the M-circles Γ whose inversions σ_Γ belong to $\mathcal{Y}$. By (8.5), $\sigma_\Gamma A = A$ if and only if $\Gamma \perp A$:

(9.1)   *A hyperbolic line is the intersection of an M-circle perpendicular to A with the interior of A.*

A *reflection in a hyperbolic line* is the inversion in the M-circle which carries the line. With these definitions, we shall now check the validity of our axioms for this new geometry. A hyperbolic entity will be denoted by the corresponding euclidean symbol with an upper index ^{H}. For example, $l^H(A,B)$ is the hyperbolic line defined by two points A and B.

axiom I^H.   *For any two distinct points A,B there exists a unique line $l^H(A,B)$ containing these points.*

By (8.5), $l^H(A,B) = \Gamma(A,\sigma_A A,B) \cap$ interior A. We shall allow ourselves the abuse of language to identify $l^H(A,B)$ and $\Gamma(A,\sigma_A A,B)$.

axiom II^H.   *All points in the plane but not on a line l^H form two non-null disjoint sets.*

The sets are the intersection respectively of the interior and the exterior of the circle which carries l^H and the interior of A.

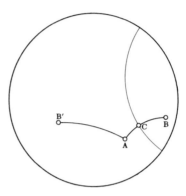

Fig. 9–2

A point C is *between* A and B if $C \in l^H(A,B)$ and if there exists a line g^H through C for which A and B are in distinct hyperbolic halfplanes (= sets defined by II^H). The segment $(A,B)^H$ is the set of all points between A and B.

axiom III^H.   *A and B are in different halfplanes of a line l^H if and only if $l^H \cap (A,B)^H \neq \emptyset$.*

This is an immediate consequence of axiom X*, which we have assumed.

axiom IV^H.   *If $B \in (A,C)^H$, then $C \notin (A,B)^H$.*

No hyperbolic line through C can intersect $l^H(A,B)$ at another point, by I^H.

axiom V^H.   *There exists a hyperbolic line.*

This again is proved by the proof of I^H.

axiom VI^H.   *For any line l^H there exists a map σ_{l^H} which maps the points of one halfplane of l^H onto the points of the other halfplane.*

σ_{l^H} is the inversion in the circle which carries the line l^H. By definition (8.4) this inversion exchanges interior and exterior of the circle, hence halfplanes in hyperbolic geometry.

axiom VII^H.   *σ_{l^H} maps all hyperbolic lines onto hyperbolic lines.*

This is a special case of (8.11).

axiom VIII^H.   *$\sigma_{l^H}^2 = \iota$.*

By definition, an inversion is an involution.

axiom IX^H.   *For all points $L \in l^H$, $\sigma_{l^H}L = L$.*

This is a reformulation of (8.6).

On the basis of these axioms we can define rays, angles, angle bisectors, and perpendicular bisectors as in the euclidean case. Also, by (8.5), $\sigma_{l^H}g^H = g^H$ if and only if $l^H \perp g^H$:

(9.2)   *Two hyperbolic lines are perpendicular if and only if their circles are perpendicular in the euclidean sense.*

axiom X^H.   *For any angle, there exists an angle bisector.*

Fɪɢ. 9–3

If Γ' and Γ'' intersect at A, the unique hyperbolic line which by inversion maps a ray on Γ' onto one of Γ'' is the circle in the pencil through A and $\sigma_A A$ which is tangent to the angle bisector of the tangents to Γ' and Γ'' at A for the corresponding rays.

axiom XI^H.   *For any pair of points there exists a perpendicular bisector.*

The perpendicular bisector of A and B is a circle Γ perpendicular to the pencil defined by Λ and $l^H(A,B)$. By definition, $\sigma_\Gamma A = B$ and, by perpendicularity,

$$\sigma_\Gamma \sigma_\Lambda A = \sigma_\Lambda \sigma_\Gamma A = \sigma_\Lambda B.$$

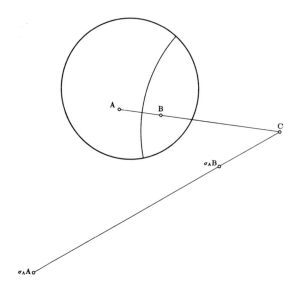

FIG. 9–4

Therefore, the center of Γ is uniquely determined as

$$C = l(A,B) \cap l(\sigma_\Lambda A, \sigma_\Lambda B).$$

axiom XII^H. *If a finite product of reflections*

$$\Sigma = \sigma_{l_k^H} \sigma_{l_{k-1}^H} \cdots \sigma_{l_2^H} \sigma_{l_1^H}$$

maps some ray a_1^H onto itself, then either $\Sigma = \sigma_{a^H}$ or $\Sigma = \iota$.

This statement will follow as a theorem from the discussion of products of hyperbolic reflections in the next section.

The main difference between euclidean and hyperbolic geometry is contained in axiom XIII, since axioms I to XII are valid in both geometries. A theorem which can be proved from axioms I to XII alone is valid in both geometries; such a theorem is called *absolute*, i.e., not relative to one of the two specific geometries in question.

We show that the euclidean axiom XIII is not true in hyperbolic geometry by a study of the common perpendiculars of two non-intersecting hyperbolic lines. The euclidean axiom implies that through a point P not on a line g

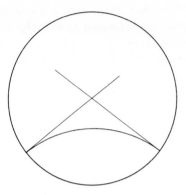

FIG. 9–5

there exists only the parallel $p[p(g,P),P]$ to g. In hyperbolic geometry there exist two hyperbolic lines through $P \in g^H$ which touch g^H on A. Since the points of the absolute are not points of our plane, these two lines are parallel to g^H. In addition, all the hyperbolic lines through P which together with g^H form a pencil of disjoint circles naturally are parallel to g^H.

(9.3) *In hyperbolic geometry, through a point not on a hyperbolic line there are an infinity of hyperbolic lines parallel to the given one.*

All the lines which intersect the absolute A at a point X form a pencil of mutually tangent circles. Such a maximal pencil of circles defined by a point of A is called an *end*. Alternatively, the point X itself is called the end. This ambiguity is permissible since the pencil and the point define one another uniquely. A line belongs to two ends. (This explains the name *hyperbolic* line and *hyperbolic* geometry from the image of the two asymptotes of a hyperbola.) Conversely, two ends X and Y uniquely define a line, namely, the circle whose center is the intersection of the tangents to A at X and Y.

The pencil of circles perpendicular to the end X is composed of the circles tangent to A at X. None of these circles is a hyperbolic line. On the other hand, if two parallel hyperbolic lines do not have an end in common, the pencil of perpendicular circles is a pencil of circles through two points of A. This pencil contains a unique perpendicular to A, i.e., a unique hyperbolic line. The hyperbolic axiom which replaces the parallel axiom therefore reads:

axiom XIII^H. *If two parallel hyperbolic lines have an end in common, they do not have a common perpendicular. If they do not have an end in common, they have a unique common perpendicular.*

It is now possible to check that all the statements of chapter I still hold with the exception of the existence statement (1.41). The existence of the circumcenter is not guaranteed in hyperbolic geometry (Fig. 9–6). But by the methods of the next section, we are still able to prove that the perpendicular bisectors

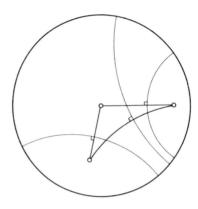

FIG. 9–6

of a triangle are in a pencil, and this was the main inference from concurrence also in euclidean geometry. Most deviations of hyperbolic geometry from the euclidean, as far as reflections are concerned, come from the fact that in hyperbolic geometry we have three types of pencils instead of two as in euclidean geometry.

Exercise 9–1

1. What are the hyperbolic lines if the absolute A is taken to be a line?

2. Find a map which transforms the hyperbolic geometry in a circle into hyperbolic geometry in a halfplane.

3. Prove theorem (1.22) for hyperbolic geometry: (a) by constructing the perpendicular in the model, (b) by proving its existence directly from axioms I^H to XIII^H.

4. Formulate and prove the congruence theorems in hyperbolic geometry. What is the definition of $\cong^H$?

5. Formulate and prove the statement corresponding to (1.40) in hyperbolic geometry.

6. Prove that two distinct perpendiculars to one hyperbolic line are parallel and do not belong to the same end.

7. Prove: for every end there exists a unique perpendicular to a given line which does not belong to the end.

2. Products of Reflections

As a special case of theorem (8.17) we obtain the three-reflections theorem in hyperbolic geometry. A set of hyperbolic lines forms a pencil if and only if the circles form a pencil in the sense of the group of circular transformations. (8.17) then gives

(9.4)   *The product of three reflections in hyperbolic lines is a reflection if and only if the three lines are in a pencil.*

The product of two reflections at intersecting lines is a *rotation*. Since a hyperbolic line through a point P of the plane also always contains the point $\sigma_A P$, the hyperbolic rotation of angle α about the point P is defined as

$$\rho_{P,\alpha}^{H} = \rho_{P,\sigma_A P;\alpha}.$$

By theorem (8.16), the group $\Re_P^H$ of hyperbolic rotations about P is isomorphic [in the inversion $\sigma_{\sigma_A P(1)}$] to a group $\Re_P$ of euclidean rotations about a point.

(9.5)   *The groups of oriented angles in euclidean and hyperbolic geometry are isomorphic.*

Therefore, we can measure angles in hyperbolic geometry by the corresponding angles in euclidean geometry.

Circles can be defined, just as in euclidean geometry, as the set of the images of a point Q under all the transformations of a group $\Re_P^H$. Any rotation about P transforms into themselves the M-circles of the pencil perpendicular to the circles through P and $\sigma_A P$. These circles, then, are the hyperbolic circles of center P if they belong to the hyperbolic plane. Since A belongs to the perpendicular pencil, a hyperbolic circle is completely in the hyperbolic plane if one of its points is in the plane.

(9.6)   *The hyperbolic circles of center P are the euclidean circles, in the hyperbolic plane, of the pencil perpendicular to the hyperbolic lines through P.*

As a consequence, euclidean and hyperbolic centers of such a circle do not coincide except at the center of A.

If the rotation is defined by reflections in perpendicular lines, we obtain the reflection in the point P,

$$\sigma_P^H = \sigma_{P,\sigma_A P}.$$

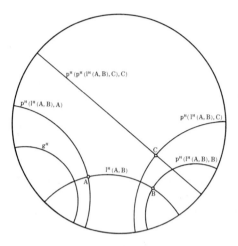

Fig. 9–7

It is still true that this is an involution [by (8.19)], but, in contrast to the euclidean case, the product of three reflections at non-collinear points is *never* a point reflection. In fact, such a product can be written as

$\sigma_C^H \sigma_B^H \sigma_A^H$

$$= \sigma_{p^H(p^H(l^H(A,B),C),C)} \sigma_{p^H(l^H(A,B),C)} \sigma_{p^H(l^H(A,B),B)} \sigma_{l^H(A,B)} \sigma_{l^H(A,B)} \sigma_{p^H(l^H(A,B),A)}.$$

By the three-reflections theorem there exists a line g^H such that

$$\sigma_{g^H} = \sigma_{p^H(l^H(A,B),C)} \sigma_{p^H(l(A,B),B)} \sigma_{p^H(l^H(A,B),A)}$$

and

$$\sigma_C^H \sigma_B^H \sigma_A^H = \sigma_{p^H(p^H(l^H(A,B),C),C)} \sigma_{g^H}.$$

$p^H[l^H(A,B),C]$ is the unique perpendicular common to $l^H(A,B)$ and $p^H\{p^H[l^H(A,B),C],C\}$. If $A \neq B$, this is distinct from g^H. Hence the product of the three point reflections is the product of reflections at two non-perpendicular hyperbolic lines; it is not a point reflection.

The product of two reflections at parallel lines which do not have an end in common is a *translation*. By XIII^H, a translation can always be written as the product of two point reflections. The two points of reflection are still not uniquely determined, but they must be on the unique perpendicular to the lines defining the translation. As a consequence, the translations belonging to collinear pairs of points (vectors) still form an abelian group. In general, however, the product of two translations need not be a translation, and it is not commutative.

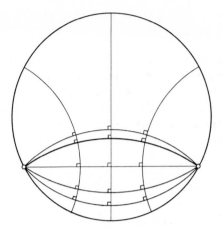

FIG. 9-8

The unique perpendicular g^H to the lines defining the translation inter-sects Λ in two points. All circles of the pencil of M-circles through these two points are mapped into themselves by the translation. Any two segments, de-fined on the perpendiculars to g^H by points of one fixed circle of the pencil and the intersection of the perpendicular with g^H, are mapped into one another by some translation whose vector is on g^H. Therefore, all these segments are congruent in hyperbolic geometry. In the pencil, no M-circle other than g^H is a hyperbolic line.

(9.7)   *The curves of constant distance from a hyperbolic line are the M-circle of the pencil defined by the ends of the line; they are not lines.*

The product of two reflections at parallel lines which belong to the same end is a *horocyclic movement*. A horocyclic movement which belongs to a certain end transforms into themselves all circles of the pencil of M-circles perpendicular to the hyperbolic lines of the end. These circles are called *horocycles* (i.e., limit circles). The curves of constant distance from a horo-cycle are the horocycles of its pencil.

The product of three reflections in hyperbolic lines not in one pencil is a *glide reflection*. The proof of (2.44) applies here also to show that a glide reflection can be represented either as a product of a point reflection and a line reflection, or as the product of a translation and a line reflection at the common perpendicular to the lines defining the translation. Hence it follows here also that the square of a glide reflection is a translation.

According to (8.23), there exist products of four inversions which are not reducible to products of a smaller number of inversions. However, this is not the case for hyperbolic reflections.

(9.8)   *A hyperbolic motion is the product of at most three reflections in hyperbolic lines.*

Every maximal pencil of hyperbolic lines contains a line through a fixed point (for instance, the center of A). As in the proof of (8.23), we consider successive pencils defined by two reflections in a given product. Then every product of four reflections is equal to the product of three reflections in concurrent lines and one additional reflection. Hence, by the three reflections theorem, it is equal to the product of two reflections. This proves (9.8).

    To sum up:

(9.9)   *A hyperbolic motion is one of the following:*
    (a) *line reflection*
    (b) *rotation* (*including point reflection*)
    (c) *translation*
    (d) *horocyclic movement*
    (e) *glide reflection.*
    Each of these operations is the product of at most two involutions.

A check on this list now proves axiom XII^H since only line reflections and rotations have a fixed point, and only line reflections have a fixed ray.

Exercise 9–2

1. Prove: if two hyperbolic lines are parallel without a common end, there exists a unique point $M(a,b)$ such that

$$b = \sigma^H_{M(a,b)}\, a.$$

2. Prove: a transversal intersects two lines a and b under equal angles if and only if the two lines are parallel without a common end and the transversal contains $M(a,b)$ (problem 1).

3. Prove that the product of three point reflections cannot be horocyclic.

4. Prove: the reflections at perpendiculars to a given line map into themselves all curves of constant distance to that line.

5. What are the orthogonal trajectories of the pencil of perpendiculars to a given line?

6. A triangle always has an incircle. Show that it may have 0, 1, 2, or 3 excircles.

7. Prove that the perpendicular bisectors of a triangle are in a pencil.

8. Prove that the altitudes of a triangle are in a pencil.

9. Prove that the angle bisectors of a triangle are in a pencil.

10. Prove that in an acute triangle, the altitudes are the angle bisectors of the pedal triangle.

11. Prove theorem (4.5) in hyperbolic geometry.

12. (a) Prove that (4.11) holds in hyperbolic geometry if the common perpendicular to $l(A,C)$ and $l(B,D)$ passes through the center of the given circle.

(b) Prove the main theorem of sec. 4–2 for hyperbolic geometry.

13. Prove that all horocycles are congruent.

14. Find all line reflections which map a horocycle onto itself.

15. Let Σ be any hyperbolic movement. For any segment s of a hyperbolic line, prove that the points $M^H(X,\Sigma X)$, $X \in s$, either coincide or they form a segment. [In the latter case, the hyperbolic line which carries the segment is *Hjelmslev's midline* $h(s,\Sigma s)$.]

16. Prove the statement of problem 15 for euclidean geometry.

17. Prove: if a^H and Σa^H are hyperbolic lines without a common end, and if Σ' is another hyperbolic movement distinct from Σ, which maps a^H onto Σa^H, then $h(a^H, \Sigma a^H) \neq h(a^H, \Sigma' a^H)$ (see problem 15).

18. Let g^H be a hyperbolic line, and Σ a hyperbolic movement such that g^H and Σg^H are parallel without a common end. Prove that $h(g^H,\Sigma g^H)$ is (for $g = g^H$)

$$l\{M^H[M(g,\Sigma g)^g,\Sigma^{-1}M(g,\Sigma g)^{\Sigma g}],M^H[\Sigma M(g,\Sigma g)^g,M(g,\Sigma g)^{\Sigma g}]\}.$$

For definitions, see problems 15 and 1.

19. Prove: if the hyperbolic lines a_1, a_2, a_3 are in a pencil, and if $(a_1,a_2) = (b_2,b_1)$, $(a_1,a_3) = (b_3,b_1)$, then also $(a_2,a_3) = (b_2,b_3)$, and all six hyperbolic lines are in a pencil.

20. Prove the existence of the isogonal conjugate relative to a triangle in hyperbolic geometry.

21. If a_i ($i = 1,2,3$) are three lines in a pencil, and B is a point distinct from the vertex of the pencil (if any), prove that the three points $B^{l^H(B^{a_i},B^{a_j})}$ are collinear.

22. What is the statement corresponding to problem 21 in euclidean geometry?

23. If four lines a_i are given in a pencil, we denote by f_{ijk} the line defined in problem 21 for the three lines a_i,a_j,a_k. Prove that the four points B^{ijk} are collinear.

24. For given A,B, and c^H prove that the product $\sigma_A^H \sigma_{c^H} \sigma_B^H$ is a line reflection if and only if $c^H \perp l^H(A,B)$.

25. Prove: if α_i and β_i ($i = 1,2,3$) are distinct elements of the hyperbolic group, and eight of the products $\alpha_i\beta_j$ are hyperbolic line reflections, then also the ninth product is a line reflection, and all nine lines are in a pencil.

26. Prove both in euclidean and in hyperbolic geometry: if a,b,c,d are four lines not in a pencil, and

$$(d,a') = (a'',a) \quad (a,b') = (b'',b) \quad (b,c') = (c'',c) \quad (c,d') = (d'',d)$$
$$(a',b') = (d',c'),$$

then $(a'',b'') = (d'',c'')$.

27. Prove: if three lines have mutually an end in common, then the perpendiculars from a point of one line onto the two others are mutually perpendicular.

28. a,b,c,d,e,f are hyperbolic lines such that

$$a \perp c,d \qquad c \neq d \qquad b \perp f$$

c,e,b in a pencil; d,e,f in a pencil. Prove: if a and b have an end in common, then the line g defined by $\sigma_g = \sigma_d\sigma_e\sigma_f$ is in that end.

29. If a and b are distinct hyperbolic lines and $P \in b$, choose a point $O \in p^H[p^H(a,P),P]$. Prove that a and b belong to one end if and only if $p^H[p^H(a,P),P] \perp l^H(O^a,O^b)$.

3. Area and Length

Any two points of the hyperbolic plane can be mapped onto one another by a hyperbolic reflection. Therefore, every hyperbolic triangle is congruent

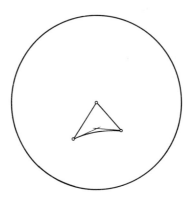

FIG. 9–9

to a triangle of which one vertex is at the euclidean center of A. In this case, two sides of the triangle become euclidean straight lines, the third side being formed by an arc of circle convex towards the center of A:

(9.10)   *The sum of the angles of a hyperbolic triangle is less than 180°.*

For the remainder of this section, we assume that the field of the geometry is that of the real numbers. In that case, we can measure the angles by the arc length of the unit circle which belongs to a given center angle. The full angle is measured by the length 2π of the circle. What we really give in this way is a homomorphism

$$\phi : \mathbf{R} \rightarrow \Re$$

of the real numbers $\mathbf{R}$ onto the oriented angles $\Re$. Two real numbers, r and r', describe the same oriented angle if and only if r and r' differ by an integer multiple of 2π:

$$\phi(r) = \phi(r') \qquad \text{if and only if } r = r' \pm k \cdot 2\pi.$$

For us the main point is that, in this setting, we may add positive angles and be sure that the result will be a positive number and not the zero.

An area function for convex polygons will be defined by the conditions A1 to A3 of sec. 5–1. Condition A4 becomes meaningless since there are no rectangles in hyperbolic geometry. In fact, by (9.10), the angle sum of any convex quadrilateral is less than 360°. The proof of (5.11) shows that two area functions coincide for all convex polygons if they coincide for all triangles. It can be shown that in any geometry *over an archimedean field* the conditions A1 to A3 define the area function up to a constant. Therefore, we will have found *the* area function if we can find *an* area function.

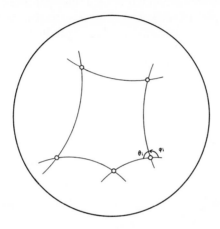

FIG. 9–10

For a convex polygon P_n we denote the positively oriented interior angles by θ_i and the exterior angles by $\phi_i = \pi - \theta_i$, $i = 1, 2, \ldots, n$. An easy check of the conditions A1 to A3 shows the following.

(9.11)   *The area function of convex polygons is*

$$\alpha^H(P_n) = \sum_{i=1}^{n} \phi_i - 2\pi = (n - 2)\pi - \sum_{i=1}^{n} \theta_i.$$

In the euclidean case, the definition would violate condition A1. Since the area is measured by angles, there is no hyperbolic equivalent of euclidean homotheties:

(9.12)   *If a map of the real hyperbolic plane onto itself preserves angles and hyperbolic lines, it preserves hyperbolic area.*

In the normalization of the area function implicit in (9.11) the area of a convex n-gon is $< (n - 2)\pi$. The area of a triangle is $< \pi$:

(9.13)   *The area of a convex n-gon in the real hyperbolic plane is, in general, greater than that of any triangle.*

There exists no triangle of area π. However, the figure bounded by three lines belonging pairwise to three ends (an *asymptotic* triangle) can be considered as a triangle whose interior angles are zero; it has area π.

We can now discuss the existence of crystallographic groups in the plane. By varying the area, it is possible to find polygons all of whose angles are either zero or an integer part of π. By indefinite reflection about the sides, the images of these polygons will cover the hyperbolic plane, and the polygon itself will be a fundamental domain in the lattice generated by the reflections. Therefore, there exist infinitely many non-isomorphic lattice groups in the hyperbolic plane. The classification of their crystallographic subgroups seems to be difficult.

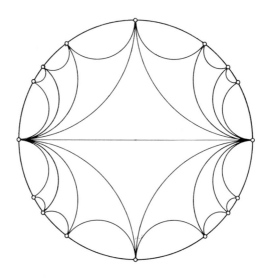

FIG. 9–11

As an example of the beautiful figures generated by the reflections, we give pictures of some triangles in the lattice generated by an asymptotic triangle. This is a lattice which does not contain points, only ends. Figure 9–12 shows some triangles of the lattice generated by a triangle of angles $\pi/2$, $\pi/4$, $\pi/8$. In both cases, the full lattice contains an infinity of triangles in the neighborhood of any point on the absolute.

Next we turn to the measure of lengths. The length $\lambda(A,B)$ is a real-valued function defined on the segments which must satisfy at least three conditions:

L1. $AB \cong^H CD$ implies $\lambda(A,B) = \lambda(C,D)$.
L2. $A \neq B$ implies $\lambda(A,B) > 0$.
L3.   If B is between A and C, then $\lambda(A,C) = \lambda(A,B) + \lambda(B,C)$.

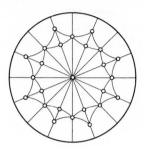

Fig. 9–12

Let M_1 and M_2 be the ends of $l^H(A,B)$ such that M_1,A,B,M_2 follow one an-other on the circle. We define the *cross ratio* of the four points in terms of the euclidean length:

$$(AB,M_2M_1) = \frac{AM_2}{AM_1}\frac{BM_1}{BM_2}.$$

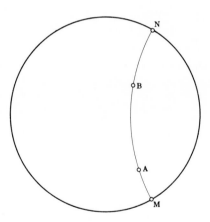

Fig. 9–13

A hyperbolic reflection is an inversion $\sigma_{O(r)}$ which transforms A into itself (or a reflection at a diameter of A). If the reflection maps A and B onto A^* and B^*, it also maps the ends onto the corresponding ends M_1^* and M_2^*. By (8.30),

$$(A^*B^*,M_2^*M_1^*) = \frac{r^2\dfrac{AM_2}{OA \cdot OM_2} \, r^2\dfrac{BM_1}{OB \cdot OM_1}}{r^2\dfrac{AM_1}{OA \cdot OM_1} \, r^2\dfrac{BM_2}{OB \cdot OB_2}} = (AB,M_2M_1).$$

The same result is trivially true for the reflections in a diameter. By the choice of our notations, $(AB,M_2M_1) > 1$. Also, if B is between A and C, then

$$(AC,M_2M_1) = (AB,M_2M_1)(BC,M_2M_1).$$

Since the cross ratio is not changed in a hyperbolic reflection, it is not changed in any hyperbolic congruence. It is then easy to check that

(9.14) $\lambda(A,B) = \frac{1}{2}\log(AB,M_2M_1)$ *is a length function in the real hyperbolic plane.*

Again, it may be shown that in any archimedean plane the conditions L1 to L3 define the length up to a constant multiple. Therefore, the measure given by (9.14) is the only possible measure of hyperbolic length up to a multiplicative constant. The value $\frac{1}{2}$ of the constant leads to the simplest formulae in trigonometry.

Exercise 9–3

1. What is ker ϕ in $\Re = R/\text{ker }\phi$ (exercise 3–2, problems 4 and 5)?
2. Prove a congruence theorem (*aaa*) in hyperbolic geometry.
3. Generalize the definition of area to polygons with an interior.
4. Let A be the center of Λ. Prove that

$$\lambda(A,B) = \tfrac{1}{2}\log\frac{1 + AB}{1 - AB}.$$

If the logarithm is taken to the base e (natural logarithm), prove that

$$AB = \tanh \lambda(A,B).$$

5. The *parallel angle* $\pi(\lambda)$ of the hyperbolic distance λ is the angle at a point at distance λ from a line g^H between the perpendicular to g^H and a line through the point which has one end in common with g^H. Prove that

$$\tan \tfrac{1}{2}\pi(\lambda) = e^{-\lambda}$$

$$\tan \pi(\lambda) = \frac{1}{\sinh \lambda}.$$

6. Prove: if the lengths of the legs of a right triangle are a^H and b^H and the length of the hypotenuse is c^H, then

$$\cosh c^H = \cosh a^H \cdot \cosh b^H$$
$$\tanh b^H = \tanh c^H \cdot \cos \alpha.$$

7. From the formulae of problem 6 derive for an arbitrary triangle

$$\cosh a^H = \cosh b^H \cosh c^H - \sinh b^H \sinh c^H \cos \hat{A}.$$

8. (a) Prove that a circle of hyperbolic radius r^H admits a circumscribed regular n-gon only if $r^H < \ln \cot \pi/2n$. (Use conventions of 4, center of the circle at A.)

(b) For a right triangle we also have

$$\tanh b^H = \sinh a^H \cdot \tan \hat{B}.$$

Use this formula to compute the perimeter of the regular n-gon circumscribing a circle of radius r^H, as

$$L = 2n \tanh \frac{\pi}{n} \sinh r^H \left(\frac{L/2n}{\tanh L/2n} \right).$$

(c) For $n \to \infty$ we obtain the perimeter of the circle as $L = 2\pi \sinh r^H/2$.

(d) Compute the perimeter for a circle of radius 1 and a circle of radius 10.

9. Show that a hyperbolic line has infinite length.

10. Show that, for very small lengths, the cosine formula of problem 6 is approximated by the formula of the pythagorean theorem.

4. The Field of Ends

The developments of the preceding section may have shown that computations based on the notions of length and area are not adequate for hyperbolic geometry. The definition of area is possible only if the group of oriented angles is representable as a factor group of the additive group of lengths and the definition of length needs the transcendental logarithmic function. Neither length nor area can be defined in that way, in general, on the fields which we have considered as a basis for our euclidean geometry. In this section we give an alternative approach to an analytic geometry for hyperbolic geometry on a general plane. It is based on the introduction of a new field which gives coordinates on the absolute Λ. If hyperbolic geometry is developed, not from a subgroup of the group of circular transformations, but in an abstract way from axioms I^H to XIII^H, the same coordinates can be introduced on the pencils which are ends.

On Λ we choose three distinct ends O,E,U (Fig. 9–14). For any end A distinct from U there exists a unique hyperbolic line a in the pencil of U such that $\sigma_a O = A$. (In the following we shall dispense with the symbol ^{H} if no ambiguity can result.) If $A \neq O,U$, there either exists a unique line a^* in the pencil of perpendiculars to $o = l^H(O,U)$ or a unique point $a^* \in o$ such that $\sigma_{a^*} E = A$. In the second case, σ_{a^*} is the product of σ_o and a reflection in a line in the pencil of perpendiculars to o. By e^* we denote the line $p^H(o,E)$. On the set of ends distinct from U, we define an order by

$$
\begin{array}{ll}
A > O & \text{if } a^* \text{ is a line} \\
A < O & \text{if } a^* \text{ is a point,}
\end{array}
$$

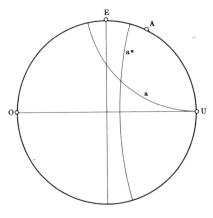

FIG. 9–14

as well as addition and multiplication by

$$\sigma_a O + \sigma_b O = \sigma_b \sigma_o \sigma_a O \qquad a,b \in U$$
$$\sigma_{a*} E \cdot \sigma_{b*} E = \sigma_{b*} \sigma_{e*} \sigma_{a*} E \qquad \sigma_{a*}^2 = \sigma_{b*}^2 = \iota$$
$$\sigma_{a*} O = \sigma_{b*} O = U$$

and

$$O \cdot X = X \cdot O = O \qquad X \neq U.$$

Then we can prove

(9.15)   *Our definitions turn the set of ends distinct from U into an ordered field of zero O and unit E.*

Addition is well defined. The associative law holds since it holds for arbitrary products of inversions. $O = \sigma_o O$ is the identity element. The inverse of $A = \sigma_a O$ is

$$-A = \sigma_{\sigma_o a} O = \sigma_o A.$$

$A > O$ means that A is in the halfplane of E for o. It follows that $A > O$ then implies $-A < O$.

Since b,o,a are in the pencil of U, it follows from (2.5) that

$$A + B = \sigma_b \sigma_o \sigma_a O = \sigma_a \sigma_o \sigma_b O = B + A.$$

Addition defines an abelian group on the ends $\neq U$.

In the same way, multiplication is well defined. The associative law holds for nonzero elements since it holds for arbitrary products of inversions. It also holds for multiplication by zero. $E = \sigma_{e*}E$ is the unit element. The inverse of $A = \sigma_{a*}E$ is

$$A^{-1} = \sigma_{\sigma_{e}*a}E = \sigma_{e}*A.$$

Either a^* and b^* are in a pencil with e^*, or one or both are points on o. In all cases

$$\sigma_{b}*\sigma_{e}*\sigma_{a}* = \sigma_{a}*\sigma_{e}*\sigma_{b}*,$$

hence

$$A \cdot B = B \cdot A.$$

Multiplication defines an abelian group on the set of ends $\neq O, U$.

For the proof of the distributive law, we note that for all hyperbolic lines perpendicular to o and all points on o, we have $\sigma_{c}*O = U$. Therefore, the product of $A = \sigma_{a}O$ and $C = \sigma_{c}*E$ can be written

$$A \cdot C = \sigma_{c}*\sigma_{e}*A = \sigma_{c}*\sigma_{e}*\sigma_{a}O = \sigma_{c}*\sigma_{e}*\sigma_{a}\sigma_{e}*\sigma_{c}*O.$$

The distributive law follows:

$$
\begin{aligned}
(A + B) \cdot C &= (\sigma_{a}O + \sigma_{b}O) \cdot \sigma_{c}*E \\
&= \sigma_{c}*\sigma_{e}*\sigma_{b}\sigma_{o}\sigma_{a}\sigma_{e}*\sigma_{c}*O \\
&= \sigma_{c}*\sigma_{e}*\sigma_{b}\sigma_{e}*\sigma_{c}*\sigma_{c}*\sigma_{e}*\sigma_{o}\sigma_{a}\sigma_{e}*\sigma_{c}*O \\
&= \sigma_{c}*\sigma_{e}*\sigma_{b}\sigma_{e}*\sigma_{c}*\sigma_{o}\sigma_{c}*\sigma_{e}*\sigma_{a}\sigma_{e}*\sigma_{c}*O \\
&= A \cdot C + B \cdot C.
\end{aligned}
$$

For multiplication by zero the distributive law also holds. If A and B both are in the halfplane of E, so is $A \cdot B$, i.e.,

$$A > O \text{ and } B > O \text{ imply } A \cdot B > O.$$

This completes the proof of (9.15).

Next we prove that our construction has a geometric meaning.

(9.16)   *The fields of ends obtained for two different choices of O,E,U are isomorphic.*

This is an immediate consequence of:

(9.17)   *There exists a unique hyperbolic movement which maps a triple O,E,U of distinct ends onto another such triple.*

Let O', E', U' be the second triple. There exists a hyperbolic reflection which maps $l^H(O,U)$ onto $l^H(O',U')$. This may be followed, eventually, by a reflection in a perpendicular to the latter line to insure that O is mapped onto O' and U onto U'. The image of E can then be mapped onto a given E' either by a translation which leaves $l^H(O',U')$ invariant, or by a translation followed by a reflection in that line. On the other hand, one checks on the list of theorem (9.9) that only the identity leaves three distinct ends fixed. Hence the map is unique.

The proof of (9.16) follows. If Σ maps O,E,U onto O',E',U', respectively, then $o' = \Sigma o$, $e'^* = \Sigma e^*$, and for the operations $+'$ and $\cdot'$ of the field defined by the second triple we have, by (1.15),

$$\Sigma(A + B) = \Sigma A +' \Sigma B \qquad \Sigma A \cdot B = \Sigma A \cdot' \Sigma B.$$

Since Σ is one-to-one, the two fields are isomorphic.

Theorem (9.17) also shows that a hyperbolic motion is uniquely determined by its action on the set of ends:

(9.18)   *The hyperbolic group is isomorphic to the group of transformations of the field of ends by hyperbolic motions.*

The advantage of the field of ends is in the very simple formula we obtain for the action of hyperbolic motions.

(9.19)   *The transformations of the field of ends by hyperbolic motions are the fractional linear maps*

$$f(X) = \frac{AX + B}{CX + D} \qquad AD - BC \neq O,$$

where A,B,C,D are constant elements of the field of ends.

First we prove that the fractional linear maps form a group. The composition of $f(X)$ and another map

$$g(X) = \frac{A'X + B'}{C'X + D'} \qquad A'D' - B'C' \neq O$$

is

$$gf(X) = \frac{(A'A + B'C)X + (A'B + B'D)}{(C'A + D'C)X + (C'B + D'D)}.$$

If we represent $f(X)$ by the matrix of its coefficients

$$\begin{pmatrix} A & B \\ C & D \end{pmatrix},$$

then the composition law is the so-called matrix product

(9.20) $$\begin{pmatrix} A' & B' \\ C' & D' \end{pmatrix} \begin{pmatrix} A & B \\ C & D \end{pmatrix} = \begin{pmatrix} A'A + B'C & A'B + B'D \\ C'A + D'C & C'B + D'D \end{pmatrix}.$$

The matrix product is studied in detail in all texts on linear algebra. One of its main properties is that the determinant of the product is the product of the determinants of its factors. Hence the determinant of $gf(X)$ is not zero; the product of two fractional linear maps is a fractional linear map. The correspondence between the transformations and the matrices is one-to-many since all matrices

$$\begin{pmatrix} MA & MB \\ MC & MD \end{pmatrix} \quad M \neq O$$

define the same map $f(X)$. The associative law holds since we are dealing with transformations. The identity map is given by

$$\begin{pmatrix} E & O \\ O & E \end{pmatrix} \quad E^2 - O^2 = E \neq O$$

and its multiples. The inverse of $f(X)$ belongs to the matrix

$$\begin{pmatrix} D & -B \\ -C & A \end{pmatrix} \quad DA - (-B)(-C) \neq O.$$

Therefore, the set of fractional linear maps forms a group.

In order to prove theorem (9.19) we show that the group of fractional linear transformations has the same structure as the group of hyperbolic motions and that it is generated by the action of reflections.

The square of a transformation $f(X)$ has the matrix

$$\begin{pmatrix} A^2 + BC & AB + BD \\ CA + DC & CB + D^2 \end{pmatrix}.$$

$f(X)$ is an involution if its square is the identity, i.e., if

$$A^2 + BC = D^2 + BC \neq O$$
$$(A + D)B = (A + D)C = O.$$

(9.21)   *A fractional linear transformation is an involution if and only if $A + D = O$ unless it is the identity.*

A hyperbolic motion is the product of at most two involutions.

(9.22)   *A fractional linear map is the product of at most two involutions.*

We show: for given f there exists an involution g of matrix

$$\begin{pmatrix} X & Y \\ Z & -X \end{pmatrix} \quad X^2 + YZ \neq O,$$

such that $h = fg$ is an involution. Then $f = hg^{-1}$ is the prcduct of two involutions. For h, the condition (9.21) is

$$(A - D)X + BZ + CY = O.$$

Since we may choose arbitrarily at least two of the elements X, Y, Z, it is possible to obtain g with a nonzero determinant. The verification of this fact is left as an exercise.

Now we come to the proof of (9.19) proper. If a is a hyperbolic line in the pencil of U, then by the definition of addition

$$\sigma_a X = -X + \sigma_a O = \frac{-E \cdot X + \sigma_a O}{O \cdot X + E}.$$

If a^* is either a line $\perp o$ or a point $\in o$, then

$$\sigma_{a*} X = X^{-1} \cdot \sigma_{a*} E = \frac{O \cdot X + \sigma_{a*} E}{E \cdot X + O}.$$

If σ is any other involution of the hyperbolic group, put $A = \sigma U, A = \sigma_a O$, where a is in the pencil of U. Then

$$\sigma_a \sigma \sigma_a O = U.$$

This means that $\sigma_a \sigma \sigma_a$ is an involution which acts like a σ_{a*}. By (9.18), it is identical to σ_{a*}, and

$$\sigma = \sigma_{\sigma_a a*}.$$

We have seen that an involution with $C = O$ is an addition, i.e., the image of a transformation σ_a. If $C \neq O$, we may assume that the matrix of any involutory fractional linear map is

$$\begin{pmatrix} A & B \\ E & -A \end{pmatrix}.$$

It is easily checked that

$$\begin{pmatrix} A & B \\ E & -A \end{pmatrix} = \begin{pmatrix} -E & A \\ O & E \end{pmatrix} \begin{pmatrix} O & -(A^2 + B) \\ -E & O \end{pmatrix} \begin{pmatrix} -E & A \\ O & E \end{pmatrix}.$$

If, therefore, we define a and a^* by

$$A = \sigma_a O \qquad -(A^2 + B) = \sigma_{a*} E,$$

it follows that the given involution is the action on the absolute of

$$\sigma = \sigma_{\sigma_a a*}.$$

This completes the proof of (9.19).

The determinant of the linear fractional map which represents addition is negative. The determinant of the map which represents multiplication is negative for $a*$ a line, positive for $a*$ a point. By the multiplication law of determinants, this gives

(9.23)   *An involutory linear fractional map is a hyperbolic point reflection if its determinant is $> O$, line reflection if its determinant is $< O$.*

A point in the hyperbolic plane uniquely defines its reflection and, therefore, the set of matrices

$$\begin{pmatrix} MX & MY \\ MZ & -MX \end{pmatrix} \quad M \neq O \quad X^2 + YZ < O$$

of its linear fractional map. The ordered triples $(X:Y:Z)$, therefore, can serve as *homogeneous coordinates* of points in the plane. This means that two triples define the same point if their members are proportional, and that there exists a unique point for each triple, subject to $X^2 + YZ < O$.

A straight line is defined by its two end points A and B. The ordered pairs (A,B), $(A \neq B)$ can serve as coordinates of the line. A point is on a line if reflection at the point maps the ends of the line onto one another. This means

$$B = \frac{XA + Y}{ZA - X}$$

or

(9.24)   *A point $(X:Y:Z)$, $X^2 + YX < O$, is on a line (A,B) if and only if $ABZ - (A + B)X - Y = O$.*

From here it is possible to develop the analytic geometry of the hyperbolic plane.

We give a last example to show how different the algebra of hyperbolic geometry is from euclidean geometry. If $A = \sigma_{a*}E > O$, $a*$ is a line, and by axiom XI^H there exists the midline $w* \ [= m^H(a* \cap o, e* \cap o)]$ of $e*$ and $a*$. For $W = \sigma_{w*}E$ we obtain

$$W \cdot W = \sigma_{w*}\sigma_{e*}\sigma_{w*}E = \sigma_{\sigma_{w}*e*}E = \sigma_{a*}E = A.$$

(9.25)   *In hyperbolic geometry, the existence of the perpendicular bisector implies the existence of a square root for all positive elements in the field of ends.*

It is possible to define a field of ends directly from the axioms, without using a model in the euclidean plane. Then one can also show that, in hyperbolic geometry, axiom XI^H implies an axiom $X*^H$ (hence X^H). Like theorem (9.23) this shows that, in hyperbolic geometry, points and lines have properties which are largely parallel.

A measure of length and angle based on the field of ends is given in the exercises.

Exercise 9–4

1. Draw the constructions for $A + B$ and $A \cdot B$.

2. $GL(2,F)$ is the group of 2 by 2 matrices of non-vanishing determinant whose coefficients are in the field F. Let F^* be the multiplicative group of the field. Show that the hyperbolic group $\mathcal{Y}$ for the geometry over the field of ends F is isomorphic to $GL(2,F)/F^*$ when F^* is identified to the group of diagonal matrices $\begin{pmatrix} M & O \\ O & M \end{pmatrix}$ ($M \neq O$).

3. Prove that a point $(X:Y:Z)$ is on a line A,U if and only if $X = ZA$.

4. Find the matrix of the fractional linear map which corresponds to a translation along a line (M,N).

5. Find the condition for a linear fractional map to represent a horocyclic movement.

6. Find the matrix of the reflection in the line (A,B) if $A,B \neq U$.

7. Prove that the cross ratio of four ends

$$(AB,CD) = \frac{A - C}{A - D} \frac{B - D}{B - C}$$

is invariant in a hyperbolic motion.

8. For any hyperbolic segment $(A,B)^H$ let A',A'' and B',B'' be the ends of the perpendiculars $p^H[l^H(A,B),A]$ and $p^H[l^H(A,B),B]$. We assume that A',B' and A'',B'' are, respectively, in one halfplane of $l^H(A,B)$. Show that $(A'A'',B'B'') > O$. (By a hyperbolic movement, bring A onto $o \cap e^*$, B into o.)

9. The *exponential* of a segment is

$$\exp(A,B) = \frac{1 + (A'A'',B'B'')^{\frac{1}{2}}}{1 - (A'A'',B'B'')^{\frac{1}{2}}}.$$

Prove that $\exp(A,B)$ is the positive end of $p^H(o,X)$ if X is the point on the ray $e^* \cap o[U]$ of o such that $(A,B)^H \cong^H (e^* \cap o,X)^H$.

10. Let A',B',C' be ends on the arc defined by E and U, and put $A = A'^{oH}$, $B = B'^{oH}$, $C = C'^{oH}$, the hyperbolic projections of the end into o. Prove that $C = A \cdot B$ implies $(e^* \cap o,A)^H \cong^H (B,C)^H$.

11. It follows from problem 9 that two segments are congruent if and only if they have the same exponential. The exponential will serve as a measure of the length of a segment. If A,B,C are collinear, prove that $\exp(A,C) = \exp(A,B)\exp(B,C)$ if B is between A and C. If $\mathbf{a}$ is the class of segments congruent to $(A,B)^H$, and $\mathbf{b}$ that congruent to $(B,C)^H$, we define $\mathbf{a} + \mathbf{b}$ to be the set of segments congruent to $(A,C)^H$. The formula to be proved then becomes $\exp(\mathbf{a} + \mathbf{b}) = \exp\mathbf{a} \cdot \exp\mathbf{b}$.

12. Show that addition of segments can be made into the operation of an abelian group on the sets of congruent segments. An isomorphic image of that group can be obtained on the group F^* (problem 2).

13. For an oriented angle (a,b) let A',A'' be the ends of a, B',B'' those of b, and assume that A',B',A'',B'' are in cyclic order.

(a) Prove that the cross ratio $(A'A'',B'B'')$ is the same for all angles equal to (a,b).

(b) Compute the cross ratio for an angle of vertex $e^* \cap o$ for which one leg is $(E,-E)$ to show that the cross ratio of an angle is not positive.

(c) Define $\tan \frac{1}{2}(a,b) = [-(A'A'',B'B'')]^{\frac{1}{2}}$ and prove that for any two oriented angles $\hat{M}$ and $\hat{N}$

$$\tan (\hat{M} + \hat{N}) = \frac{\tan \hat{M} + \tan \hat{N}}{1 - \tan \hat{M} \tan \hat{N}}.$$

Hint: prove first that a rotation about $e^* \cap o$ which maps $(E,-E)$ into $(A,-A)$ has the matrix $\begin{pmatrix} 1 & P \\ -P & 1 \end{pmatrix}$ where $P = \dfrac{A-1}{A+1}$.

14. A segment of length **a** is realized as $(e^* \cap o,P)$, $P \in o$. Let A be the positive end point of $p^H(o,P)$. The *parallel angle* of **a** (exercise 9–3, problem 5) is $(o,l^H(e^* \cap o,A))$. Prove that

$$\tan \tfrac{1}{2}\pi(\mathbf{a}) = \exp (-\mathbf{a}).$$

5. A Linear Model

Hyperbolic geometry has been developed by means of euclidean circles. Since we are speaking about "hyperbolic lines," it would be nice to have a

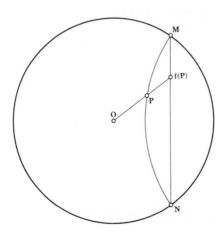

FIG. 9–15

model of hyperbolic geometry in which "lines" would be lines. This can be done in the following way. Let A be the center of Λ. If P is on a hyperbolic line of end points M and N, define

$$f(P) = l(A,P) \cap l(M,N).$$

This definition is independent of the choice of the hyperbolic line through P. In fact, $f(P)$ is the intersection of all the radical axes of Λ and the circles of the pencil through P and $\sigma_\Lambda P$. By definition, the image of a hyperbolic line is the straight segment between its end points. Since $f(P)$ is one-to-one, we see that the straight segments in the interior of Λ give a model of non-euclidean geometry. This model, however, does not conserve the euclidean angles. The construction given in Fig. 9–16 shows that two hyperbolic lines in the model

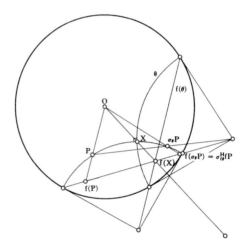

FIG. 9–16

are perpendicular if one passes through the intersection of the tangents to Λ at the end points of the other. The same figure shows the definition of the reflection of a point $f(P)$ at a line $f(\theta)$. Since the map f conserves end points, the analytic geometry developed in section 4 is equally valid in this model.

6. Elliptic Geometry

Since we succeeded in the development of a geometry in which there is an infinity of parallels to a line through one point, we may ask whether it is possible to construct a geometry in which there are no parallels at all. This is indeed possible. However, the structure of the plane in which the geometry can be found must be quite different from the planes we have studied thus far, since the absence of parallels implies the absence of any ideal, or infinite, points. While we can carry over the group theoretical approach and find the group of the new geometry as a subgroup of the Möbius group, we will have to lose most of the axioms which have a topological character. Therefore, we shall not attempt to give an axiomatic characterization of this *elliptic* geometry in this short survey.

Again we choose a fixed circle $A = O(r)$. Inversion in A is replaced by the involution

$$\sigma^* = \sigma_O \sigma_A.$$

For any point P, the point $P^* = \sigma^* P$ is called the *antipodal* point of P. The power of O for any circle Γ through a pair of antipodal points P and P^* is $\pi(O,\Gamma) = -r^2$. This means that the diameter which connects O and one point of $\Gamma \cap A$ intersects Γ again in the second point of $\Gamma \cap A$:

(9.26)   *The circles of the pencil defined by two antipodal points intersect the fixed circle in a pair of diametrically opposed points.*

Diametrically opposed points on A are antipodal. If we write a circle of the pencil as $\Gamma = \Gamma(P,P^*,X)$, where $X \in \Gamma \cap A$, it follows that

$$\sigma^* \Gamma = \Gamma(P^*,P,X^*) = \Gamma.$$

(9.27)   *The circles through two antipodal points are invariant under the action of σ^*.*

This means that a circle which contains one pair of antipodal points must contain the antipodal of any of its points.

Hyperbolic geometry presented a similar situation. A hyperbolic line is on a circle which contains $\sigma_A X$ if and only if it contains X. Instead of restricting the domain of hyperbolic geometry to the interior of A, we could have defined the hyperbolic plane with its ends as the set of unordered couples of points $(X,\sigma_A X)$. The ends then are those couples which consist of two identical points. This procedure is appropriate for elliptic geometry.

Sets and functions relating to the new geometry will be identified by an upper index E. An *elliptic point* P^E is an unordered couple (P,P^*) of antipodal points in the Gauss plane. The map σ^* has no fixed points; any couple (P,P^*) consists of two distinct points. (It would have been possible to define an elliptic point as being either a point in the interior of A or a couple of diametrically opposed points of A, and then to discard the exterior of A just as in hyperbolic geometry. This approach is inconvenient for the group theory since A in elliptic geometry does not have the invariant meaning it has in hyperbolic geometry. However, we shall use this representation when it has visual advantages.) The set of the elliptic points is the *elliptic plane*. The map *e* of the Gauss plane onto the elliptic plane,

$$eP = P^E,$$

is a one-to-two map since $e^{-1}P^E = P \cup P^*$. We say that the Gauss plane is a double covering of the elliptic plane. The involution σ^* is a *covering map* whose image in the elliptic plane is the identity

$$e\sigma^*e^{-1} = \iota^E,$$

since

$$e\sigma^*e^{-1}P^E = e\sigma^*(P \cup P^*) = e(P^* \cup P) = P^E \cup P^E = P^E.$$

An *elliptic line* is the image under *e* of a circle through a pair of antipodal points. By (9.27), a circle gives rise to an elliptic line if and only if

$$e^{-1}e\Gamma = \Gamma.$$

A *reflection in an elliptic line* $l^E = e\Gamma$ is

$$\sigma_{l^E} = e\sigma_\Gamma e^{-1}.$$

We have to show that this is well defined, i.e., that for any P^E both points P and P^* of $e^{-1}P^E$ define the same elliptic point $e\sigma_\Gamma P = e\sigma_\Gamma P^*$. But (9.27) implies

$$\sigma_\Gamma = \sigma^*\sigma_\Gamma\sigma^*,$$

or

(9.28) $\sigma_\Gamma\sigma^* = \sigma^*\sigma_\Gamma$ *if and only if* Γ *is the original of an elliptic line.*

It follows that

$$(\sigma_\Gamma P)^* = \sigma_\Gamma P^*,$$

and this is the desired relation.

Since we cannot draw the elliptic plane, we prefer to work in the Gauss plane instead.

Axiom I of euclidean geometry holds in the elliptic plane since there exists a unique elliptic line through two distinct points P^E and Q^E. This line is the image by *e* of

$$\Gamma(P,P^*,Q) = \Gamma(P,P^*,Q^*) = \Gamma(P,Q,Q^*).$$

The axioms about halfplanes do not hold. This is seen most easily if for the moment we represent the plane by the points in the interior of A and the antipodal pairs of A. Any two points not on a line l^E can be joined by an arc disjoint from l^E (Fig. 9–17).

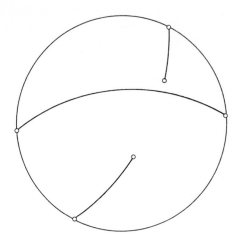

Fig. 9–17

The same representation shows that, given two pairs of diametrically opposed points and an M-circle joining the points of one of the pairs, the points of the other pair are in different domains for that circle. This implies:

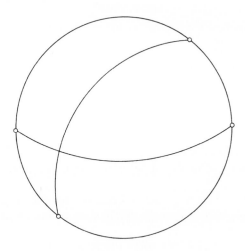

Fig. 9–18

(9.29)   *Two elliptic lines always intersect.*

Not only do we not have halfplanes, but also it is impossible to define a sense of orientation. In fact, the two M-triangles which cover one E-triangle have opposite orientation (Fig. 9–19).

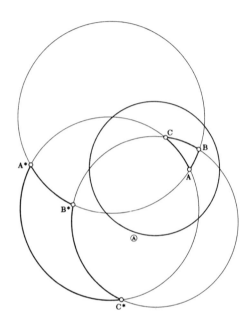

FIG. 9–19

The main lemma for the study of the group $\mathcal{E}$ of elliptic motions is:

(9.30)   *There exists a unique elliptic line perpendicular to all lines of a pencil of elliptic lines.*

By (9.29), all pencils of elliptic lines are formed by the images of the circles through one elliptic point (P,P^*). As always, two elliptic lines are perpendicular if the reflections in them commute, i.e., if they are images of perpendicular M-circles. Since the centers of the M-circles of the perpendicular pencil are on $l(P,P^*)$, the only circle in that M-pencil which defines an elliptic line is the circle through the points of $\Lambda \cap p(l(P,P^*),O)$.

Theorem (9.30) implies its converse:

(9.31)   *The perpendiculars to an elliptic line are concurrent.*

The elliptic point $P^E = (P,P^*)$ at which the perpendiculars to l^E are concurrent is called the *pole* of l^E. Now l^E is the unique perpendicular of the elliptic lines through P^E; it is the *polar* of P^E. Since the reflection in a line maps the perpendiculars onto themselves, it follows that

(9.32)   *The pole of an elliptic line is invariant in the elliptic reflection in the line.*

This means that an elliptic line reflection always has a fixed point other than the points of the line. In the Gauss plane, the reflection naturally exchanges interior and exterior. If l^E is the image of Γ, then $\sigma_\Gamma P = P^*$.

As always, the reflection in a point is defined as the product of the reflections in any pair of perpendiculars through that point. (9.30) then implies:

(9.33)   *The polar of an elliptic point is invariant in the reflection in the point.*

By now the reader will be ready to accept the fact that we cannot distinguish between line reflections and point reflections:

(9.34)   *If P^E is the pole of g^E, then $\sigma_{pE} = \sigma_{gE}$.*

We choose two perpendiculars a^E, b^E through P^E. The pole of a^E is $A^E = g^E \cap b^E$ since both b^E and g^E are perpendicular to a^E. We want to prove that

$$\sigma_{pE}\sigma_{gE} = \sigma_{aE}\sigma_{bE}\sigma_{gE} = \iota^E.$$

Let X^E be a point not on any of the three lines. Then

$$X^E = l^E(X^E,P^E) \cap l^E(X^E,A^E).$$

The first line passes through P^E and is perpendicular to g^E, hence

$$\sigma_{pE}\sigma_{gE}\, l^E(X^E,P^E) = l^E(X^E,P^E).$$

By the same argument,

$$\sigma_{pE}\sigma_{gE}\, l^E(X^E,A^E) = \sigma_{AE}\sigma_{aE}\, l^E(X^E,A^E) = l^E(X^E,A^E).$$

Hence

$$\sigma_{pE}\sigma_{gE}X^E = X^E.$$

An even simpler argument shows the same if X^E is on one of the three lines.

The fact that a point reflection is a line reflection at once gives us the structure theorem of the elliptic group:

(9.35)   *Every elliptic motion is equal to the product of two line reflections.*

For one reflection, this is (9.34). We have to prove the statement only for products of three reflections. But, by (9.34), any product of three line reflections is equal to some product of four line reflections. By (8.17) this can be reduced to the product of two reflections in the usual way (see sec. 2–6).

By (9.34), we can write (9.35) as

(9.36)   *Every elliptic motion is equal to the product of two point reflections.*

The preceding results suggest the possibility of an axiomatics of elliptic geometry which is completely symmetric in the notions of point and line, join and intersection. It is, in fact, possible to give a description of elliptic geometry in which every true theorem is transformed into a true theorem if "point" is replaced by "line" and vice versa and, simultaneously, "join of two points" is replaced by "intersection of two lines." For this reason, elliptic geometry is called a *self-dual* theory. However, we shall not develop elliptic geometry further and only give a spatial interpretation of this geometry. Since we did not develop solid geometry in this book, the discussion must be informal.

In space we take a sphere (Fig. 9–20) whose intersection with the plane Π of our geometry is the circle Λ. That plane is taken as horizontal, and the south pole of the sphere is denoted by S. Any point P, which is not in the

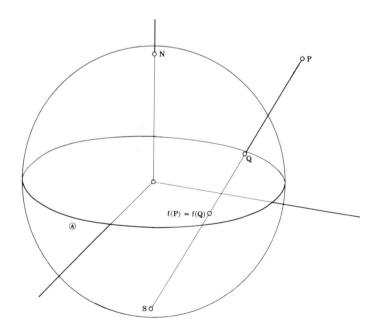

Fig. 9–20

tangent plane Π to the sphere at S, can be mapped into Π by central projection from S:

$$f(P) = l(P,S) \cap \Pi.$$

The restriction of this map to points on the sphere is called the *stereographic projection*. It is one-to-one outside S since a line through S has at most one other point of intersection with the sphere. If we define $f(S) = \infty$, we obtain a map of the sphere onto the Gauss plane which is one-to-one without exception.

Stereographic projection preserves elementary angles. Let us consider two tangents t_1, t_2 attached to a point P on the sphere. The planes defined by S and the lines t_i ($i = 1,2$) cut out two circles from the sphere. These

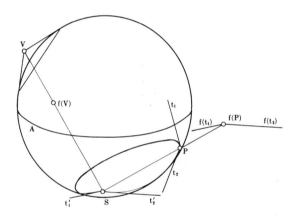

FIG. 9–21

two circles form a figure called a lune. A lune is symmetric with respect to the plane normal to the chord $l(S,P)$ at $M(S,P)$. If t_1', t_2' are the tangents at S to the circles of the lune, the symmetry implies

$$\angle (t_1,t_2) \cong \angle (t_1',t_2').$$

The line t_i' is the line of intersection of Π′, tangent to the sphere at S, and the plane spanned by S and t_i. And $f(t_i)$ is the line of intersection of Π and the same plane spanned by S and t_i. Hence $f(t_i) \parallel t_i'$, and

$$\angle (t_1,t_2) \cong \angle (f(t_1),f(t_2)).$$

Stereographic projection maps circles onto circles. For a given circle Γ on the sphere, consider the tangents to the sphere which are normal to the circle. These tangents form a cone. Let V be its vertex. The tangents are mapped onto the lines through $f(V)$. By the preceding remark, $f(\Gamma)$ is a curve perpendicular to all lines through $f(V)$; it is a circle of center $f(V)$.

The points of A are fixed in the stereographic projection. A circle on the sphere is a *great circle* if it is the intersection of the sphere and a plane through the center of the sphere. The great circles are the circles that intersect any other great circle, e.g., the equator A, in a couple of diametrically opposed points. All great circles through a point on the sphere meet again at the antipodal point. This shows that *the geometry obtained from the euclidean geometry on the sphere by identification of antipodal points, and in which great circles define straight lines, is isomorphic to elliptic geometry by stereographic projection.*

Exercise 9–6

1. Characterize the pole of an elliptic line in the geometry on the sphere.

2. The reflection in a great circle can be defined either as the reflection in the plane of the circle, or as follows: Through a point P (on the sphere) draw all circles perpendicular to the great circle l. All these circles intersect at a second point $Q = \sigma_l P$. The reflection of P in a point X is the point Q on the great circle through P and X for which X is the midpoint of the arc PQ.

(a) Prove that the image in Π of the reflection in l is the inversion in $f(l)$.

(b) If L is one of the poles of the line l, show that

$$\sigma_l P = (\sigma_L P)^*, \qquad \sigma_L P = \sigma_{L^*} P$$

where * denotes the antipodal map on the sphere.

(c) Let $O(3)$ be the group of motions of the sphere generated by the products of reflections at great circles. The two maps ι, * define a subgroup A of $O(3)$. Prove that A is a normal subgroup of $O(3)$ and that $\mathcal{E} = O(3)/A$.

3. In elliptic geometry, two points do not define a distance but an angle. The *angle* of two points is the oriented angle of their polars. The *polar triangle* of an elliptic triangle is the triangle defined by the poles of the sides, taken as vertices of the new triangle. (Elliptic triangles are conveniently treated as *complete* triangles.) Prove that the sides of the polar triangle are the polars of the vertices of the original triangle, and find the relations between the line-angles and point-angles of a triangle and its polar triangle.

4. Use problem 3 to prove that any metric relation in elliptic geometry must be symmetric in point-angles and line-angles.

5. Prove formula (2.52) in elliptic geometry.

6. (a) Prove that the circles intersecting two given (non-parallel) lines under given angles form two families of homothetic circles.

(b) Prove that formula (2.52) implies that a triangle is determined by three independent data and that, therefore, (2.52) contains all of elliptic trigonometry.

7. Prove that an elliptic motion either has one fixed point or it has a line of fixed points and an isolated fixed point.

8. Prove that the existence of a midpoint for any pair of elliptic points implies the existence of an angle bisector for any pair of elliptic lines.

9. (a) Prove that two points in an elliptic plane admit a midpoint if and only if the product of the reflections in the two points is the square of an element of $\mathcal{E}$.

(b) Prove that the existence of either angle bisectors or midpoints implies that all elements of $\mathcal{E}$ are squares.

10. By projection from the center of the sphere, obtain a model of elliptic geometry in which every elliptic line is covered by a straight line.

Appendix

A NON–ARCHIMEDEAN PLANE

In this appendix we construct the so-called Hilbert plane. This is a non-archimedean plane which satisfies the axioms of our geometry. The elements of the field F of lengths will be the formal power series

$$x = \sum_{-\infty}^{+\infty} a_i t^i,$$

where the a_i are real numbers and t is an "indeterminate," i.e., a symbol. We allow only a finite number of nonzero coefficients with negative indices. This means that for each x there exists an integer $N(x)$ such that

$$a_i = 0 \quad \text{if } i < N(x).$$

We do not speak about convergence of the power series since t does not have any numerical value. The sum of x and another power series $y = \sum_{-\infty}^{+\infty} b_i t^i$ is defined as

$$x + y = \sum_{-\infty}^{+\infty} (a_i + b_i) t^i.$$

This is again an element of F since the coefficients are zero for i less than the smaller of the N defined for x and y. The product of two formal power series is

$$x \cdot y = \sum_{-\infty}^{+\infty} c_i t^i \qquad c_i = \sum_{j=-\infty}^{+\infty} a_j b_{i-j}.$$

This is well defined since only a finite number of terms in the sum which is c_i are different from zero, and $c_i = 0$ for i smaller than some integer N. The real numbers are identified to the power series for which $a_i = 0$ if $i \neq 0$. It is easy to see that addition defines an abelian group with identity element 0.

260

In the definition of multiplication we may replace the summation over the index j by the summation over $k = i - j$,

$$\sum_j a_j b_{i-j} = \sum_u a_{i-k} b_k.$$

Since j and k are just names introduced for the summation and not fixed indices, it is possible to replace one name by the other. This shows that the definition of multiplication is symmetric in the coefficients of x and y; multiplication is commutative. A similar argument shows that it is also associative. For a third power series $z = \Sigma e_i t^i$ we write

$$(xy)z = \Sigma A_i t^i \qquad x(yz) = \Sigma B_i t^i,$$

where

$$A_i = \sum_j \sum_k a_k b_{j-k} e_{i-j}$$

and

$$B_i = \sum_j a_j \sum_k b_k e_{i-j-k}.$$

In the definition of B_i we change the name j into k and k into $j - k$. Then $i - j - k$ is changed into $i - j$ and $A_i = B_i$.

The real number 1 is the multiplicative unit. The existence of an inverse is shown by direct construction. If $N(x) = 0$, then $a_0 \neq 0$ and for

$$x = a_0 + a_1 t + \cdots$$

it is possible to find

$$y = b_0 + b_1 t + \cdots$$

such that $xy = 1$. In fact, the definition of the product leads to a string of equations:

$$a_0 b_0 = 1$$
$$a_0 b_1 + a_1 b_0 = 0$$
$$a_0 b_2 + a_1 b_1 + a_2 b_0 = 0$$
$$\cdots$$

Each new equation contains only one new unknown b_i multiplied by the non-zero number a_0. Therefore, the equations can be solved stepwise in a unique way. In the general case,

$$x = a_N t^N + a_{N+1} t^{N+1} + \cdots \qquad\qquad a_N \neq 0$$
$$= t^N(a_N + a_{N+1} t + \cdots),$$

the preceding construction shows the existence of

$$x^{-1} = t^{-N}(a_N + a_{N+1}t + \cdots)^{-1}.$$

This shows that the formal power series indeed form a field.
An order is defined on the field by:

$$x > 0 \text{ if and only if } a_N > 0,$$

and, accordingly, $x > y$ if and only if $x - y > 0$. It is an easy exercise to show that this definition turns F into an ordered field. This order is non-archimedean since, e.g., 1 is greater than any integer multiple of t. Here t plays the role of an "infinitely small" element. If r is any positive real number, an order preserving automorphism of F onto itself can be defined by

$$\phi(\Sigma a_i t^i) = \Sigma r^i a_i t^i.$$

ϕ is not the identity unless $r = 1$. By theorem (8.3) this gives a new proof that F is not archimedean.

Every element $1 + x^2$ has a square root in F. In fact, an element

$$a_0 + a_1 t + \cdots, \qquad\qquad a_0 > 0$$

has a square root $c_0 + c_1 t + \cdots$, where the c_i can be determined step by step from the system of linear equations

$$c_0^2 = a_0$$
$$2c_0 c_1 = a_1$$
$$2c_0 c_2 + c_1^2 = a_2$$
$$\cdots$$

Therefore, every element $a_N t^N + \cdots$, N even, $a_N > 0$ admits a square root in the field. On the other hand, not every positive element admits a root. For example, $t > 0$, but there is no x in F such that $x^2 = t$.

Our *plane* now is the set of all ordered couples (x,y) of elements of F. The *coordinates* of (x,y) are x and y. A *line* is the set of all couples which satisfy a linear equation

$$l(x,y) = ax + by + c = 0 \qquad\qquad a^2 + b^2 \neq 0; \ a,b,c \in F.$$

The *halfplanes* of the line are the two sets of points characterized by $l(x,y) > 0$ and $l(x,y) < 0$. The *reflection* of a point (u,y) in the line l is the point $\sigma_l(u,v)$ of coordinates

$$\left[u - \frac{2a}{a^2 + b^2} l(u,v), \ v - \frac{2b}{a^2 + b^2} l(u,v) \right].$$

This is an involution which leaves $l(x,y) = 0$ pointwise fixed and exchanges halfplanes since

(*) $$l[\sigma_l(u,v)] = -l(u,v).$$

The unique line through two points (x_1,y_1) and (x_2,y_2) is

$$(y_2 - y_1)x + (x_1 - x_2)y + (x_2 y_1 - x_1 y_2) = 0.$$

The equation of the line is in *normal* form if $a^2 + b^2 = 1$. For a general expression of $l(x,y)$ the normal form is

$$\frac{a}{(a^2 + b^2)^{\frac{1}{2}}} x + \frac{b}{(a^2 + b^2)^{\frac{1}{2}}} y + \frac{c}{(a^2 + b^2)^{\frac{1}{2}}} = 0.$$

The normal form always exists since $(a^2 + b^2)^{\frac{1}{2}}$ exists in F. If a second line g is given by

$$g(x,y) = Ax + By + C = 0,$$

then

$$g[\sigma_l(u,v)] = g(u,v) - 2\frac{aA + bB}{a^2 + b^2} l(u,v)$$

$g \perp l$ if $g(x,y) = 0$ implies $g[\sigma_l(x,y)] = 0$ and $l(x,y) \neq g(x,y)$. Hence the condition of perpendicularity is

$$aA + bB = 0.$$

Therefore, the *perpendicular bisector* of two points (x_1,y_1) and (x_2,y_2) is the line

$$g(x,y) = -(x_2 - x_1)x + (y_2 - y_1)y + C = 0$$

for which $g(x_1,y_1) = g(x_2,y_2)$. This condition determines C:

$$2C = -x_1^2 + x_2^2 + y_1^2 - y_2^2.$$

The *angle bisector* of two lines $g = 0$ and $h = 0$ is a line l such that $g(x,y) = 0$ implies $h[\sigma_l(x,y)] = 0$. Since the equation of a straight line is defined only up to a constant, we may assume that the coefficients of $l(x,y) = 0$ have been chosen so that for $g(x,y)$ in *normal* form $h[\sigma_l(x,y)]$ also is a linear expression in normal form. If A,B,C are the coefficients of h, and a,b,c those of l, then l is an angle bisector if and only if

$$h[\sigma_l(x,y)] = h(x,y) - 2\frac{aA + bB}{a^2 + b^2} l(x,y) = \pm g(x,y).$$

The sign is indefinite since a straight line has two normal forms. Again we may disregard a common factor and obtain: *The angle bisector of two lines whose equations are in normal form is* $g(x,y) \pm h(x,y) = 0$. g *and* h *are parallel if and only if they have equal slope* A/B. In this case l is unique and is the *mid-line*.

All axioms of euclidean geometry are now checked easily. The only axiom that might cause some trouble is XII. But the action of a product Σ of reflections can be described by

$$g[\Sigma(u,v)] = g(u,v) - S(u,v),$$

where, by construction, $S(u,v)$ is a linear expression with constant coefficients

$$S(u,v) = ru + sv + t \qquad\qquad r,s,t \in F.$$

From the discussion of the angle bisector we know that the coefficients can be chosen so that both $g(x,y) = 0$ and $g[\Sigma(x,y)] = 0$ are equations in normal form. If $g(x,y) = 0$ implies $g[\Sigma(x,y)] = 0$, then $S(u,v)$ is a multiple of $g(u,v)$ and

$$g[\Sigma(u,v)] = \pm g(u,v).$$

If Σ maps not only g onto itself but also some perpendicular $p(x,y) = 0$ onto itself, the preceding result also holds for p. If Σ maps a ray of g onto itself, it cannot change the sign of p, $p[\Sigma(u,v)] = p(u,v)$. Since the equations of both g and p are in normal form,

$$g(u,v) = Au + Bv + C$$
$$p(u,v) = -Bu + Av + C',$$

we may compute the coordinates as

$$u = A(g - C) - B(p - C'),$$
$$v = B(g - C) + A(p - C').$$

If $g[\Sigma(u,v)] = g(u,v)$, then Σ is the identity. If $g[\Sigma(u,v)] = -g(u,v)$, then, by (*), $\Sigma(u,v) = \sigma_g(u,v)$.

The analytic geometry which we have constructed satisfies the axioms I to XIII, but not A and X*. The formulae derived for the plane over the field F are also valid in the analytic geometry over the field of real numbers.

Exercise (Appendix)

1. Prove in detail that $\phi(\Sigma a_i t^i) = \Sigma r^i a_i t^i$ is an automorphism of F for $r \neq 0$.

2. A new order can be defined on F as follows: $x \succ 0$ if and only if $\phi(x) > 0$ for some fixed r. For $r = -1$, find some x such that $x > 0$, $x \prec 0$.

3. (a) Show that a square in an ordered field is always positive.

(b) Show that $1 + x^2 \succ 0$ for all possible orders in F.

4. A main property of the real numbers is: every bounded monotone increasing sequence converges. Show that in F the positive integers form a bounded, monotone increasing sequence which does not converge.

5. (a) From the proof of theorem (8.3) extract a proof that every archimedean field is isomorphic to some subfield of the real numbers.

(b) Use problem (a) to show that every euclidean archimedean plane can be realized by some subset of the cartesian plane of all couples of real numbers.

6. Prove that the two angle bisectors of two concurrent lines are mutually perpendicular.

REFERENCES

[1] Artin, E. Geometric Algebra. Interscience, New York, 1957.

[2] Bachmann, F. Aufbau der Geometrie aus dem Spiegelungsbegriff. Springer, Berlin, 1959.

[3] Blumenthal, L. A Modern View of Geometry. Freeman, Los Angeles, 1961.

[4] Boltyanskii, V. G. Equivalent and Equidecomposable Figures. Topics in Mathematics. Heath and Co., Boston, 1963.

[5] Burckhardt, J. J. Die Bewegungsgruppen der Kristallographie. Birkhäuser, Basel, 1957.

[6] Court, N. A. College Geometry. 2nd ed. Barnes and Noble, New York, 1952.

[7] Coxeter, H. S. M. Introduction to Geometry. Wiley, New York, 1961.

[8] Coxeter, H. S. M. Non-Euclidean Geometry. 4th ed. University of Toronto, 1961.

[9] Coxeter, H. S. M., and W. O. Moser. Generators and Relations for Discrete Groups. 2nd ed. Springer, Berlin, 1965.

[10] Eves, H. A Survey of Geometry. vol. 1. Allyn and Bacon, Boston, 1963.

[11] Fejes-Tóth, L. Lagerungen in der Ebene, auf der Kugel, und im Raum. Springer, Berlin, 1953.

[12] Fejes-Tóth, L. Regular Figures. Macmillan, New York, 1964.

[13] Forder, H. G. Coordinates in Geometry. Auckland Univ. Coll. Math. Series, 41. No. 1, 1953.

[14] Freudenthal, H. Lie Groups in the Foundations of Geometry. Advances in Mathematics. vol. 1, fasc. 2, pp. 145–190, Academic Press, New York, 1964.

[15] Gerretsen, J. C. H. Die Begründung der Trigonometrie in der hyperbolischen Geometrie. Akad. Wetensch. Amsterdam, Proc., 45, pp. 360–366, 479–483, 559–566, 1942.

[16] Gonseth, F. La géométrie et le problème de l'espace. Griffon, Neuchâtel, 1955.

[17] Hadamard, J. Leçons de géométrie élémentaire. vol. 1. Géométrie plane. 2e éd. Armand Colin, Paris, 1906.

[18] Hilbert, D. Neue Begründung der Bolyai-Lobatschefkyschen Geometrie. Math. Ann. 57, pp. 137–150, 1903. Appendix III in: Grundlagen der Geometrie, 8th ed. Teubner, Stuttgart, 1956; 9th ed., 1961.

[19] Ijzeren, J. van. Moderne vlakke meetkunde. W. J. Thieme & Cie., Zutphen, 1941.

[20] Jeger, M. Transformation Geometry. Wiley, New York, 1966. English version by A. W. Deicke and A. G. Howson.

[21] Kazarinoff, N. D. Geometric Inequalities. New Mathematical Library. Random House, New York, 1961.

[22] Klein, F. Famous Problems of Elementary Geometry. Transl. by W. W. Beman and D. E. Smith. Chelsea, New York, 1955.

[23] Klein, F. Vorlesungen über nichteuklidische Geometrie. 3rd ed. Springer, Berlin, 1928.

[24] M'Clelland, W. J. A Treatise on the Geometry of the Circle. Macmillan, London, 1891.

[25] Moise, E. E. Elementary Geometry from an Advanced Standpoint. Addison-Wesley, Reading, Mass., 1963.

[26] Oppenheim, A. The Erdös and Other Inequalities for a Triangle. Am. Math. Monthly 68, pp. 226–230, 1961.

[27] Pontrjagin, L. S. Topological Groups. 2nd ed. Princeton, 1956.

[28] Rouché, E., and C. de Comberousse. Traité de géométrie. 7e ed. (In particular, note III.) Gauthier-Villars, Paris, 1900.

[29] Thomsen, G. The Treatment of Elementary Geometry by a Group Calculus. Math. Gazette 17, p. 232, 1933.

[30] Yaglom, I. M. Geometric Transformations. Transl. by Allen Shields. New Mathematical Library. Random House, New York, 1962.

[31] Yaglom, I. M., and V. G. Boltyanskii. Convex Figures. Transl. by P. J. Kelly and L. F. Walton. Holt, Rinehart and Winston, New York, 1961.

[32] Zassenhaus, H. Theory of Groups. Chelsea, New York, 1949.

SUGGESTIONS FOR FURTHER READING

Philosophy of axiomatics: 16.
Geometry based on reflections and groups of transformations: 2, 6, 17, 20, 29, 30.
Unsolvable problems in elementary geometry: 22, 25.
Planes with only partial systems of axioms: 1, 3, 13, 19.
Abstract groups: Any book on modern algebra and 32.
Groups in geometry: 2, 6, 14, 23, 27, 29.
Crystallographic groups: 5, 6, 8, 12.
Theorems of Pappus and Desargues: 1, 3, 13, 18, 19.
Theory of area: 4, 10, 25.
Field in which $1 + x^2$ is a square: 2.
Similitude: 24.
Geometry of the triangle and the circle: 9, 24, 28.
Geometric inequalities: 11, 21, 26, 31.
Circular transformations: 17, 19, 24, 28, 30 (vol. 2).
Hyperbolic geometry: 2, 6, 7, 15, 16, 18, 23, 30 (vol. 2).
Billiard ball problem: R. Sturm, Crelle's J.f.d.r.u.a. Math., 96, 97 (1884).

SOLUTIONS FOR EXERCISES

1–1

3. Use IV. **4a.** No condition. **b.** Use problem 3. **6.** In Fig. 1–4 fill in the third point on each line by (1.7). New lines by I. Process will never stop. **7.** Pasch on $\triangle(D,B,C)$ and (1.5). **8.** For A,B in kernel choose $C \in (A,B)$ and $D \in (C,X)$ for fixed X. By problem 7 there is $F \in (B,X)$, $D \in (A,F)$. And $F \in S$, hence $D \in S$, hence $[C,X] \subset S$. **9.** $\emptyset$, point, open and closed intervals, open interval $\cup$ one endpoint, ray, ray $\cup$ vertex. See **4.**

1–2

3. If you are interested in set theory, see G. Cantor, Contributions to the founding of the theory of transfinite numbers, Dover, New York, reprint. sec. 9, 122–128. **4.** $\pi_A^2 \neq \pi_A$. Prove that $\pi_A^2 \cap \pi_B^2 \cap \pi_C^2 = \emptyset$. See proof (1.26). **5.** $\sigma_{t(a_2,b_1)}\sigma_{t(a_1,b_1)} = \sigma_{p(a\ P)}\sigma_a$ by XII. **7.** $\sigma_{l(B,C)} = \sigma_{m(A,B)}\sigma_{l(A,C)}\sigma_{m(A,B)}$. **10.** $M(A,A) = A$. $m(a,a)$ any line $\ni A$. **11.** $p[l(A,B),B]$. **12.** If $\Omega = \Sigma T$, then $\Omega\Sigma = \Sigma(T\Sigma) = \Sigma$, $\Omega = \iota$. **14a.** See (1.26); $C \in [A,B]$ implies $p(g,C) \subset \pi_{p(g,A)}^1 \cap \pi_{p(g,B)}^1$. **b.** $S^g = A$ iff $S \subset p(g,A)$. **c.** (1.26) for A^g, B^g,C^g. **15.** $p(p(g,P),P)$. **16.** $\sigma_{t(b_1,c_1)}\sigma_{t(a_1,b_1)}\sigma_{t(b_1,c_1)}\sigma_{t(a_1,b_1)} = \iota$. **17.** (1.21) and (1.24).

1–3

4. (1.4). **6.** (1.33). **7.** Point invariant for σ_t. **8.** $\cong$ by σ_t. **9.** E.g., 3 edges, 2 suitable angles, indication of halfplanes. **11.** $\sigma_t A = B$. **12.** Problems 9, 3; $\sigma_{l[C,M(A,B)]}\triangle[C,A,M(A,B)]$.

1–4

1. $\sigma_{m(fA,A)}\sigma_{t(A[B],\sigma_{m(fA,A)}fA[fB])}$ (times, eventually, σ_c).

1–5

1a,c. $\sigma_{t_C}A = B$. **b.** $\sigma_{h_c}A = B$. **d.** (1.37).   **2a.** No.   **b.** Yes.   **3.** No.   **4.** (1.33).
5. Base angles congruent by (1.44).

2–1

1. $\sigma_{l(O,B)}$.   **3.** $h = \sigma_a h$; h,b,c pencil.   **4a.** (1.16).   **b.** Use **4a**, (2.3), and (1.15).
5a. Use **4a**.   **6.** Opposite vertex.   **7.** $\sigma_{\sigma_{t_C}t_B}$.

2–2

2. Common perpendicular mapped into common perpendicular.   **4.** Proof of
(1.30).   **5.** Given $a \parallel b$, α, P. Foot of perpendicular: $b \cap \rho_{P,\alpha}a$.   **6.** Lines p,q,r.
Choose $A \in p$. $C = r \cap \rho_{A,+\frac{1}{2}\alpha}q$.   **7.** $X = g \cap l(A,\sigma_g B)$.   **8.** $l(\sigma_a B, \sigma_b B)$.
9. $C = \sigma_g B$. In isosceles triangle of leg $l(A,C)$, third vertex on g, $X = g \cap t_C$.

2–3

1. Prove second line identical to parallel to first through intersection with transversal.   **2.** Not odd.   **3.** $(n - 2) \cdot 180°$, $(n - 2)/n \cdot 180°$.
4. $\frac{1}{2}(l(P,A),l(P,B)) + \hat{A} - \frac{1}{2}(l(Q,A),c) + \hat{B} - \frac{1}{2}(c,l(B,Q)) = 180°$.
7. $x = m(P,Q)$.   **9.** Draw $\sigma_{l[M(A,D),M(B,C)]}l(A,D)$ and $\sigma_{l[M(A,D),M(B,C)]}l(B,C)$.
11. $\sigma_{M_c}\sigma_{M_a}\sigma_{M_b}A = A$.   **12.** Vertex = fixed point of product of reflections at all
midpoints, in order. Cf. (2.24), (2.7).   **13.** Cf. exercise 2–1, problem 4.   **14.** Vertex:
$c \cap \rho_{A,90°}b$.   **15.** $b = \rho_{M,90°}a = l(Q,\rho_{M,90°}P)$.   **18.** P,Q,R,S parallelogram.
$X = a \cap \sigma_s b$.   **19a.** $\sigma_F\sigma_E\sigma_C\sigma_D = \sigma_F\sigma_E\sigma_B\sigma_A\sigma_A\sigma_B\sigma_C\sigma_D = \iota \cdot \iota = \iota$. Similarly,
case b.   **20.** E.g., $\sigma_P\sigma_Q = \sigma_P\sigma_Q\sigma_R\sigma_R = \sigma_R\sigma_Q\sigma_P\sigma_R = \sigma_{l''}\sigma_{m'}\sigma_m'\sigma_{k'}$
$= \sigma_{l'}\sigma_{l'}\sigma_{l''}\sigma_{m'}\sigma_m''\sigma_{k'}\sigma_{k''}\sigma_{k''} = \sigma_{l'}\sigma_m\sigma_k\sigma_k\sigma_l\sigma_l\sigma_m\sigma_{k''} = \sigma_{l'}\sigma_{k''}$.

2–4

1. $a = p[l(A,B),A]$; $b = p[l(A,B),B]$.   **2.** $B = p(a,A) \cap y$, $\sigma_y = \sigma_{p[p(a,A),A]}\sigma_b\sigma_a$.
4. $[\![AB]\!] = 2[\![CB]\!]$, $C = M(A,B)$.   **5.** $\sigma_a\sigma_b = \sigma_R\sigma_Q$.   **8. a** vector of length a, $\parallel l_1$.
Angle bisectors of l_1, $\tau_a l_2$. Segments in strip between l_2 and $\tau_a l_2$. (Two possibilities
for **a**.)   **9.** $\sigma_a\sigma_b[\![PQ]\!] + [\![QP]\!] = 0$.   **10.** $M(A,\tau_v A)$.   **11.** Reflect in base.
12. $\sigma_G\sigma_{M_c}\sigma_G\sigma_{M_c}\sigma_G\sigma_C = \sigma_G\sigma_{M_c}\sigma_G\sigma_C\sigma_G\sigma_{M_c} = \sigma_G \cdot \sigma_{M_c}\sigma_G\sigma_{M_a} \cdot \sigma_{M_a}\sigma_C \cdot \sigma_G\sigma_{M_c}\sigma_{M_a} \cdot \sigma_{M_a}$
$= \sigma_G \cdot \sigma_{M_a}\sigma_G\sigma_{M_a} \cdot \sigma_{M_a}\sigma_C \cdot \sigma_{M_a}\sigma_{M_c}\sigma_G\sigma_{M_a} = \sigma_G\sigma_{M_a}\sigma_G\sigma_{M_c}\sigma_B\sigma_{M_c}\sigma_G\sigma_{M_c}$
$= \sigma_G\sigma_{M_a}\sigma_G\sigma_{M_a}\sigma_B\sigma_{M_c}\sigma_G\sigma_{M_c} = \sigma_A\sigma_G\sigma_B\sigma_{M_c}\sigma_G\sigma_{M_c} = \sigma_A\sigma_{M_c}\sigma_B\sigma_{M_c} = \iota$.
14. Draw $l[B,(\sigma_q\sigma_p)^2A]$.   **15.** M center of square; given A,B,C,D. σ_M is auto-
morphism of square, $\sigma_M A \in b$. Hence $b = l(B,Q)$, $[\![QD]\!] \perp [\![AC]\!]$, $QD = AC$.
16. Problem 15 for two coinciding points.   **18b.** Reduce to **a**.   **19.** Take $d \parallel b$.
20. Use **19**, or prove $(a,b) = (p(a,X),p(b,X))$.   **22.** (2.38).

2–5

3. Use **1**. **4.** $\sigma_a[\![AB]\!] = [\![BA]\!]$. **5.** The condition that a certain vector is mapped by σ_a into another vector (draw a picture) implies congruence of base angles. **6.** Use **4**. **7.** Use exercise 2–3, problem 13c, or for the isotomic points P',Q',R' prove $l(P',Q') \parallel l(Q',R') \parallel l(R',P')$.

2–6

1. Center of $\rho_1^{-1}\rho_2$, $\alpha_1 \neq \alpha_2$. **2.** If $b = l(C_1,C_2)$, $\rho_2 = \sigma_b\sigma_c$, $\rho_1 = \sigma_a\sigma_b$, then $\rho_1\rho_2\rho_1^{-1} = \sigma_{\sigma_a c}\sigma_b$, center $\in b$. **3.** $l = l(C_1,C_2)$, $\rho_1 = \sigma_l\sigma_a$, $\rho_2 = \sigma_b\sigma_l$, center $(\rho_2\rho_1) = a \cap b$, center $(\rho_1\rho_2) = \sigma_l a \cap \sigma_l b$. **4.** A fixed point of $\rho_{A_3,\alpha_3}\rho_{A_2,\alpha_2}\rho_{A_1,\alpha_1}$. For $\Sigma\alpha_i = k \cdot 360°$, either no solution or every point in the plane is a possible vertex.

3–1

2. Vectors on edges of triangles are not multiples of one another. **3.** $aa^{-1} = \iota \in H$. $\iota a^{-1} = a^{-1} \in H$. Hence $HH = H$, $H^{-1} = H$. **4.** E.g., H positive integers. **6.** 2. **8.** $c = xy, x^2 = y^2 = \iota$. $c^2 = x \cdot y(xy) = x(xy)y = x^2y^2 = \iota$. **10a.** $\{\iota\}$ **b.** 3. **12.** Homo: $axya^{-1} = axa^{-1}aya^{-1}$. Mono: $axa^{-1} = aya^{-1}$ implies $x = y$. Epi: $b = axa^{-1}$ gives $x = a^{-1}ba$. See (1.15). **13.** (1.11). **14.** $f(x^k) = x'^k$. **15.** $n + 1$. **17.** 6. **19.** Isomorphic $\mathbf{Z}_3$. **20a.** 8 elements **b.** Isomorphic $\mathbf{Z}_4$. **c.** 4.

3–2

1. One group isomorphic $\mathbf{Z}_3$, two groups isomorphic $\mathbf{Z}_2$. Spaces have 2,3 elements. **3.** $F(gg'^{-1}) = \iota'\iota' = \iota'$, hence subgroup. $F(xgx^{-1}) = F(x)'F(x)^{-1} = \iota'$, hence normal. **4.** $F^*(gg') = gg'$ ker $F = gg'$ ker F ker $F = g$ ker F g' ker $F = F^*(g)F^*(g')$. Epi: obvious. Mono: see proof (3.19). **5,6.** $F(m) =$ greatest non-negative remainder of m in division by n; similarly, problem 6. **7.** $F(x) = 2\pi\{x\}$, $\{x\} = x -$ (greatest integer $\leqslant x$). **8.** If $x \in H$, left cosets H, xH; right cosets H, Hx. Hence $xH = Hx$. If two elements ι, α in group, $\alpha^2 = \iota$. Isomorphism $F(\iota) = 0 + 2\mathbf{Z}$, $F(\alpha) = 1 + 2\mathbf{Z}$ (problem 2). **9.** $\mathfrak{M} = \mathfrak{M}^+ \cup \sigma_l\mathfrak{M}^+$, arbitrary l. **10,11.** (3.19). **12.** $\mathfrak{M}^+$ both times. **14.** $\{\iota\}$. **17.** yes. **18.** $xCx^{-1} = xx^{-1}C = C$. **20.** (3.7).

3–3

4. Choose the lattice for double mesh size, isomorphic to D_1kk. **5.** Turn drawing by 45° and look for rhombic lattice. **7.** Two vertices and two centers form a square. **8.** C_6. **9.** $\mathcal{Z}_4$. **14.** Lattice of centers (white circles in Fig. 3–9). **15.** Midpoints of edges.

4–1

1. Lines through vertices and not through interior. All except vertices. **2.** All lines through endpoints. **3.** All lines through the angle which does not contain points of S. **6.** One vertex is on $\Gamma_1 \cap \sigma_g \Gamma_2$; intersection must exist. **7.** $B \in \Gamma_2 \cap \tau_v \Gamma_1 (\neq \emptyset)$. **8.** (4.1). **9.** Translate Γ_1 until the image intersects Γ_2. **10.** $\Sigma[O(r)] = \Sigma O(r)$. **11.** $(d, l(O, E)) = (d, g) + (g, l(O, E)) = (d, g) + (l(D, O), g)$ $= (d, g) + 2(d, g)$. **13.** See problem 7. **14.** Investigate $\sigma_{l(O_1, O_2)}$. **15.** $\sigma_{l(P, O)}$. **16.** $\rho_{O, \alpha}$. **17.** Necessity from problem 15. Assume theorem false. Opposite edges determine two circles which touch three consecutive edges. Two segments between points of contact at two circles cannot cancel, contradiction.

4–2

1. (4.16). **2,3,4.** (4.17). **5.** $\angle IBI_a \cong \angle ICI_a \cong \perp$, $I_a \in \Gamma(B, I, C)$, X_a on diameter, equidistant from B, C. **6.** $g \cap h$, ΣA, ΣB, ΣC concyclic. Four congruent circles through $g \cap h$ (Σ proper motion: two circles). **7.** Formulate (4.17) for the half-angle. Replace $t(a, c)$ by $m(a, c)$. **8.** $l(A, Y_a) = l(I_b, I_c)$. **11.** (4.17). Split angles by intermediary point. **12.** Lines l_i, circles $\Gamma(l_i \cap l_{i+1}, l_{i+1} \cap l_{i+2}, l_{i+2} \cap l_i)$. Proof like problem 11. **13.** Two angles constant in $\triangle[A_1, A_2, l(A_1, Q) \cap l(A_2, R)]$. **14.** (4.17). **15.** $\triangle(Y_1, Q, T_1)$ and $\triangle(Y_2, Q, T_2)$ isosceles. **16a.** Circles through P, (4.17). **b.** Use **a.** **17.** E.g., $(l(D, A), l(D, C)) = 2\hat{A} + (l(Q, A), l(Q, R)) + (l(Q, P), l(Q, C))$ $= 2(\hat{A} + \hat{C} + \hat{Q})$. **19.** Intersection of the two loci (4.18). **20.** (4.17). **21.** $\sigma_{M(P, Q)} \Gamma$. **22.** σ_a. **24.** (4.15), compare $\hat{C}$. **25.** $120°$ (4.18). **26.** Compute angles subtended by edges. **27a.** Angles at transversal. **b.** Compute angles on concircular quadrilateral of point, one vertex, two feet. **28.** Invert proof of **27a**. **29.** (4.17). **30.** Use problem 27. Simson lines belonging to antipodal points are perpendicular. **31.** ρ (Simson line). **32.** By (4.20), isogonal image of parallel pencil. **33.** Circumcircle without vertices. **34.** Length c of chord known. From P_1 draw tangent to $P_2(c)$.

4–3

6. Follow the order of the hexagons in the statement. **7.** Not if two edges are parallel to the corresponding lines $l(A_i, B_i)$. **9.** Vertices of hexagons on b, e. **10.** Vertices on a, a^*. **11.** Associative law: $A, B, C, A + B, P_o, B + C$ form Pascal hexagon, $l(P_o, A + B + C) = l(P_o, N)$. **12.** Associative law: A, B, C, AB, P_1, BC form Pascal hexagon, $l(P_o, ABC) = l(P_o, N)$.

5–1

2. Draw a transversal and divide each trapezoid by parallels to one edge into triangles and a trapezoid whose height is the height of the other rectangle. Translate trapezoids along transversal. **3.** Choose $\hat{A}$ biggest elementary angle. h_a and $l(M_b, M_c)$. **5.** (5.9). **6.** g the parallel to base at distance h. **a.** $A = g \cap p(a, M_a)$. **b.** $O = m_a \cap B(R)$. **c.** $A = g \cap M_a(s_a)$.

7. $\alpha(ABCD) = \alpha[\triangle(A,D,l(A,B)) \cap \tau_{[\![DC]\!]}l(B,D)]$. **8.** Fig. 5–27. **9.** $\frac{1}{5}$. **10.** Dissect into triangles. Common vertex: center of circle. $r = \alpha/p$.
11. $\alpha = (h/2)(b_1 + b_2)$. Draw a diagonal. **12.** Draw two lines through P and compare areas by σ_P. $P = M_a$.
15. $PE/EA = \alpha[\triangle(P,E,\tau_{[\![CE]\!]}B)]/\alpha[\triangle(A,E,\tau_{[\![CE]\!]}B)]$. **16.** Prove for triangle. Then use induction: $\alpha°(A_1, \ldots, A_k) = \alpha°(A_1, \ldots, A_{k-1}) - \alpha°(P,A_{k-1},A_1) + \alpha°(P,A_{k-1},A_k) + \alpha°(P,A_k,A_1) = \alpha°(A_1, \ldots, A_{k-1}) + \alpha°(A_{k-1},A_k,A_1)$.
17b. E.g., P interior point. Draw q through P parallel to $l(A,D)$.
$\alpha\{\triangle[A,q \cap l(A,B),C]\} = \alpha[\triangle(A,P,D)]$. $\alpha\{\triangle[q \cap l(A,B),C,A]\} = \alpha[\triangle(P,C,A)]$.
18. Two vectors: **17b**; then induction. **19.** For arbitrary Q, define B_i by $[\![QB_i]\!] = [\![A_{2i-1}A_{2i}]\!]$. $f(P) = \Sigma\alpha°(P,Q,B_i) + \Sigma\alpha°(Q,A_{2i-1},A_{2i})$. Define R by $[\![QR]\!] = \mathbf{v}$. $\alpha°(P,Q,R) = f(P) - \Sigma\alpha°(Q,A_{2i-1},A_{2i})$. **22.** Define X so that A,B,X,C form a parallelogram. Use **17a** and **21**. **23.** Special case of **22**, $C \to A$, $D \to C$.
24. If $l(A,B) \parallel l(C,P)$, use **21, 22** with $P = D$. If $S = l(A,B) \cap l(C,P)$, use **23** for A,B,S. **29.** Change one point at a time. $\triangle(A_1,A_2,P)$ and $\triangle(A_4,A_1,P)$ have a common base $[P,A_1]$.

5–2

1. $l(P,A)$ bisects the parallelogram. **4.** $x = q_1$, $y = q_2$, (4.15). **5.** In the right triangle compare s_c, h, $CF_c^{s_c}$. **6.** Necessity: compute PA, PB, PC by Pythagoras. Sufficiency: $G = [p(a,E) \cap p(b,F)]^c$. **7.** $A_i\sigma_h A_j = A_j\sigma_h A_i$. **8.** Exercise 2–3, problem 13. **9.** $(1 + \lambda\mu\nu)^2/(\mu\nu - \mu + 1)(\nu\lambda - \nu + 1)(\lambda\mu - \lambda + 1)$. **12.** Fig. 4–10.
14. (5.17) on P; A,G,M_a. **15.** (5.19). **16.** Multiply Stewart by $\frac{1}{4}AB \cdot PP^{a^2}$.
17. Use **16** for $A \to A$, $B \to B$, $C \to l(A,B) \cap l(C,D) = C'$, $P \to D$, and multiply by $CD^2/C'D^2$. **18.** Four cyclic permutations in **17**, add. **19.** See **18**.

5–3

1. Fig. 4-10, (5-9). **2.** Stewart and (5.24), $t_A^2 = bc - a^2bc(b + c)^{-2}$. **3.** (5.24).
5. (5.24) for $\triangle(I,B,I_a)$. **6.** (5.24), $\triangle(C,P,D)$. **10.** (5.20) for vertices E,G. **11.** T_i a point of contact of tangents to $O_i(r_i)$. $\triangle(P,T_1,O_1)$ and $\triangle(P,T_2,O_2)$ equiangular. $P \in$ circle (5.25) for $\lambda = r_1/r_2$. **12.** $t = l(P,T)$. $T \in O(r) \cap M(O,P)(\frac{1}{2}OP)$.
13. $(a/b)^3$. **14.** $\lambda = a_1/a_2$, $a_1^2 + h^2 = r_1^2$, $a_2^2 + h^2 = r_2^2$, $a_1 + a_2 = O_1O_2$. **15.** E.g., $3 \in F$, $\sqrt{3} \notin F$. **16.** No, $(a + \sqrt{b})^{\frac{1}{2}} \in \Omega$ only if $(a - \sqrt{b})^{\frac{1}{2}} \in \Omega$. X* does not hold. **17.** $a > 0$ means $a = x^2$. Second condition independent of notion of order.
19a. $(s/2)(\sqrt{5} - 1)$. **b.** Isosceles, vertex angle 36°. **20.** $\cos \alpha = 4\cos^3 \alpha/3 - 3\cos \alpha/3$. All equations $4x^3 - 3x - a = 0$, $-1 \leq a \leq +1$ must have solution in field. **21a.** Yes. **b.** No.

5–4

2a. Add to formula of **1.** **b.** Through F,G draw parallels to $l(A,P)$. **5.** Compute ratios, e.g., for $l(C,D)$, Fig. 5–15. **6.** As in the proof of Ceva's theorem, express all quantities as functions of BE/EC, CF/FA, AG/GB. **7.** $\triangle(A,B,E)$, $\triangle(A,C,E)$

equiangular. **8.** Desargues, see **10.** **9.** (5.36). **10.** Desargues on $\triangle(A,P_b,P_c)$, $\triangle(P_a,B,C)$. Then converse Desargues on $\triangle[P_c,P_b,l(B,P_c) \cap l(C,P_b)]$, $\triangle[P_a,l(C,P_a) \cap l(A,P_c), l(A,P_b) \cap l(B,P_a)]$. **11.** Let the lines be $l(i,j)$. Prove that the ratio of division of $l(1,3) \cap l(1,2)$ is equal to that of $l(1,3) \cap l(2,3)$ on $(a_1 \cap b_3, a_3 \cap b_1)$ by Menelaus for $\triangle(a_1 \cap b_3, A_3, a_3 \cap b_1)$, $\triangle(a_1 \cap b_3, A_1, a_3 \cap b_1)$. **12.** Menelaus for triangle defined by midpoints of pairs of non-opposite vertices. By (5.20) reduce to Menelaus on the triangle of non-opposite vertices and fourth line of quadrilateral. **13.** Four times Ceva. **18.** Multiply Menelaus formulae for $l(A_{2k-1}, A_{2k+1})$ and $\triangle(A_{2j-1}, A_{2j}, A_{2j+1})$. **19.** Product of ratios: $+1$. **21.** -1. **22.** On a triangle formed by vertices not on the diagonal take Menelaus for the diagonal and Ceva for lines through the intersection of two diagonals.

5–5

1. Still true. Note: Every $P \in g$ may define a circle $P(t)$. **2a.** $CP_a = CP_b$ and cyclic. **b.** Ceva and **a.** **c.** Exercise 5 4, problem 6, exercise 5–1, problem 10. **3.** Menelaus for the two lines and power theorem for A: $[\![BA_1]\!]/[\![A_1C]\!] = [\![CA_2]\!]/[\![A_2B]\!]$. **4.** Points of contact symmetrical with respect to midpoints. Directions to central. **7.** Radical axes equal altitudes. **8.** On radical axis. **9.** (5.38) for $P(t)$. **10.** Prove for two circles. (4.10) and (5.22). **11.** (i) = (ii). **12.** Second fixed point $P:[\![BP]\!] \cdot [\![BA]\!] = \pi(B,\Gamma)$. **14.** $A \in$ radical axis, consider angles. **15.** Vertices equal power, not collinear. **16.** (5.41). **17.** Circle defined by condition for one circle.   Compute for the others.   **19a.** Prove first $\pi(P,\Gamma)/\pi(P',\Gamma) = \alpha[\triangle(\sigma_a P, \sigma_b P, \sigma_c P)]/\alpha[\triangle(\sigma_a P', \sigma_b P', \sigma_c P')]$.   Choose $P' = O$. **b.** $P \in \Gamma(A,B,C)$. **20.** Problem 7. **21.** $B \in P([\pi(P,\Gamma)/\lambda]^{\frac{1}{2}})$. **22.** $P = g \cap l(A,B)$. $\Gamma \cap g = C \cup D$. $PA \cdot PB = PC(PC + d)$.

6–1

1. (6.6) independent. **2.** $\eta_{B,1/\lambda}\eta_{A,\lambda} = \tau_{(\lambda-1)/\lambda[\![AB]\!]}$. **3a.** Use problem 2. **b.** Cosets: all homotheties of fixed ratio. **c.** Plane, (3.19). **4.** (6.7). **5.** $\eta_{A,1/2}g$. **6.** $\eta_{M(A,B),1/3}$. **7.** $g = \eta_{P,2}$ (Simson line); $\sigma_a H, \sigma_b H, \sigma_c H \in \Gamma(A,B,C)$; $(l(\sigma_a P,H),h_a) = (h_a, l(\sigma_a H,P)) = (b, l(C,P))$. **8.** $P = \Gamma(A,B,C) \cap \Gamma(B,C,D) \cap \Gamma(A,C,D) \cap \Gamma(A,B,D)$. **9.** $\eta_{\text{center }\Gamma}$. **10.** $O_1 O' = [(\lambda_2 \lambda_1^2 - 1)/\lambda_1(\lambda_2\lambda_1 - 1)]O_1 O_2$. **13.** Common tangents to Γ_1, $\sigma_g \Gamma_2$. **14.** $\eta_{A,AO/(AO+r)}O(r)$. **15.** All configurations homothetic; line through P. **16.** $A_2 \in \Gamma_2 \cap \eta_{P,-1/\lambda}\Gamma_1$. **17.** Draw a circle $O(r)$ to fulfill the angle condition. Then homothety of center $l[O,M(A,B)] \cap g$. **18.** Two lines through $g_1 \cap g_2$. **19.** $t_A = [A,X]$. $C \in A(b) \cap \eta_{X,-b/c}A(c)$. **20.** $\Gamma =$ circle (5.25). $[B,C]$ known. $M_b = B(s_b) \cap \eta_{C,1/2}\Gamma$. **21.** Draw a rhombus whose edge is on one diagonal. **22.** Choose $X \in g$. Solution:

$$Y = \eta_{g \cap h,\,(g \cap h)[X(XX^h) \cap l(P,g \cap h)]/(g \cap h)P} Y.$$

23. $\eta_{\text{point of contact}}$. **24.** $\eta_{P,\lambda}\Gamma \cap \Gamma \neq \emptyset$. **25.** $\eta_{\text{vertex},1/2}\Gamma$.

6–2

1a. $S^-S^- = S^+$. **c.** $\mathfrak{R}$. **d.** Z_2. **e.** Similitudes with same angle of rotation.
2. Proof of (1.15). **4.** Solve $\eta^{-1}C = \rho C$. Draw isosceles $\triangle(A,X,\eta^{-1}A)$, $\hat{X} = \alpha$.
By direct similitude of center P, map onto $\triangle(B,O,B^*)$, $\eta\rho B = \eta B^* = B$.
5. Equality of angles, equality of ratios of corresponding edges. **6.** $\theta_2\theta_1$ a homothety, no triangle of lines. **7.** Image of point as intersection of two lines. **8.** (5.34).
9. Problem 8, (6.22). **10a.** (6.22). **b.** Check angles. **11.** Compute angles.
12. $\rho_{C,2\hat{C}}\rho_{B,2\hat{B}}\rho_{A,2\hat{A}} = \iota$ implies $\rho_{\sigma_R C,2\hat{C}}\rho_{\sigma_Q B,2\hat{B}}\rho_{\sigma_P A,2\hat{A}} = \iota$. **13.** Draw $\triangle$: One
vertex P, others on lines. By parallels, homothetic triangle. Join vertices.
14. Isosceles triangles similar, by direct similitudes of centers B,C. Look for angles
$\hat{A}$, $\hat{B}$, $\hat{C}$ in the configuration. **15.** Given A,b,c. $C = \eta_{A,\sqrt{2}}\rho_{A,45°}B$. Hence
$C = (\eta_{A,\sqrt{2}}\rho_{A,45°}b) \cap c$. **16.** See problem 15; $B = b \cap \eta_{A,\sin \hat{C}/\sin \hat{B}}\rho_{A,\hat{A}}C$.
17. Parallel g, cosets of S^+/G. $B = \tau A$, $\theta\tau$ is homothety. **18.** Vectors define
triangle inversely similar to given $\triangle$. **19.** Find loci (4.18) for intersection of
diagonals. **20.** Similar triangle is known. **21.** $\theta = \eta_{O,b/c}\rho_{O,\alpha}$. **22,23.** (6.17).
24. Must be homothety. Look for fixed point.

6–3

1. Corresponding lines through invariant points. **2.** Image of O in homothety
with $\triangle(S_a,S_b,S_c)$. **3.** Problem 2. **4.** At N. **6a.** P midpoint of chord on y_c.
$\triangle(C,M_b,M_a)$ similar to $\triangle(C,P,B)$; hence $\theta_1\triangle(B,C,P) = \triangle(C,A,P)$, $\theta_1P = P$.
c. Triangles on one edge and one first Brocard point are similar. **7.** Exercise 6–2,
problem 11. **8.** Center of similitude. **10.** Pedal triangle similar to given ones.
12. Define X by $l(A,A_1) \cap \Gamma(A_1,B,C) = A_1 \cup X$. Use angles to show X solves A;
$A_2 \in \Gamma(B_1,C_1,X)$ and cyclic. **13.** $(l(X,B^g),l(X,C^g)) = (l(M_a,M_c),l(M_a,M_b))$.
$X \in$ nine point circle. **14.** $\triangle(A,X_a,C) = \theta\triangle(A,B,Y_a)$. **15.** $AI^b = p - a$, $AI_a^b = p$.
16. α from (5.19a). **17a.** Problem 15. **b.** $(r + r_c)/R = \cos \hat{A} + \cos \hat{B}$.
18. Problem 15. **19.** Problem 16c, $2\alpha = ah_a$.

6–4

1c. See **1a.** **d.** See **1c**, **1b.** **4.** Draw circles: center the intersection on adjacent
sides, $\perp$ original circle. Then (6.33) and problem 3. **5.** $A \in \Gamma_1 \cap \Gamma, B \in \Gamma_2 \cap \Gamma$.
Draw diameters d_1 through A, d_2 through B.
$d_1 \cap d_2[(d_1 \cap d_2)A] = d_1 \cap d_2[(d_1 \cap d_2)B]$. (6.33) or problem 3. **6.** Compute
on central. **9.** Given: the ratios of homethety and the M_i, D_i, A_i.

7–1

1. $\|$ central. **2.** Complete the parallelogram of diagonal $2s_a$. **3.** $\triangle(A,D,C)$ in
Fig. 5–19. Use exercise 5–2, problem 5. Cf. F. Leuenberger, *El. Math.* 17, 1962,
45–46. **4.** Fig. 5–19, $\triangle(A,X,C)$. **5.** Prolong $l(B,P)$ to intersection with b.
6. Problem 7. Take the PA_i in pairs. E.g., $A_4 \in \triangle(A_1,P,A_2)$ means
$A_1P + PA_2 > A_1A_4 + A_4A_2$, $PA_4 + PA_3 \geqslant A_4A_3$. **9.** Introduction from problems 6,8. **11.** Draw $l(A,\tau_{\mathbf{v}}^{-1}B)$, where $\mathbf{v}$ is the vector defined by segment.

12. Example 1. **13.** A,B given, X unknown, $\hat{X}$ maximal in $\triangle(A,X,B)$. Reduce to the same halfplane, locus (4.18). **14.** Solution only if λ,μ,ν may form a triangle $\triangle$. On edges of $\triangle(A,B,C)$ construct triangles in the exterior, similar to $\triangle$. Then example 2. **15.** (1.33).

7–2

1. Ratio of similitude of original and associated triangles, $OM_a = \frac{1}{2}HA$.
2. Problem 1. **3.** See Fig. 7–9. **4.** $f = \sigma_b \sigma_c \sigma_a b$. **5.** Translation. **8.** Angle conditions. **9.** All projections on edges: pedal minimal. One edge a diameter: pedal quadrilateral degenerates to triangle. Center outside quadrilateral: no minimal quadrilateral, only triangle. **10.** Fig. 7–11. **13.** $\sigma_a \sigma_b \sigma_a \sigma_c = \rho_{C,2\hat{C}} \rho_{B,-2\hat{B}}$. If not isosceles, $\hat{C} = \hat{B} \pm 90°$, obtuse: no solution. **14,15.** Fig. S–1. **16.** Must be of

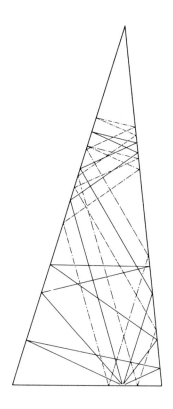

Fig. S–1

type $\sigma_{\sigma_a \sigma_b c}\sigma_c$. **17a.** Otherwise the incircle is bigger. **b.** See **a,c. c.** There is none; look for triangle of perimeter $2p + \epsilon$. **19.** $M(\sigma_a\sigma_d\sigma_c\sigma_b\sigma_aM) = 5p$.

7–3

Note: Inequalities at the triangle are the subject of many recent publications. For problems taken from recent journals, references are given instead of hints. Abbreviations: MONTHLY (American Mathematical Monthly), E (Elementary problems), *El. Math.* (Elemente der Mathematik).

Practically all known geometric inequalities in the plane are discussed, with proofs, in D. S. Mitrinovič, P. M. Vasič, R. Z. Dordevič, R. R. Janič, *Geometrijske Nejednakosti*, Izdavac, Beograd, 1966. The book is in Serbo-Croatian, but the formulae are easily understood.
2. L. Carlitz, MONTHLY *71*, 881–885, 1961. See also exercise 5–4. **3.** L. Bernstein and J. Steinig, *El. Math. 19*, 8–10, 1964; L. Bankoff, MONTHLY *70*, 1101, 1963, E 1564. **4.** F. Leuenberger, **a.** *El. Math. 16*, 127–129, 1961, **b.** *El. Math. 18*, 35–37, 1963, **c.** *El. Math. 19*, 132–133, 1964. **5.** F. Leuenberger, MONTHLY *71*, 93, 1964, E 1573. **6.** L. Carlitz, MONTHLY *71*, 687, 1964, E 1628. Also see J. Schopp, MONTHLY, E 1675. **7.** D. Pedoe, MONTHLY *70*, 1012, 1963, E 1562. **8–16.** See MONTHLY *71*, 915–916, 1964, E 1644. **17.** F. Leuenberger, *El. Math. 20*, 89–90, 1965. **18.** J. Steinig, *El. Math. 20*, 64–65, 1965.

7–4

4. *a* given edge. $P \cup \sigma_a P$ has given perimeter: regular. Angle at *a*, 90°. Adjacent edges, half the length of the others. **5,6.** $P \cup \sigma_a P$ circumscribed to a circle, center on base edge. **6a.** $\triangle$: circle tangent at midpoint. **7.** Circumscribed circle, remaining edges and angles equal. **9.** Use **8. 10.** Shortest: cuts off isosceles triangle from the legs of the smallest angle. Longest: longest median.
11. $\lambda_1 L_1 + \lambda_2 L_2 = c$, $\lambda_1^2 A_1 + \lambda_2^2 A_2 = $ maximum. **13a.** σ_P. **16.** Similar triangles.

8–1

1. $X \in l(A,B)$ means $X = \sigma_{l(A,B)}X$.
2. $A(AB) \cap l(C,D) = A(AB) \cap \sigma_{l(C,D)}A(AB)$. **3.** $X \in m(A,B)$ (Fig. 5–25a), $Y = X(AX) \cap A(AB)$, $C = A(AB) \cap Y(YA) \in l(A,B)$. **4.** Parallelogram.

8–2

1e. $\sigma_{O(1)}$.
2. Center: $\Gamma \cap p(g,A)$, point X on complement of $A[A^g]$. $\sigma_{X([2a(a+AA^g)]^{\frac{1}{2}})}$.
4. $\sigma_{O(r)}$, $O \in \Gamma$. **5a.** Fig. 8–3. **b.** Use ratios and $l[O,p(X_1) \cap p(X_2)] \perp l(X_1,X_2)$. **c.** (*b*). **d.** $p(O)$ not defined. **7a.** Line $\eta_{D,DO/DC}l(A,C)$. **b.** A,N,M,C concyclic.

8–3

1. $\theta\Psi$, $\sigma_\Gamma\Sigma\Psi$. **3.** $\eta = \sigma_{\Gamma_2}\sigma_{\Gamma_1}$ (8.13). **4.** $\sigma_a P = Q$. **5.** (8.22). **6.** Direct similitude $[A_1,A_2] \rightarrow [B_1,B_2]$. **7.** If not in pencil, invert at unique common perpen-

dicular circle.   **9a.** See **b.**   **b.** (8.13).   **c.** $T_1 \perp T_2$.   **10.** $\sigma_\Gamma \eta_{O,\lambda} \sigma_\Gamma = \eta_{\sigma_\Gamma O,\lambda}$.
12. Always disjoint circles.   **13.** Equivalence classes of rotations of constant α, horocyclic transformations of constant $(r_2 - r_1)/r_1 r_2$.   **14.** $I = \{\rho_{A_1,A_2;\alpha} \mid \text{all } \alpha\}$.

8–4

1. Exercise 2–1, problem 4.   **2.** Exercise 2–3, problem 13.   **3.** Exercise 2–1, problem 3.   **4.** $\sigma_{P(r)}$. (4.23).   **5.** Problem 4 for A_1,A_3,B_4; A_3,B_1,A_2.   **6.** σ_O exercise 4–2, problem 4.   **7.** $\sigma_{a \text{ point of contact } (r)}$. Prove collinearity by angles.
8. (2.48), necessity by (8.22).   **9.** Exercise 2–5, problem 3.   **10.** σ_O Simson line.
11. $h_i = \sigma_O \sigma_{O(R)} \Gamma(O, \sigma_O A_i, \sigma_{m_i} A_i)$.   **12.** $\sigma_{\Gamma(A,B,C)} \Gamma(A_1,A_2,M_a) = I(A,A_1)$.
13. $\sigma_{O(r)}$ radical axis of $\sigma\Gamma(A,B,C)$, $\sigma\Gamma(E,F,G)$.   **14.** $\sigma_{O(r)}$.   **15.** $g \cap I(O_1,O_2)$.
16. $\sigma_{A_1(r)}$; two circles through A_1,A_2. Angle with Γ:45°.   **17.** $\sigma_{A_3(\sqrt{A_2 A_1 \cdot A_2 A_3})}$;
$\sigma\Gamma_3 = \Gamma_3$, $\sigma K_3 = K_3$.   **18.** $\sigma_{A(r)}$ angle bisectors.
19. $\sigma_{A[\pi(A,\Gamma')]} \cdot \sigma\Gamma = I(A',B')$, $\sigma\Gamma' = \Gamma'$.   **20.** $\sigma_{C[\pi(C,\Gamma')]}$.   **21.** $\sigma_{A(r)}$.
23. Check the midpoints of the edges of $\triangle$.   **24,25.** Transform Γ into a line.
26. Either transform into two concentric circles or two intersecting lines, or by inversion reduce to the case of common tangents to two circles.   **27.** Use methods of **26,** first suggestion.

8–5

1. $\sigma_{I(r)}$.   **3.** (8.31).   **4.** $\sigma_{A(r)}$ on Stewart's formula.   **5.** ST.   **6.** 6.   **8,9.** (8.30).

9–1

1. $O(r)$, $O \in A$; $l \perp A$.   **2.** $\sigma_{O(r)}$, $O \in A$.   **6.** axiom XIII^H.

9–2

5. Curves of constant distance.   **6.** See Fig. 9–6.   **7.** $\sigma_{\underset{ma}{H}} \sigma_{\underset{mb}{H}} \sigma_{\underset{mc}{H}} B = B$, similarly **8,9.**   **13.** Find mapping $\tau^H \rho^H$.   **14.** End of horocycle.   **15,17.** Check on (9.9).   **19.** $\sigma_{a_2}\sigma_{a_3} = \sigma_{a_1}\sigma_{a_1}\sigma_{a_2}\sigma_{a_3} = \sigma_{a_1}\sigma_{a_1}\sigma_{a_2}\sigma_{a_1} = \sigma_{b_1}\sigma_{b_1}\sigma_{b_1}\sigma_{b_2} = \sigma_{b_1}\sigma_{b_2}$. Pencil a_1, a_2 = pencil b_1, b_2.   **21.** a line in pencil of B. $\sigma_{a_i}\sigma_a\sigma_{a_j} = \sigma_{l^H(B,Bl^H(B^{a_i}B^{a_j}))}$:
$\sigma_{a_1}\sigma_a\sigma_{a_2}\sigma_a\sigma_{a_3} = \sigma_{l^H(B^{a_1},B^{a_2})}\sigma_{a_1}\sigma_{l^H(B^{a_1},B^{a_3})}$.   **22.** Simson line.
23. $\sigma_{a_1}\sigma_a\sigma_{a_2}\sigma_a\sigma_{a_3}\sigma_a\sigma_{a_4} = \sigma_{p^H(J_{123},B)}\sigma_{l^H(B^{a_1},B^{a_2})}\sigma_{p^H(J_{124},B)}$.
25. $\alpha_3\beta_3 = (\alpha_3\beta_2)(\alpha_1\beta_2)^{-1}(\alpha_1\beta_3)$. Use the other relations to show the three lines in pencil.   **29.** Use **28.**

9–3

2. If false, two parallels have two common perpendiculars.
5,6. Move point to A, problem 4.   **8b.** $L = 2n \tan \pi/n \sinh r/2 \left(\dfrac{L/4n}{\tanh L/4n} \right)$.
d. 3.28, 465.   **10.** Taylor expansion.

9–4

1. Fig. S–2. **4.** $M + N = (A + B)/C$, $MN = -B/C$.

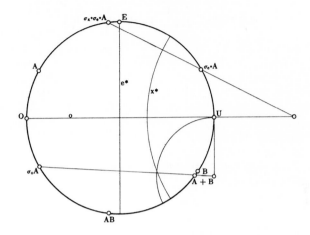

Fig. S–2

5. $(A + D)^2 + BC = 0$. **6.** $\begin{pmatrix} A + B & 2AB \\ 2 & -(A + B) \end{pmatrix}$.

9. By problem 7, $(A'A'',B'B'') = \left(\dfrac{X' - E}{X' + E}\right)^2$. **11.** Problem 10. **12.** By exp.

13. $e^* \cap o$ is the point $(O,E,-E)$; a rotation about $(O,E,-E)$ has matrix $\begin{pmatrix} P & Q \\ R & S \end{pmatrix}$,
$PR + QS = O$, $P^2 + Q^2 = R^2 + S^2$.

9–6

1. North and South pole if great circle is equator. **2a.** (8.5). **c.** $\sigma_t^* \sigma_l = {}^*$;
* is product of three line reflections. Then use definitions. **3.** Line angle = point
angle in polar $\triangle$ and vice versa. **7.** Rotation or point reflection. **8.** (9.34).
9a. $\sigma_Q = \sigma_S \sigma_P \sigma_S$ implies $\sigma_Q \sigma_P = (\sigma_S \sigma_P)^2$. If $\sigma_A \sigma_B = (\sigma_R \sigma_S)^2$, then $R,S \in l^E(A,B)$,
and there exists C, $\sigma_C = \sigma_A \sigma_R \sigma_S \cdot \sigma_B = \sigma_C \sigma_A \sigma_C$.

Appendix

2. E.g., $t > 0$, $t \prec 0$. **4.** $n < t^{-1}$. **5.** Isomorphism $\varphi(m \cdot 2^{-k}) = m \cdot 2^{-k}$.
6. $(A_g - A_h)(A_g + A_h) + (B_g - B_h)(B_g + B_h) = 0$.

INDEX OF NOTATIONS

INDEX OF GROUPS

Symbol	Page	Meaning
$\mathfrak{M}$	60	motions
$\mathfrak{M}^+$	60	proper motions
$\mathfrak{R}_P$	60	rotations about point P
$\mathfrak{I}$	60	translations
$\mathfrak{L}$	60	segments (length)
$\mathcal{I}_P$	60, 68	isotropy group at P
$\mathcal{Z}_{P,n}$	61	rotations of angle $(k/n) \cdot 360°$ about P
$\mathbf{R}$	61	real numbers (additive group)
$\mathbf{R}^*$	61	positive real numbers (multiplicative group)
$\mathbf{Z}$	61	integers (additive group)
$\mathbf{Z}_n$	61	integers modulo n
$\mathbf{R}_{2\pi}$	61	reals modulo 2π
$\mathfrak{R}$	68	oriented angles
$\mathfrak{IC}$	157	homotheties
$\mathfrak{IC}_P$	157	homotheties of center P
$\mathcal{S}$	159	similitudes
$\mathcal{S}_P$	163	similitudes of center P
$\mathcal{S}^+$	163	direct similitudes
$\mathfrak{C}$	208	circular transformations
$\mathcal{Y} = \mathfrak{M}^H$	225	hyperbolic motions
$\mathfrak{R}_P^H$	231	hyperbolic rotations about P
$\mathcal{E}$	254	elliptic motions

LIST OF AXIOMS

axiom I. For any two distinct points A,B there exists a unique line $l(A,B)$ containing these points.

axiom II. All points in the plane but not on a line l form two non-null disjoint sets.

axiom III. A and B are in different halfplanes of a line l if and only if $l \cap (A,B) \neq \emptyset$.

axiom IV. If $B \in (A,C)$, then $C \notin (A,B)$.

axiom V. There exists a line.

axiom VI. For any line l there exists a map σ_l which maps the points of one halfplane of l onto the points of the other halfplane.

axiom VII. σ_l maps straight lines onto straight lines.

axiom VIII. $\sigma_l^2 = \iota$.

axiom IX. For all points $L \in l$, $\sigma_l L = L$.

axiom X. For any angle, there exists an angle bisector.

axiom XI. For any pair of points, there exists a perpendicular bisector.

axiom XII. If some product of reflections maps some ray a_1 onto itself, then it is either σ_a or ι.

axiom XIII. If $a \parallel b$ and $d \perp a$, then $d \perp b$.

axiom (A). If $a \geqslant 0$, $b > 0$, and $a < \frac{1}{n} b$ for all natural numbers n, then $a = 0$.

axiom X*. If a line has a point in the interior of a circle, it meets the circle in two points.

axiom XIII^H. If two parallel lines have an end in common, they do not have a common perpendicular. If they do not have an end in common, they have a unique common perpendicular.

INDEX